Plate 1. Red wolf of the Lower Mississippi Valley (*Canis niger gregoryi*)

The Wolves

of

North America

By

STANLEY P. YOUNG *and* EDWARD A. GOLDMAN

Senior Biologists, Section of Biological Surveys, Division of Wildlife Research, Fish and Wildlife Service, Department of the Interior.

PART I

Their History, Life Habits, Economic Status, and Control

By

STANLEY P. YOUNG

DOVER PUBLICATIONS, INC.

NEW YORK

Published in Canada by General Publishing Company, Ltd., 30 Lesmill Road, Don Mills, Toronto, Ontario.
Published in the United Kingdom by Constable and Company, Ltd., 10 Orange Street, London WC 2.

This Dover edition, first published in 1964, is an unabridged and corrected republication of the work first published in 1944 by the American Wildlife Institute. Certain plates which were color plates in the original edition are reproduced in black and white in this edition.

This work originally appeared in one volume but now appears in two volumes.

International Standard Book Number: 0-486-21193-2
Library of Congress Catalog Card Number: 64-15510

Manufactured in the United States of America

Dover Publications, Inc.
180 Varick Street
New York, N. Y. 10014

FOREWORD

IN THIS volume we have attempted to bring together the widely scattered literature of historical import concerning the wolves of North America, from the earliest times to the present day. This has entailed a review of thousands of published records, some contained in very rare volumes, covering the entire Christian era. It also outlines the general results of field studies of the animals, carried on during more than a quarter of a century, in connection with control of their depredations, by the Biological Survey (now the Fish and Wildlife Service). As the work progressed we have been increasingly impressed with the importance of the part these master predators have played in complex relation to human welfare.

Owing, in part, to the wide diversity of color in wolves many names were proposed for supposed species, and this led to much confusion, dating from early American exploration. A number of names prove to be without specific basis, or are applicable only to subspecies. On the other hand the geographic races, or subspecies, of the true wolves are numerous, and a detailed classification of those inhabiting North America is presented for the first time. It is hoped that this volume on the animals in North America will afford a substantial foundation for the use of future workers in bringing together more comprehensive knowledge of the wolves of the world.

STANLEY P. YOUNG
EDWARD A. GOLDMAN

Washington, D. C.
January 20, 1944

v

ACKNOWLEDGMENTS

IN THE preparation of this volume, the authors have received most hearty cooperation from many individuals and sources, for all of which sincere appreciation is herewith expressed. We particularly desire to mention certain firms and individuals who so generously aided in making possible the various color plates. These are The KRO Co. of Springfield, Ohio, through the late Frank Connable; The Animal Trap Co. of America, through Kenneth Witmyer; The Hoffman-LaRoche Co., represented by Nelson F. Petersen and John Vance; Tappan Gregory, noted wildlife photographer, of Chicago; Wetmore Hodges, conservationist, of Tucson, Ariz., and Ennis, Mont. To these we express our profound appreciation and hearty thanks.

In addition to material in the U. S. National Museum, the specimens examined included 178 from other American museums and private collections. Many of these were of critical importance in determining the status of the species in particular regions. For the loan of specimens and other courtesies, our gratitude is due to H. E. Anthony, of the American Museum of Natural History; Thomas Barbour and the late Glover M. Allen, of the Museum of Comparative Zoology of Harvard College; G. Clifford Carl, of the Provincial Museum, Victoria, British Columbia; Stuart C. Downing, of the Royal Ontario Museum of Zoology, Toronto, Ontario; Charles M. B. Cadwalader, of the Academy of Natural Sciences of Philadelphia; Alfred M. Bailey, of the Colorado Museum of Natural History; E. Raymond Hall and Seth Benson, of the Museum of Vertebrate Zoology, University of California; Clifford C. Gregg and Wilfred H. Osgood, of the Chicago Natural History Museum; Charles D. Bunker, of the Kansas University Museum of Natural History; W. J. Breckenridge, of the Minnesota Museum of Natural History; John F. Stanwell-Fletcher, of Dimock, Pa.; R. E. Dimick, of Oregon State College; and Arthur Einarsen, of the Fish and Wildlife Service. The distribution maps and sketches were drawn by Katheryne C. Tabb. The illustrations of skulls are by Gurney I. Hightower, photographer, under direction of A. J. Olmstead, of the U. S. National Museum.

Other individuals who were most helpful are E. W. Jeffery, Professor of American History, Woodrow Wilson High School, Washington, D. C., who aided materially in our bibliographical research; Richard P. Eckels, of the University of Mississippi, University, Miss.; Arthur Dean, at present Treasurer of Bent County, Colo., and Secretary of the Bent-Prowers Cattle and Horse Growers Association, who so kindly lent us the historically valuable minutes of the annual meetings of this organization; Carl Lomen, of Seattle, Wash., and Nome, Alaska; Joseph N. Neal, of Meeker, Colo.; Remington Kellogg, of the U. S. National Museum; Vilhjalmur Stefansson and Donald B. MacMillan, the Arctic explorers, of New York, N. Y., and Provincetown, Mass., respectively; J. Stokley Ligon, of Albuquerque and Carlsbad, N. Mex.; Hartley H. T. Jackson, for advice, Clona C. Whitaker, Frances W. Shibley, Emma M. Charters, and Blanche W. Mahlman, of the Fish and Wildlife Service of the Department of the Interior, for their general aid and meticulous care in connection with copy work; and finally we are greatly indebted to W. L. McAtee, of the Fish and Wildlife Service, for critical suggestions and editorial review of the entire manuscript.

THE WOLVES OF NORTH AMERICA

PART I

Their History, Habits, Economic Status, and Control
by
Stanley P. Young

═══

CONTENTS

═══

ILLUSTRATIONS

Plates

xi

Text Figures

Tables

THE WOLVES OF NORTH AMERICA

Part I

Their History, Habits, Economic Status, and Control

by

Stanley P. Young

I

INTRODUCTION

THROUGH the centuries the wolf has left a record symbolizing power, ferocity, sagacity, courage, fighting ability, and ruthlessness. It has left a mark upon the pages of literature and legend, even to modern slang which applies the name of the animal to the human love predator, and to another extreme—the enemy submarines of the second World War. There also exists the "Timber Wolf Division" of the present American Army. Its finest soldiers after passing many crucial, exacting commando tests are dubbed "Wolf Scouts."

It found a place in early day medicinal formulas, and has been a problem for the lawmakers from the days of ancient Greece down to the present.

The gray wolf (*Canis lupus*) has had a more important role in relation to human welfare than any other wild carnivore. Once numerous throughout Europe, most of Asia, and North America, it had a geographic range greater, perhaps, than any other land mammal; and this dispersal brought it in contact and conflict with the majority of the peoples of the world. The wolf was not only a menace to human life, but was everywhere so destructive to domestic stock that constant warfare had to be waged against it. Through the use of modern firearms, poison, and steel traps, the wolf has been

1

extirpated over much of its former range, but still populates vast areas in Asia and North America. The red wolf (*Canis niger*) is a distinct American species, comparatively restricted in range.

The peculiar social instincts and behavior of the wolf led to domestication and the evolution of the many breeds of domestic dogs that have been intimately associated with diverse human races since the dawn of history. The place of the wolf in folk-lore and the extent of the literature amply attest the hold of the animal on the popular imagination and its bearing on human affairs. The historical summary establishes the fact that expensive control measures, including bounty acts, date back at least to ancient Greece. Intolerable depredations by wolves finally led to federal appropriations to control predatory animals in the United States.

In the treatment of the classification and geographic distribution of these predators 23 races of gray and 3 of red wolves, respectively, are recognized as having inhabited North America.

The wolves should not be confused with the coyotes, sometimes called prairie or brush wolves, but which are smaller with more fox-like habits. Confusion in the field has sometimes been due to close superficial resemblance and to the fact that wolves and coyotes inhabit much of the same range. Wolves are distinguished from these smaller members of the genus *Canis* by much larger size and less pointed features, especially the rounded ears and heavier muzzle. In the adult wolf the nose pad exceeds an inch in diameter, while in a coyote of the same age the pad is less than an inch in this dimension.

Nature's fingerprint records—the asphalt deposits of southern California and limestone caves in the midwest—show that during the Pleistocene period when the true wolves first appeared, some were much larger than those of the present time. Nearest in size to their prehistoric ancestors are the three races of wolves now occurring in the Arctic (*Canis lupus alces, C. l. pambasileus* of Alaska, and *C. l. occidentalis* of Mackenzie, Canada).

When man, says the archaeologist, was armed with only the stoneheaded club and stone knife, there was room for both him and the larger predators, and food for both.

What was the cause of the passing of these great wolves of earlier days—prolonged drought, glacial climate, or was it Mother Nature and her slow acting checks?

It seems probable then that the huge predators of another day were unable to adjust themselves wholly to some great change that came about with too great speed and perhaps was marked by a decrease in food.

Whatever may have been the cause, it seems possible that it raised the predatory instincts of these killers even to cannibalism. It may have been this, indeed, that lured them into the open oil pools which trapped them in such numbers and embalmed their skeletons for modern biologists to find and speculate upon thousands of years later.

Civilization appears to have brought the next crisis upon the survivors of these prehistoric predators. They had given trouble to the Indians and the early day stockmen, but it was a casual warfare—there were still other sources of food than the red man's cayuse and the white man's cattle. But the white man kept spreading out with his cleared and cultivated lands, driving the wolf's main food prey back farther and farther into the wilder country, reducing the cover through which this mammal might roam unmolested—shooting, trapping and poisoning this predator along the forced march of civilization.

The American continent was repeating the extermination of the wolf in Europe a few centuries earlier. History indicates that the wolf disappeared from England during the reign of Henry VII (1485-1509) from Scotland by 1743 and from Ireland by 1776 (Harting, J. E., 1880: 204).

Ranging on the North American continent during the years of its maximum numbers from Alaska and the northern Arctic to the tableland of Mexico, the wolf has to date resisted extinction perhaps more successfully on the new continent.

Even though the animal may finally be exterminated from the earth its imprint nevertheless is left on history, fiction, medicine, poetry, myth, legend, and even the nursery rhyme, and modern slang. One author likened the Roman empire "to a huge wolf, the jaw and fangs of which were her farflung legions, with the city of Rome as the belly of the beast into which the rich morsels flowed after they had been sufficiently pulverized by the molars and grinders" (White, Bouck. 1913: 46).

Necessity, reward, sport and nature all combined to drive the animal out of most of Europe. Early writings reveal that, in the ninth century, wolf hunting was a part of the young nobleman's training. The breeding of dogs specially developed and trained to hunt wolves was practiced in Britain.

Much later, on the American continent, we find the predator being destroyed by divers methods, one of which was the circular ring hunt, which seems to have served as a sort of pattern for the jackrabbit and coyote drives still in use on the western plains today.

There are numerous tales in European literature about children that have been reared by wild animals. The legend of Romulus and Remus is popularly accepted as one of these. In the tale pertaining to the founding of Rome in 753 B.C., these two were said to have been suckled in their infancy by a she-wolf. However, Topsell suggested, in the sixteenth century, another explanation for the tale.

"Lupa and lupula," he says, "were the names of noble deuoringe harlots. ... It is doubtful whether the nurse of Romulous and Remus were a harlot or a she-wolf. I rather think it was a harlot than a wolfe that nursed those children" (Topsell, E., 1607: 734).

Traditions of similar import existed in Asia and furnished the basis of Rudyard Kipling's tale, "Mowgli," so popular that it has not only been printed in numerous editions but also has been the theme of a full-length motion picture.

As late as 1920 "wolf-children" were reported taken in Midnapore, India, the country in which Kipling's scenes were laid. According to this account, the Rev. J. A. L. Singh, an Anglican missionary, rescued the children from a wolf den in remote northwest India. They were aged about two and eight years at the time of their removal from the wolf den, and were both girls. The younger died shortly after being removed to an orphanage maintained by Dr. Singh, but the other lived to be about seventeen years of age. At the time of the removal of the children from the den, three adult wolves, one apparently a female, and two young were likewise occupying the den.

Wolf traits manifested by these two girls were stated to include lapping of milk; preferring the company of dogs to that of humans; tearing off, at first, of all clothing put on their bodies; and howling like wolves; besides scratching at a door entrance after approaching it on all fours. Upon removal from the den, they could not walk, and even with teaching "neither of the children ever mastered man's upright position well enough to run, but they did learn to walk upright, though somewhat awkwardly" (Zingg, R. M., 1941: 135).

Greek and Roman literature tells that men became wolves; the Middle Ages attributed wolflike characteristics to those accused of witchcraft; folklore adopted it in Red Riding Hood (Beddard, F. E., 1902: 421).

Tales of were-wolves, of loups garou, of skin changers abound in the legends and literature and in history of medieval times; even later, "Belief in them still lingers in parts of Europe where wolves are to be found. . . . The Emperor Sigismund convoked a council of theologians in the Fifteenth century who decided that wer-wolves did exist" (The Harvard Classics, 1910: 268).

From Aesop's Fables down through the "Three Little Pigs," so recently popularized as an animated cartoon, the wolf skulks through the pages of folklore. Scores of Greek and Roman writers discussed its evil characteristics, its gruesomeness, its ferocity.

In the Badianus manuscript where is found the Aztec Herbal of 1552 occurs the earliest known assertion of the therapeutic values to be found in the North American wolf. It includes wolf's liver as an ingredient of a medicine for the cure of "black blood" or melancholia and suggests also the pricking of the breast with the "sharpened bone of a wolf." Montezuma's gardens which, it is believed "furnished animals and plants for the use of the court physicians," in their ministrations to the sick, contained wolves (Emmart, E. W., 1940: 54, 281, 324).

Pliny the Elder suggested use of a wolf's tooth as an aid to infant teething, of the dung in relieving cataract and in curing colic. An early Greek doctor, Paulus Aegineta, prescribed for arthritis a bath, prepared by boiling whole wolves in oil. And so on, well toward the close of the eighteenth century.

Isadore of Seville, sometimes called the first encyclopedist, related a superstition among "country people" that "a man loses his voice if a wolf sees him first. And therefore, if a person is suddenly silent, they say 'it is the wolf in the fable'" (Brehaut, E., 1912: 225).

Topsell, writing in the sixteenth century, sought to trace the name to its origin: "Lupus, as some say in Latine, is quasi Leopos, lyon-footed: because that it resembleth a lyon in its feet. . . . Others deriue it from Lukes, the light, because in the twilight of the euening or morning it deuoureth his prey, auoiding both extreme light as the noone day, and also extreme darkness as the night" (Topsell, E., 1607: 734).

Said Topsell, also:

"There are diuers kinds of wolues in the world. . . . The first which is swift hath a greater head than other wolues, and likewise greater legs fitted to run, white spots on the belly, round members, his colour betwixt red and yellow, he is very bold, howleth fearefully, hauing firy-flaming eies, and continually wagging his head. The second kind hath a greater and larger body then this, being swifter then all other; betimes in the morning he being hungry, goeth abroad to hunt his prey, the sides and taile are of a siluer colour, he inhabiteth the Mountaines, except in the winter time, wherein he descendeth to the Gates of Citties or Townes, and boldy without feare killeth both Goates and sheepe, yet by stealth and secretly.

"The third kind inhabiteth . . . . sharp and inaccessible places, being worthily for beauty preferred before the others, because of his Golden resplendent haires: and therefore my Author saith: . . . . that he is not a wolfe but some wilde Beast excelling a wolfe. He is exceeding strong, especially being able with his mouth and teeth to bite asunder not only stones, but Brasse and Iron: He feareth the Dog star and heate of summer, reiocying more in cold then in warme weather, therefore in the Dog daies he hideth himself in some pit or gaping of the earth, vntill that sunny heat he abated. . . . The fourth and fift kinds . . . . haue short necks, broad shoulders, rough Legs and feet, and small snouts, and little eies: herein they differ one kind from the other, because that one of them hath a backe of a siluer colour, and a white belly, and the lower part of the feet blacke and this is Ictinus canus, a gray Kite-wolfe: the other is black, hauing a lesser body, his haire standing continuously vpright, and liueth by hunting of Hares" (Ibid., p. 735). And so, was the wolf classified by the early seventeenth century.

In earliest days courage and fighting ability were always associated with the wolf, so it was not surprising to find the heroes of those days adopting names which would claim those traits for themselves. Among the early Anglo-Saxons such qualities as fighting, stamina, and courage, regarded as superb, were evidently associated with this predator. All of us who took a beginner's course in English literature recall the struggle we had in reading about Beowulf, or Beado Wulf; the War Wolf, the legendary Teutonic heroic figure that was printed in Old English. Anglo-Saxon history is interpreted with respect to the use of the prefix or suffix "Wulf" or "Wolf," when applied to a human name, as associated with the brute force exemplified as a trait of the wolf. Individuals exhibiting wolf traits were in earlier times held high in the scale of social distinction. During certain periods of the seventh, eighth, ninth, and tenth centuries we find therefore, certain of the Anglo-Saxon kings and other nobles taking the name of Berthwolf, Cynewolf, Wulfstan, Wulfred, Wolfwig, and Ceowulf. In other words a "wolfish" king, one exemplifying the brute force, tenacity, or courage of the wolf, in dealing with his subjects, was one of the prime requisites of these early rulers.

Biblical references to the wolf, indicate a conception of ferocity and bloodthirstiness. For instance, Christ in his caution to the disciple group said metaphorically: "I send you forth as sheep in the midst of wolves." Bouck White, in his "Call of the Carpenter," says: "To repel wolves with moral suasion is not christianity." Wolves in this instance were the Roman aristocrats and their dealings with the earliest Christians following the death of Christ.

In later years references to the wolf emphasized some less commendable qualities. The Puritan Roger Williams called it "a fierce, bloodsucking persecutor." Theodore Roosevelt characterized the animal as "the beast of waste and desolation." Said Horace Greeley: "a scoundrel." Others called it the "Shark" or "Ghoul" of the Plains.

Efforts to destroy the wolf in this country were instrumental in the formation of the Oregon territory. The "wolf meetings" of Oregon—officially the formal sessions of the Oregon Wolf Organization—drew pioneer leaders of the northwest together as did no other objective. Out of these eventually came the plans for a civil government for the territory. These meetings symbolized the acknowledgment that the wolf was the outstanding predator of western North America.

And finally, some of this mammal's habits have been responsible for the adoption of several expressive terms in our language. These, generally colloquial in use, include one descriptive of hurried eating; "he wolfed his food." Various plants or parts of plants are named out of association with the wolf as wolfbane and wolfberry.

Also, we find the animal named in classical quotations, such as: Homo homini lupus (Man to man is a wolf); Homo homini aut lupus (Man is to man either a god or a wolf); Lupus pilum mutat non mentem (The wolf changes his hair, but not his nature); and, Ovem lupo committere (To entrust the sheep to the wolf).

The animal seemed to have an understanding of man's stratagems that enabled it to evade capture as did no other of the wild mammals of the nineteenth century. Its keen sense of smell, its sagacity continued to balk every device undertaken for its extermination. It still promises to avoid extinction, even though it has been driven into the farthest and most inaccessible portions of the continent—the wilds of Alaska, the Canadian Arctic, and northern Mexico; certain parts of far western Canada, northern, western, and certain portions of the southern United States.

From a biological as well as from an historical viewpoint the wolves, linked with the dogs, are of surpassing interest as an outstanding group of predatory animals. In the more remote parts of North America, especially in Alaska, northern Canada, and on the other extreme, even in Mexico, suitable habitats remain where these large killers can exist in no direct conflict with man. No reason is, therefore, apparent to us why they should not always be tolerated, and even accorded a permanent place in the fauna of the continent; rigid control, however, must be maintained where their presence clashes with human welfare.

II

DISTRIBUTION OF THE WOLF IN NORTH AMERICA, PAST AND PRESENT

ORIGINALLY the wolf occurred from the Plateau of middle Mexico near Mexico City to the extreme polar regions, and from the Atlantic to the Pacific, except in such extreme desert regions as southwestern Arizona, southern Nevada, and southern California. Heat and aridity of these regions were not to its liking, but again they are no bar to the coyote, which is found in most of the desert areas of North America. The wolf occurred on the island of Newfoundland and on the coastal fringes of Greenland, in which latter area they are found in sparse numbers to this day. According to Jensen, the wolf of Greenland has the same distribution as the musk ox, in that it occurs on the north coast and northern part of the east coast as far south as the Scoresby Sound region. He reports that it is only found scattered and comparatively rarely seen (Jensen, A. S., 1928-29: 319).

In the course of the ill-fated Greely Expedition, and while based at Fort Conger on Ellesmere Island, nearly 1,100 miles north of the Arctic Circle, in latitude of approximately 81° 45', Brainard recorded the occurrence of wolves during the early 1880's (Brainard, D. L., 1940: 29, 33, 103).

Similarly General Greely records that:

"The wolf or his fresh tracks have been seen, or his howling

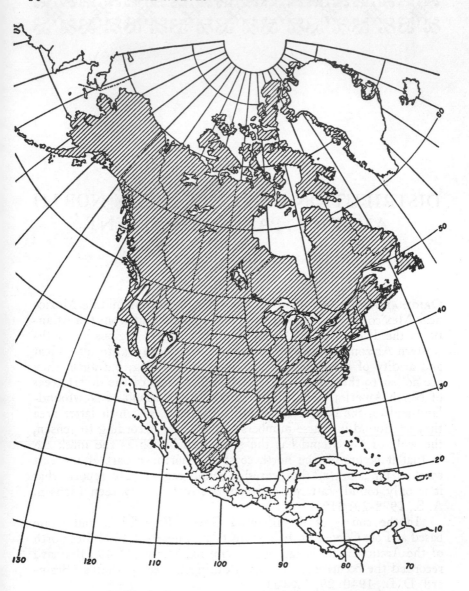

Figure 1. Former distribution of the gray and red wolves of North America

Plate 2. The red wolf, a distinct American species—specimen from Texas

Plate 3. Open oil pool in which Pleistocene wolves and other mammals became mired, and their skeletons preserved for our present-day wonderment. (From drawing by Robert Bruce Horsfall.)

Plate 4. Tracks of Pleistocene wolf from a sandstone quarry at Nevada State Penitentiary, Carson City, Nevada

Plate 5. Live wolf (left) and live coyote (right), showing marked differences in facial appearance

Plate 6. Wolf (left); coyote (right); depicting general external differences

Plate 7. The Mexican wolf which crosses the international boundary from the states of Chihuahua and Sonora

Plate 8. Stanley P. Young with Mexican wolf (*Canis lupus baileyi*), shown in Plate 7, brought to camp alive, Huachuca Mountains, Arizona, November 1, 1917

14

heard in Grinnell Land every winter month except November. . . . The most northerly specimen known is undoubtedly the animal whose tracks were observed April 15, 1876, by Markham near Cape Joseph Henry, 82° 50' N.

"A band of eighteen crossed the harbor-floe within several hundred yards of Fort Conger September 15, 1881. In the summer of 1883 a band of about a dozen was seen passing near the station. They stopped for a while and howled dismally and in concert, but discreetly remained out of gunshot" (Greely, A. W., 1888, v. 2, p. 3).

MacMillan, in the course of 33 years of work in the Arctic, observed the wolf in "Ellesmere Land, Axel Heiberg, Ellef and Amund Ringnes Island, and in Grant Land, four hundred and thirty miles from the Pole." He also "saw their tracks at Cape Morris Jesup, three hundred and eighty miles from the Pole . . . ." This latter distribution places the wolf on the "most northern point of land in the world."[1]

Thus the wolf ranged from the polar cap of North America to the tropical latitude of middle Mexico. It apparently occurred in every State of the Union, as well as in all of the Canadian provinces, and the Territory of Alaska. An account of both the former and present distribution of the animal as revealed by search through available records and by field observations, follows:

ALABAMA

Howell records that:

"Wolves in former times doubtless ranged over the greater part of Alabama, but are now on the verge of extinction. Their last stronghold appears to be the rough, hilly country stretching from Walker County northwestward to Colbert County.

"Little is known of the habits of the Alabama wolves except that they roamed the mountains in small droves and fed considerably on the smaller domestic animals—sheep, goats, pigs, and sometimes calves (Howell, A. H., 1921: 30).

ALASKA

Writing of the wolf in extreme northern Alaska, as noted in the operations of the International Polar expeditions to Point Bar-

---

[1]Letter from Explorer Donald B. MacMillan to E. A. Goldman, March 31, 1941, from Provincetown, Mass. In files of Fish and Wildlife Service.

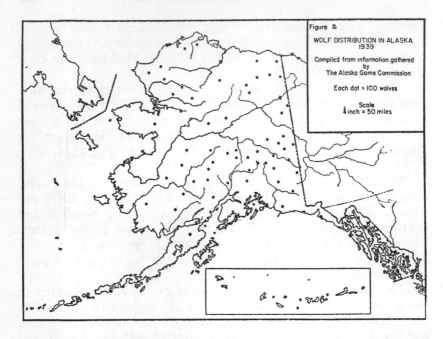

Figure 2

WOLF DISTRIBUTION IN ALASKA
1939

Compiled from information gathered
by
The Alaska Game Commission

Each dot = 100 wolves

Scale
¼ inch = 50 miles

row, Alaska, for the years 1881, 1882, 1883, Sgt. John Murdock, connected with the Signal Corps, U. S. Army, states:

"The wolf never appears to come near the coast in the vicinity of Point Barrow. The natives, however, have a good many of their skins and prize them very highly for trimming their deer skin clothes, especially for making the frill round the hood of the jacket. . . . The natives speak of them as rather plenty inland along the rivers where the reindeer abound and say they chase the deer in packs. Our hunting and exploring parties which went inland in the spring of 1882 and 1883 saw wolves several times but were unable to secure any specimens. The only skin we obtained, a very large male, was shot by a native hunter near Meade River in the spring of 1883. One of the Eskimo trading parties which went east in the summer of 1882 succeeded in catching a couple of male cubs alive. These were brought home early in September, and carefully fed till late in December at which time their fur was supposed to be fit for use. . . . We obtained one skin and six skulls" (Murdoch, J., 1883: 93).

Plate 9. Gray wolf as a southern Arizona invader (*Canis lupus baileyi*)

Nelson observed that:

"The wolf ranges north to beyond the 71st degree of latitude to the Arctic Coast, and in Venaiminoff's account of the Territory (Alaska), written the first part of this century, it is stated that two wolves were killed on Akun Island in 1830, and that they are among the resident animals of Unimak Island. Both these islands are at the extreme eastern end of the Aleutian chain, and this animal is unknown elsewhere among these islands" (Nelson, E. W., 1888: 238).

In his Contributions to the Natural History of Alaska, Turner states:

"This wolf ranges all over the mainland of Alaska. On the Aleutian Islands it occurs only on Unimak; attaining that locality by crossing on the ice, from the north, jamming into 'False' or Isanotsky Pass, separating that island from Alaska" (Turner, L. M., 1886: 208). This records the wolf in its most westerly habitat in North America. Frank Dufresne, Executive Secretary of the Alaska Game Commission, said in 1939 there were no wolves on the Aleutians, and he knew of no wolf being reported on these islands in his 20 years in Alaska.

On June 2, 1937, Clarence J. Rhodes, of the Alaska Game Commission, reported a large wolf killed during the winter of that year near Togiak River on the coastal area north and west of Dillingham. It was the first wolf ever seen in that section; it measured 7 feet in length. Mr. Rhodes believed it to be one of a number of wolves that had recently moved into this part of Alaska. With the exception above-noted, this is the most westerly recording of a wolf in our continent.

The Alaska Game Commission reported in 1938 that:

"Wolves have increased in most parts of the Territory during the past year, particularly in the region occupied by caribou, mountain sheep, and reindeer. In the southeastern islands, their inroads have been checked to some extent by year-long trapping. In a few isolated sections near Cordova and Fairbanks there have been encouraging reports indicating slight decrease in numbers. But taking the Territory as a whole it appears that wolves are far too numerous, and are raising havoc among valuable game and fur animals, and semi-domestic reindeer" (Alaska Game Commission, 1938: 14).

Frank Glaser, during October of 1938, noted 60 wolves the

first week—34 in one band—while in the White Mountains, Alaska, and also stated that it was the first time he had ever seen more than one family of wolves in a band so early in the fall, as in the Alaska Range wolves do not ordinarily band up until about the middle of February.

ARKANSAS

Nuttall, one of the earliest scientific explorers of this region, found the animal northwest of Little Rock where, he states, ". . . . wolves (black and grey) are in considerable abundance in this country" (Nuttall, T., 1821: 118).

The topographical features of this State make for excellent wolf habitat and the animal was once found in goodly numbers throughout most of Arkansas. In later years, up to and including the present time, its range is confined to the Ozark Mountains.

ARIZONA

M. E. Musgrave, formerly of the Fish and Wildlife Service, shot and killed a wolf in the vicinity of Truxton, Ariz., in northeastern Mohave County in 1920. This is the most westerly record of the wolf in the State.

Wolves have been taken in all the counties with the exception of Yuma and Maricopa. In these latter counties Fish and Wildlife records show rare occurrence. Their most frequent occurrence is along the Mexican border in Pima, Santa Cruz, Cochise, Graham, and Greenlee Counties.

CALIFORNIA

The occurrence of the wolf in most of California has been rare. An early diary records it from the vicinity of the San Gabriel Mission in southern California—a part of the State, however, where it seems to have been scarce.

"Thurs. (Jan.) 4th (1827) Still at the Mission; nothing new, ... Myself and Mr. McCoy went up into the mountains to see if we could fine [find] some dear [deer]; I saw two and wounded one, killed a wolf and two ducks; Mr. McCoy saw two dear [deer], and got one shot but missed" (Rogers, H. G., 1918: 218).

Newberry makes the following observations concerning the size and the predominant color of the wolf in California:

"Though much less common than the 'coyote,' the large grey wolf is found in all the uninhabited parts of California and Oregon.

Very few were seen by members of our party, none were killed, and we had everywhere evidence that this species is much less numerously represented on the Pacific Coast than on the upper Missouri. In the Cascade mountains we saw tracks of some of these wolves of most portentous size. All the large wolves seen by any of our party were grey, and all the skins which I saw in the possession of Indians or whites were also grey, and it is probable that the white and black varieties are never found in California. On the upper Columbia, in Oregon and Washington Territories, where the wolves are more numerous and the winters are colder, the same variations occur which are common on the upper Missouri" (Newberry, J. S., 1857, vol. 6, p. 37).

Brewer reports that:

"Jul. 3, 1863. We botanized, etc. during the morning, and in the afternoon returned to Soda Springs. On our way we saw a large wolf, the only large animal of any considerable size that we have seen here" (Brewer, W. H., 1930: 412). (Near Mono Lake and Mount Dana, Calif.)

"August 8, 1863. Two men have wintered here, and in the winter have killed several rare animals—two gluttons, stone martens, silver-gray foxes . . ., large gray wolf, etc." (Ibid., p. 434). (Near Bigtrees, Calaveras County, Calif., not far from Mokelumne River.)

While driving a band of mules during the spring of 1860 from the Sacramento Valley, Calif., to The Dalles, in Oregon, John K. Lord had an encounter with wolves on Shotgun Creek near the Mount Shasta region. While camped at this point on May 11 he "twice . . . . drove them [wolves] out of my camp with a fire log" (Lord, J. K., 1866: 250). On May 12 Lord passed a group of mining packers camped nearby on Mary's Creek. They had likewise been troubled by wolves, for "The rascally wolves had pulled down one of their mules, and torn it almost to pieces" (Ibid.).

One of General Fremont's party on his Second Expedition, Mr. Preus, on March 5, 1844, while entering the Sacramento Valley in California, "had collected firewood for the night when he heard at some distance from the river the barking of what he thought were two dogs, and walked in that direction as quickly as he was able hoping to find there some Indian hut, but met only two wolves; . . . ." (Fremont, J. C., 1887: 349).

In the course of his second expedition, and while in California along the San Joaquin River on April 7, 1844, Fremont states:

"We made on the 7th, a hard march in cold, chilly rain from morning until night—the weather so thick that we travelled by compass. This was a traverse from the San Joaquin to the waters of the Tule Lakes, and our road was over a level prairie country.

"We saw wolves frequently during the day—prowling about after the young antelope, which cannot run very fast" (Ibid., p. 359).

It is quite possible that these "wolves" may have been coyotes, but as Fremont knew the distinguishing features of the two animals, his observations as to their being wolves should not be discredited.

Frank Stephens, in his California Mammals, states: "A very few gray wolves live in the high Sierras and in the mountains of northeastern California." Mr. Stephens also states he knew of no "California example in any museum or private collection" (Stephens, F., 1906: 217). Prior to the publication of this volume, no general work covering the mammals of California had been published since 1857, when Baird's Vol. 8, of the Pacific Railroad reports, was issued.

Dr. Joseph Grinnell, regarding the wolf in California, states:

"We have the skull of a veritable wolf taken within the eastern boundary of California the past winter."[2]

Dr. Grinnell further states:

"Formerly, doubtless, occurred far and wide through northern and eastern portions of the State; no available evidence indicates presence within historic times in west-central California or in southern California west of deserts. Now probably altogether extinct within our boundaries . . . . The last veritable wolves have held out along our eastern borders, in Modoc, Lassen, and eastern San Bernardino Counties, where individuals were captured in 1922, 1924, and 1922, respectively." (Grinnell, Dixon, and Linsdale, MS.) (Grinnell, J., 1933: 114.)

CANADA

In recording the existence of mammals occurring in Newfoundland, Bonnycastle stated:

"The wolf (*Canis lupus occidentalis*) of Richardson grows very large, is frequently traced near the capital, and does much injury

---

[2]Letter of Dr. Joseph Grinnell of Museum of Vertebrate Zoology, University of California, to Ernest Thompson Seton, April 25, 1923.

to young cattle; a price is put by the legislature on its head" (Bonnycastle, R. H., 1842: 224).

It is apparent that Newfoundland contained a goodly population of wolves during the first part of the last century, dwindling in numbers toward its close. An account of 1875 states, "There can be no doubt that in the interior of Newfoundland wolves are in strong force. . . . Few winters are passed without some wolves being trapped along the shores. They often prowl near the houses of the settlers, or pass them in the chase" (Anonymous, 1875: 390).

Adams listed the animal among the quadrupeds of New Brunswick, stating that by 1873 it was found only in the northern part of this province (Adams, A. L., 1873: 295).

In Labrador near the turn of the century, Bangs reported its being common in the barrens and semi-barrens of the North, but in the southern wooded region, owing to the diminution of the woodland caribou, it was becoming rare (Bangs, O., 1898b: 505).

Describing the country on the east side of the Rockies, Harmon, one of the partners in the N. W. Fur Co., stated:

"That part of it which lies between the 44th and 52nd degrees of north latitude is a plain or prairie country, almost wholly destitute of timber, of any kind. It is, in general, sufficiently dry for any kind of cultivation; and is covered with grass, which commonly grows to the height of from six inches to a foot, though in marshy places it is much higher. This grass furnishes food for innumerable herds of buffaloes, which are constantly roving about from place to place followed by thousands of wolves, . . ." (Harmon, D. W., 1820: 331).

Harmon spent 19 years (1800-1819) in the service of the N. W. Fur Co., eight of them in the Rocky Mountains, or between these mountains and the Pacific. Starting as a clerk in the company, he eventually became Superintendent of all the N. W. Fur Co. beyond the Rockies.

In a bulletin issued by the Bureau of Provincial Information, Victoria, British Columbia, it is stated that the wolf is "found more or less all over the Province, but particularly numerous on Vancouver Island and along the northern coast" (British Columbia, Province of: 1910: 27).

An interesting observation was recorded by Bernard Gilpin with respect to the fluctuations of the wolf in Nova Scotia. In 1868 he stated:

". . . the wolf in his white or grey variety, endeavoring in vain to re-habit the Province. During the last sixty or seventy years [this would mean for the period that began approximately with the year 1800] they have constantly appeared, single and in pairs, at each extremity of the Province and then have been unheard of for years" (Gilpin, J. B., 1870: 60).

It is obvious from these early, as well as from later, records that the wolf during earlier times was fairly well distributed over the entire Dominion of Canada from coast to coast, and from the present southern boundary northwest to and including much of the Arctic regions, on the mainland as well as on the islands.

THE CAROLINAS

In the seventeenth century the term Florida was applied some-what indefinitely to all of the southeastern United States. On Cape Fear River, in what is now southern North Carolina, Hilton reported:

". . . we heard several Wolves howling in the woods and saw where they had torn a Deer in pieces" (Hilton, W., 1911: 47).

In the vicinity of Charleston, S. C., Hilton also reported:

". . . from the abundance of their Feeding great numbers (cattle) forsake their own Plantations, running wild in the Woods, the Tyger, Wolf, and Wild Cat, by devouring them, oftentimes goes Share with the Planter" (Ibid., p. 149).

Near Abbeville County, S. C., Cuming stated:

"March 13, 1730. . . . This Day William Cooper killed a Buffalo, a Viper, a Fox Squirrel, and wounded three wolves, which set upon their great Dog and tore out Part of his Entrails" (Cuming, Alexander, 1928: 21).

Catesby, an early authority, recorded:

"The wolves in Carolina are very numerous, and more destructive than another animal. They go in droves by night, and hunt deer like hounds, with dismal yelling cries" (Catesby, M., 1743: vol. 2, p. 26).

Between the Yadkin and Catewba Rivers, Daniel Boone asserted:

". . . wild turkeys were easy prey . . . while wolves, panthers, and wildcats overran the country" (Thwaites, R. G., 1902: 18).

COLORADO

A statement by Emerson Carney concerning Colorado and Wyoming is descriptive of the time when the wolf was apparently still holding its own in spite of the warfare against it: "Owing to the openness and natural advantages for hunters in that region, all big game animals are disappearing faster than they ever did in any of our eastern forests, but what of the wolf? . . . With four practicable ways open for his undoing in the West, he not only grows more abundant, but adds new territory to his possessions and refuses to be 'ousted,' while all other of the larger animals of the West are rapidly disappearing" (Carney, E., 1902: 84).

FLORIDA

In this State it was recorded that:

"Wolves are found in all the unsettled parts of the Territory; but except in purloining a calf, occasionally, they are little known. Their attention is usually directed to the sheep and of these, there are, as yet, very few in the Territory" (Goodrich, A. T., 1837: 63).

Many years after a protracted hunting trip in Florida, Whitehead recorded his experiences in a narrative that includes much humanized description. He relates that:

"These wolves are funny fellows. You would hear one howl away down the river just audibly above the insect hum. Then an instant's pause, and another answers from the opposite shore and then one close at hand gives a yelpish whine as though he had been intending to howl, but a bone that he had in his mouth stopped him until he laid the bone down and hurriedly had his howl out. Most of the wolves in the Gulf coast are black. . . .

"The first sleeper had just begun to emit a hoarse breathing . . ., when we heard, 'Ah- ha- whoo-a-whoo-oo-oo!' from a little way down shore. 'Bow-ow-owe-owe!' said every dog in camp, in different tones of shrillness . . . .

"Everybody turned over; wolves are never dangerous unless to your provisions, . . . a sound of strangulation from the Doctor . . . forboded . . . sleep when 'Ooh-ooh ooough,' came the old note, followed by the rush of the dogs . . . .

"There seemed to be a concert near us; for the moment one wolf would get tired, another would take up the refrain until it was soon apparent there was no more sleep for that night. We only took cat naps, . . . talking and conjuring up all the old stories of wolves that we had ever heard of . . . .

"Mike's opinion of him was that he was a 'dratted mean cuss, feared to hunt deer alone and fodderin' on his own young ones when he can't ketch nothin' else.' "

A curious legend concerning wolves was to the effect that:

"The negro boys entertained the belief that the luminous appearance from their eyes at night arose from their feasting on the slain in battle, and a suspicion that they sometimes visited graveyards for other purposes than pensive meditations" (Whitehead, C. E., 1891: 258).

Cory, in his book on hunting and fishing in Florida, published in 1896, recorded that the wolf in Florida was: "still not uncommon in some localities. In the vicinity of the Big Cypress and in the extreme Southern Florida wolves still occur in some numbers. A wolf was seen in the spring of 1895 near Little Fish Crossing, southwest of Lake Worth. They are usually black, although examples have been killed which were brown, shading into gray on the belly and breast.

"I have heard of gray wolves in Florida, but have never seen one. Robert Osceola killed a female with two cubs near the Big Cypress in the spring of 1894. He captured the little ones alive and took them to his camp; but they would not eat, and, after keeping them a day or two, he killed them. The mother and both pups were black" (Cory, C. B., 1896: 110).

Wolves doubtless ranged over the greater part of Florida in primitive times, but they were gradually reduced in numbers as the country became settled, and were finally exterminated early in the present century. In 1774 William Bartram, on his journey through the State, observed wolves at several places. While he was camping on the shore of Lake George one night, a wolf circled his camp and carried off a piece of broiled fish. Near the Alachua Savanna he observed a company of wolves feeding on the carcass of a horse; they sat on their haunches until the travelers approached within about gunshot, when they trotted off towards the forest. He described the Florida wolves as being "perfectly black except the females, which have a white spot on the breast!" (Bartram, W., 1928: 232.) At another place in his narrative he says he had been informed that they "are frequently seen pied, black and white, and of other mixed colours" (Ibid., p. 232).

The type specimen of the Florida subspecies in the U. S. National Museum was taken August 12, 1890, on the St. Johns River in Putnam County, and was presented to the Museum by Dr. W. L. Ralph. It was described by G. S. Miller, Jr. (1912b: 95).

R. D. Hoyt, in a letter to H. H. T. Jackson in 1903 stated that there were at that time some wolves "on the prairie next the Everglades."

Maynard was of the opinion that the wolves in Florida did not "occur south of the Everglades" (1872: 138).

GEORGIA

While journeying in northeast Georgia in the vicinity of Broad and Little Rivers north and west of Augusta in the late spring of 1773, William Bartram mentions in his travels:

"Bears, tigers (this creature is called in Pennsylvania and northern states, panther, but in Carolina and the southern states is called tiger; it is very strong, much larger than any dog, of a yellowish brown, or clay colour, having a very long tail; it is a mischievous animal, and preys on calves, young colts, etc.) *wolves* . . . are numerous enough" (1928: 63).

The animal no doubt formerly occurred throughout all of the State in numbers.

Harper feels that Okefenokee Swamp of southeastern Georgia was "one of its last strongholds, and may even yet [1927] shelter a few survivors" (1927: 260). However, at the present time, indications are that the wolf is now extinct in Georgia.

ILLINOIS

It is stated in an early account of what is now Illinois:

"There are but few beavers, but to make amends, there is a large number of buffaloes or bears, large wolves, stags, *sibolas* (Spanish for buffalo), hinds and roe deer in abundance; . . ." (de Tonty, H., 1917: 302).

"The winter of 1830 and '31 [the first that the Lincoln family spent in Illinois] was the celebrated winter of the deep snow. . . . such a snow has never since been known. The settlers were blockaded in their cabins. . . . A great deal of stock was frozen to death. . . . The deer and wild turkeys, which had been very numerous, were almost exterminated. The wolves, on the other hand, had a pleasant time of it. They played around over the snow, caught all the deer they wished, and were bold and impudent" (Duis, E., 1874: 9).

During the middle of the past century, Kennicott mentions the animal as formerly common, and that it "has been found throughout the state" (Kennicott, R., 1855: 578).

INDIANA

At the turn of the 19th century, Warden recorded that in Indiana "The woods abound with deer. Bears and wolves are also numerous" (Warden, D. B., 1819: vol. 2, p. 292).

Marcus Ward Lyon, Jr., states:

"Undoubtedly wolves were once abundant throughout the whole of Indiana. The first naturalist to write of Indiana mammals, the Prince of Wied, says they were not rare in the great forests about the Wabash and in New Harmony one heard their howlings on cold nights (winter of 1832-33)" (1936: 153).

According to Lyon's reckoning from available Indiana records, "the wolf in Indiana was practically extinct toward the end of the first decade of the present century. One was reported killed on December 19, 1908, near Monroe City in Knox County, but Lyon questions that this was a true wolf" (Ibid., p. 153).

He further states:

"The true wolf is too large and conspicuous an animal and not cunning enough to compete with man in a thickly settled state like Indiana" (Ibid., p. 155).

McAtee mentions the occurrence of a female wolf with a litter of young taken in Brown County in south central Indiana during 1902 (McAtee, W. L., 1907: 6).

IOWA

Western Iowa appears to have harbored the greatest number of wolves during the early settlement of that State, the animals occurring but sparingly in its other sections. The species is completely extirpated at the present time, and most of the old wolf range is inhabited by the coyote.

In 1869 Allen wrote: Wolves "were rather common less than twenty years since, they are now scarce, especially in the more settled districts. They are usually termed mountain wolves, in distinction from the prairie wolves (coyotes)" (Allen, J. A., 1871a: 181).

KENTUCKY

Dr. Thomas Walker, in his Journal, records the following:

"(May) 31st (1750) We crossed 2 mountains and camped just by a Wolf's Den. They were very impudent and after they had been twice shot at, they kept howling about the Camp.

"June ye 1st (1750) We found the Wolf's Den and caught 4 of the young ones (Magoffin County, Kentucky)" (Walker, T., 1898: 65).

Funkhouser states that "Wolves were very abundant in Kentucky in early days, but seemed to disappear more rapidly with the establishment of settlements than any of the other wild animals," . . . and he associates this with the probability that it was due to "the cutting of the forests." Also by 1809 "wolves had ceased to be a serious menace . . . ," "for on Feb. 1st" of that year the state bounty law was repealed. However, on January 26, 1810, the state legislature passed an act which gave the various counties of the state the right to pay bounties at the stipulated price of $1.50 for each wolf over six months old that was killed. (Funkhouser, W. D., 1925: 41). By the early 1890's Garman listed the animal as not common in the Blue Grass State. (Garman, H., 1894: 63).

LOUISIANA

During my visit to Louisiana in October of 1934, red wolves (but no large greys) were found to exist in Madison Parish in considerable numbers. They were also found in W. and E. Carroll as well as Franklin and Tensas Parishes. In fact, the whole of N. E. Louisiana seems to contain a fair representation of wolves today. They are also reported from the extreme southwestern part of Louisiana in Cameron and Calcasieu Parishes. I have also received information as to their occurrence in La Salle and W. Feliciana Parishes. In Louisiana, the red wolf in 1934 was holding its own, if not slightly increasing.

MARYLAND

The wolves that formerly occurred in this State were confined mainly to northern and northwestern Maryland. According to an old record:

"In the upper parts of the Countrey there are Bufeloes, Elkes, Lions, Beares, Wolves, and Deare there are in great store, . . ." (Anonymous, 1910b: 80).

An old-time Maryland hunter, Meshach Browning, gives a good idea of the occurrence of wolves in this State during early times— some of his comments are used later in the text.

MEXICO

According to Gregg:
"The large gray wolf of the prairies is also to be found in great

abundance in northern Mexico. They sometimes make dreadful havoc among the cattle, frequently killing and devouring even mules and horses; . . ." (Gregg, Josiah, 1905, vol. 19, p. 327).

This wolf of Gregg's, now recognized as the wolf of the Sierra Madres, is a distinct geographic race. They have always occurred in large numbers throughout most of northern Mexico, and up to the present time do not seem to have diminished appreciably in numbers.

Along the southern border of the United States, in the Mexican states of Sonora, Chihuahua, and Coahuila, I found the wolf to be fairly numerous in 1916-17-18. However, it seems that the wolf never occurred at any time in Lower California. According to Nelson, he was "unable . . . to find any definite record of wolves ever having occurred in the peninsula, and conditions there do not appear to be favorable for them" (Nelson, E. W., 1921: 132).

MICHIGAN

In early times they were found to occur throughout the entire State. Wood mentions their being destructive to sheep along the southern border in present-day Washtenaw County during the 1830's (Wood, N. A., 1922: 8).

Their later range has been confined mainly to the upper peninsula and at present but few remain. In the early 1920's they gave some concern in conjunction with the coyote to those inhabitants of the upper peninsula who had ventured into livestock production. During the interval of State cooperative efforts with the Federal Government in wolf control measures, covering approximately a decade, a total of 551 wolves were removed, mainly from northern Michigan.

The State at present allows a bounty on the animals, and during 1940 paid on 33; the same number were bountied in 1939, 49 in 1938, and 37 in 1937. All of these wolves apparently came from the upper peninsula.

MINNESOTA

Of wolves in Minnesota, Keating says:

"The . . . prairies as seen by the bright moonlight, the freshness of the night air, the stillness of the scenery, interrupted only by the . . . howlings [of wolves] suggests to the mind melancholy yet not unpleasant reflections" (Keating, W. H., 1825: 19).

As late as 1932 Surber stated: "In the more remote sections of the northern third of the state . . . [the wolf] is still fairly common, its abundance dependable upon the food supply." Also that in spite of a scarce food supply "enough of them remain to have become a rather serious menace to the deer herds in all the border counties" (Surber, T., 1932: 55).

MISSISSIPPI

The reported presence of wolves in Mississippi was investigated in June 1932 by Roy Moore (Assistant Regional Director) of the Fish and Wildlife Service.

"Three small packs of wolves [red] were located in western Mississippi. One pack of three ranging in Jefferson and Franklin Counties centering around Oldenburg of Franklin County. These are very destructive, killing more than 700 goats and 20 calves. One pack of two old and three young were located north of Carlisle, eastern part of Claiborne County. Their headquarters are west of Dentville, Copiah County, where another small pack of three or four are located permanently. The above-mentioned seem to have crossed the river during the flood of 1927. One was located ranging in Jackson County. . . .[3]

At the time this investigation was made (June, 1932), it was believed that there were about a dozen wolves, all of the red species, in the entire country within a radius of 50 to 60 miles east of Natchez, Miss., and circumstances indicated that these wolves had been forced to cross the Mississippi River by the flood waters on the Louisiana side during the high water of 1927.

In early day Mississippi, according to Wailes:

"The Wolf, like the Bear, has been driven into retirement, and is now rarely seen in the older settled parts of the country. Wolves are still numerous, however, in the sparsely settled districts of the State, and emerge in packs occasionally from their fastnesses, on marauding excursions to the neighboring sheepfolds, and, with a wasteful prodigality of blood, destroy and mangle ten times as many as they can devour.

"They are taken in pens or traps made of poles, and baited with fresh meat, which is previously dragged over the ground for miles through the woods near their haunts, to lure them to the trail. Pits

---

[3]Official letter from Roy Moore, together with report, in files of Fish and Wildlife Service.

are also constructed with a slight covering of twigs and leaves, into which they fall in attempting to reach the bait suspended over them" (Wailes, B. L. C., 1854: 314).

MISSOURI

Missouri probably contained the so-called plains, or buffalo, wolf, as well as the present-day wolf known as the Mississippi Valley wolf, a geographical race of the Texas red wolf. For the past 20 years these latter wolves have been taken in Missouri in cooperative predatory animal control work in connection with livestock depredations. During the fiscal year ending June 30, 1940, a total of 59 wolves were captured. The majority of these came from the counties south of the Missouri River. It is believed that the so-called buffalo wolf, formerly found in Missouri, is now extirpated from that State.

NEVADA

According to recorded observations with respect to mammal life in Nevada, the wolf has always been scarce. Only six wolves have been taken in more than two decades of predatory animal operations in the cooperative predatory work of the Fish and Wildlife Service in this State. Of this number, 3 were taken in Elko County near Mountain City; 1 near Eureka in the same county; 1 in White Pine County; and 1 near Leadville in Washoe County.

Turnbull recorded while along the Humboldt River in Nevada:

"July 15—Camp'd 4 o'clock. Good grass and plenty of it. A large grey Wolfe came to a dead horse about 50 rod from us. . . .

"July 16—Stopped at 1 o'clock and fed. Good grass all along. Saw one very large grey wolfe" (1913: 164, 195, 200, 208).

While approaching Humboldt Sink in western Nevada, he further wrote:

"July 22—Plenty wolves howl all night, very large grey fellows" (Ibid., pp. 164, 195, 200, 208).

The following citations were apparently made while Turnbull was in the Carson Valley, western Nevada:

"August 1—Stopped all day. Seen wolves here in every direction at night.

"August 2—This country around here looks something like a country for mining. Passed 2 dead cattle. . . . wolves plenty" (Ibid., pp. 164, 195, 200, 208).

Plate 10. Wolf taken in the vicinity of Truxton Canyon, northwestern Arizona, on September 1, 1921—the most westerly record for the State

Plate 11. Black phase of red wolf (*Canis niger gregoryi*)

Plate 12. Alaskan wolves. On the average, wolves of this region and of the Canadian northwest territories are the largest in North America

Plate 13. Seventy-nine pound wolf trapped in northern Wisconsin; winter of 1931

Plate 14. Wolf taken during 1928, Highwood Mountains, Montana. Some wolves in this state have averaged more than 100 pounds in weight

Plate 15. Part of one trapper's fur catch, season of 1933, on the Savage River, 15 miles west of Healey, Alaska. The two light-colored wolf skins shown in the center measured 8 feet 6 inches and 8 feet 4 inches, respectively. (Photo courtesy of Frank Glaser)

THE NEW ENGLAND STATES

All of New England contained wolves, as recorded by Trumbull, who states:

"The wolf, wild cat, and other animals, common in New England, were equally so in Connecticut. Wolves were numerous in all parts of New England when the settlers commenced, and did great damage to the planters, killing their sheep, calves, and young cattle" (Trumbull, B., 1818: 39).

Goodwin records that

"In the past, the wolf ranged throughout the State of Connecticut. In 1842, Linsley says, 'Only three years since, a very large wolf was killed near Bridgeport by Mr. Moses Bulkley; and one 10 years since, in Newtown, by Mr. Aaron Glover.' Other than these two records, however, we do not seem to have any further history of the wolf in Connecticut" (1935: 82).

The instance cited from Goodwin was approximately 100 years after the famous episode of General Israel Putnam's finding a wolf den 35 miles northeast of Hartford, which will be recounted later in the text.

Morton, who gives one of the first accounts, said of the New England wolves:

"The wolfes are of divers coloures: some sandy coloured; some griselled, and some black, their foode is fish which they catch when they passe up the rivers, into the ponds to spawne, at the spring time. The Deare are also their pray, and at summer, when they have whelpes, the bitch will fetch a puppy dogg from our dores, to feede their whelpes with. They are fearefull Curres, and will runne away from a man (that meeteth them by chance at a banke end) as fast as any feareful dogge. These pray upon the Deare very much. The skinnes are used by the Salvages, especially the skinne of the black wolfe, which is esteemed a present for a prince there.

"When there ariseth any difference betweene prince, and prince, the prince that desires to be reconciled to his neighbouring prince does endeavour to purchase it, by sending him a black wolfes skinne for a present, and the acceptance of such a present is an assurance of reconciliation betweene them; and the salvages will willingly give 40 beaver skinnes for the purchase of one of these black wolfes skinnes; and although the beast himselfe be a discommodity, which other Countries of Christendome are subject unto, yet is the skinne of the black Wolfe worthy, the title of a commodity, in that respect that hath been declared" (Morton, T., 1637: 79).

Wood, an even earlier recorder, says:

". . . . there would be more of them (bears) if it were not for the wolves, which devour them; a kennell of those ravening runnagadoes, setting on a poor single Beare, will teare him as a dogge will teare a Kid; it would be a good change if the countrey had for every Woolfe a Beare, upon the condition that all the Woolves were banished; so should the Inhabitants be not only rid of their greatest annoyance, but furnished with more store of provisions. . . ." (Wood, W., 1635: 17, 18, 20, 21).

He continues:

". . . . These poore beasts (moose) are likewise much devoured by the Woolves: . . . . The ordinary Deare desire to be neare the Sea, so that they may swimme to the Islands when they are chased by the Woolves: It is not to be thought into what great multitudes they would encrease, were it not for the common devourer the Wolfe: They have generally three at a time which they hide a mile one from another giving sucke by turnes; thus they doe, that if the Wolfe should find one, he might misse the other" (Ibid., p. 18).

And then inclines to fable:

". . . . The Woolves be in some respect different from them in other countries; it was never knowne yet that a Woolfe ever set upon a man or a woman. Neither doe they trouble Horses or Cowes; but Swine, Goate and red Calves, which they take for Deare, be often destroyed by them, so that a red Calfe is cheaper than a blacke one in that regard in some places; in the time of Autumn and in the beginning of the Spring, these ravenous rangers doe most frequent our English habitations, following the Deere which come down at that time to those parts. They be made much like a Mungrell, being big boned, lanke paunched, deepe breasted, having a thicke necke, and head, pricke ears, and long snoute with dangerous teeth, long staring haire, and a great bush taile; it is thought of many that our English Mastiffes might be too hard for them; but it is no such matter, for they car no more for an ordinary Mastiffe, than an ordinary Mastiffe cares for a Curre; many good dogges have been spoyled by them. Once a faire Grayhound hearing them at their howlings run out to chide them, who was torne in peeces before he could be rescued. One of them makes no more bones to runne away with a Pigge, than a

Dogge to runne away with a Marrow bone. It is observed that they have no joynts from their head to the taile, which prevents them from leaping, or sudden turning, as may appeare by what I shall shew you. A certaine man having shot a Woolfe, as he was feeding upon a Swine, breaking his leg onely, he knew not how to devise his death; on a suddaine, the Woolfe being a blacke one, he was loath to spoyle his furre with a second shot, his skin being worth five or sixe pound Sterling; wherefore hee resolved to get him by the tayle, and thrust him into a river that was hard by; which effected, the Woolfe being not able to turne his joyntless body to bite him, was taken (Ibid., p. 20).

"... . That they cannot leape may appeare by this Woolfe, whose mouth watering at a few poore impaled Kiddes, would needes leape over a five-footed pale to get at them; but his foote slipping in the rise, he feel shorrt of his desire, and being hung in the Carpenters stockes, howled so loud, that he frightened away the Kids, and called the English, who killed him. These he killed daily in some place or other, either by the English, or Indian; who have a certaine rate for every head. Yet there is little hope of their utter destruction, the Countrey being so spacious, and they so numerous, travelling in the Swamps by Kennels: sometimes ten or twelve are of a company. Late at night, and early in the morning, they set up their howlings and call their companies together, at night to hunt, at morning to sleepe; in a word, they may be the greatest inconvenience the Countrey hath, both for matter of dammage to private men in particular, and the whole Country in generall" (Ibid., p. 21).

Lechford found in New England that:

"There are Bears, Wolves and Foxes and many other wilde beasts, as the Moose, a kind of Deere, as big as some Oxen and Lyons, as I have heard. The Wolves and Foxes are a great annoyance" (1642: 111).

In our most northeasterly state, Williamson said of the animals:

"... . The fox is sometimes mischievous. But no wild creature has been more troublesome to the husbandman than the *Wolf*. Till the separation[4] a bounty of four pounds currency was provided by law for every one killed. It weighs about 80 or 90 pounds" (Williamson, W. D., 1839: 137).

[4]The term *separation* here refers to the separation from Massachusetts in 1820, when Maine became a State.

Later writing by Norton reveals that:

"Wolves were numerous in the Portland (Maine) region, and existed at least down to 1740 in the immediate vicinity of the present city" (Norton, A. H., 1930: 41).

Loomis and Young report the occurrence of wolf skeletal remains from the Sawyer's Island shell heap (Loomis, F. B., and Young, D. B., 1912: 24, 25, 27).

From the foregoing and from a resume of early colonial bounty acts, it is clear that the wolf occurred throughout all of the New England States, and varied as to density of population, congregating at times in large numbers around the early colonial habitations that possessed swine, sheep, and cattle where it did much damage. Of early Rhode Island it is said:

"The Indians had no fowls. . . . There was, says Williams, 'wonderful plenteous hunting.' Sometimes 'they pursue in twentie, fortie, fiftie, yea two hundred in a company. . . .' They were ingenious trappers, well knew the habits of the waterfowl and land birds, of the deer and wolf, and ready to take advantage of them" (Dorr, H. C., 1885: 146). (This was written of Rhode Island district near Narragansett Bay. Dorr in this quotes from Roger Williams' "Key into the language of America," London, 1643.)

Roger Williams, founder of the colony of Rhode Island in 1636, writes of the Indians trapping deer and wolves as follows:

". . . They are very tender of their traps, where they lie and what comes at them; for they say the Deere (whom they conceive to have a Devine power in them) will soon smelle and be gone. . . . Nummishkommin—I have found a Deere; which sometimes they doe, taking a Wolfe in the very act of his greedy prey, when sometimes (the Wolfe being greedy of his prey) they kill him: sometimes the Wolfe having glutted himselfe with the one halfe, leaves the other for the next bait; but the glad Indian finding of it prevents him. . . .

"I remember how a poor Deere was long hunted and chased by a Wolfe, at last (as their manner is) after the chase of ten, it may be more, miles running, the stout Wolfe tired out the nimble Deer, and seasing upon it kill'd; In the act of devouring his prey, two English Swine, big with Pig, past by, assaulted the Wolfe, drove him from his prey and devoured so much of that poore Deere as they both surfeited and died that night.

"The Wolfe is an Embleme of a fierce blood-sucking persecutor.

... Neummootamuch qun natoqus, The Wolfe hath rob'd me.

"When a Deer is caught by the leg in a trap, sometimes there it lies a day together before the Indian come, so lies a pray to the raging Wolfe, and other wild Beasts (most commonly the Wolfe) who seaseth upon the Deere and Robs the Indian (at his first devouring) of neere halfe his prey, and if the Indian come not sooner, hee makes a second greedie Meale and leaves him nothing but the bones, and the torn, Deereskins, especially if he call some of his greedy Companions to his bloody banquet.

"Upon this, the Indian makes a falling trap called Sunnuckhig (with great weight of stones), and so sometimes Knocks the Wolfe on the head with a gainefull revenge, especially if it bee a blacke Wolfe, whose Skin they greatly prize" (Williams, R., 1827: 142).

Again, this smallest of the states is described as follows:

"Road-Island is of a considerable bigness. . . . It abounds with all things necessary for the life of Man, is excellent for Sheep, Kine and Horses; and being environed by the Sea, it is freed from the dangers of Bears, Wolves, and Foxes, which molest and damnifie those that live on the Continent" (Kimball, G. S., 1900: 13).

The expression "the continent" in the foregoing is interpreted to refer to parts of the mainland adjacent to Narragansett Bay, as distinguished from the island of Rhode Island, which lies between the lower Sakonet River and the Eastern Passage of the bay. This usage appears in a number of early journals.

Samuel Williams' "Native Animals" gives an interesting record of this early Vermont historian's impressions of the New England wolf:

"One of the most common and noxious of all our animals is the Wolf. In the form of his body, the wolf resembles much the dog. He has a long head, a pointed nose, sharp and erect ears, a short and thick neck, with sharp and strong teeth. His eyes generally appear sparkling; and there is a wildness and a fierceness in his looks. The colour of the wolf in Vermont, is a dirty grey; with some tinges of yellow about his ears and legs. This animal is extremely fierce, sanguinary, and carnivorous. When a number of them associate, it is not for peace but for war and destruction. The animal at which they most of all aim, is the sheep. When they can find a flock of these, they seem to delight in slaughter; tearing their flesh and sucking their blood, after they are fully satisfied with the fat of their tender parts. They attack the deer, foxes, rabbits, and are enemies to all other animals; and their attacks are generally attended with the most horrid howlings. They generally flee before the face of the hunter; but when they have once tasted of human flesh, they become more fierce, and daring, and seem to be inflamed with greater fury. In such a state, there have been instances in Vermont, in which the wolves have ventured to make their attacks upon men; but they generally retire upon their approach. They are not often to be seen in the day, but in the night venture into our yards and barns. These animals are yet in great numbers, in this state; They destroy a great many of our sheep in the night; and find a safe retreat in our woods and mountains. The wolf is a very prolific animal. The female is in season in the winter, but the male and female never pair. The time of gestation, is about three months and a half; and the young whelps are found from the beginning of May, until the month of July. The hunters have sometimes found in their dens, a male, a female, and a litter of nine young whelps. One of the largest wolves in Vermont, weighed ninety-two pounds. There is nothing valuable in these animals but their skins, which afford a warm and durable fur" (Williams, S., 1809: 101).

Jacob Green recounts an interesting observation of a wolf "in the wilds of Vermont" a few years prior to 1821. He describes an encounter between a wolf and a wild razor-back boar aided by a herd of swine, of which the boar was apparently the leader. The wolf received a fatal thrust from the boar's tusks (Green, J., 1822: 309).

By the close of the 18th century wolves had practically disappeared from most of New England, though they remained fairly common in the southern parts of Maine, Vermont, and New Hampshire, as well as in the mountainous sections of western Massachusetts.

NEW JERSEY

The early inhabitants of New Jersey, as will be noted later, used pits as a means of wolf control. On the animal's occurrence in this State, we find that:

"Adjacent to the Delaware River and bay and the sea coast, there are wide tracts of salt meadow which are in a few places improved by embankments. The climate near the coast is so mild that herds of cattle subsist through the winter upon these meadows, and in neighboring thickets, without expense to the proprietors, . . . wolves and bears are sometimes seen in the wilds of New Jersey" (Pierce, J., 1823b: 241).

Thomas, in giving an early record of New Jersey, says:

"As to Wild Vermin, There are Otters, Beavers, Foxes, . . . Likewise there were some Wolves and Bears, but now they are very rare to be seen, by reason the Indians destroy them. . . ." (Thomas, G., 1912: 348).

Smith, an early New Jersey historian, recorded that the wolf was common to all parts of the State, being one of the main predators on the deer (Smith, S., 1765: 502).

NEW MEXICO

As will be noted later, Abert found the wolf numerous enough to be troublesome in the 1840's in the vicinity of Raton Pass in northeastern New Mexico, as did Pancoast, but a short distance from Albuquerque in the summer of 1849. Apparently, wolves were very common in New Mexico at the beginning of its settlement by the Spaniards and later by the Americans. Today wolves continue to invade the state from Mexico, particularly along its southwestern border.

Woodhouse reported the wolf as "very common throughout the Indian territory, Texas, and New Mexico" (Woodhouse, S. W., 1853: 45).

A few years previous to the observations made by Abert, Pancoast, and Woodhouse, Gregg had observed that the gray wolf was abundant in northern Mexico (present day New Mexico), where "they sometimes make dreadful havoc among the cattle, frequently killing and devouring even mules and horses; . . ." (Thwaites, R. G., 1904-07, vol. 19, p. 327).

NEW YORK

With regard to the occurrence of the wolf in this State, Pierce records that:

"Of wolves, two varieties inhabit the Catskill mountains; one called by hunters the deer wolf from its habit of pursuing deer, for which his light grey hound form adapts him. The other of a more clumsy figure with short legs and large body, more frequently depredates upon flocks under the protection of man" (Pierce, J., 1823a: 93).

The occurrence of the animal in this State will be more fully detailed in the discussion of bounties. Wolves made their final stand in the Adirondack section of New York. De Kay, in his Natural History of New York in 1842, states: "In some of the Southern counties, where they were formerly so numerous as to require legislative enactments, they are now nearly extirpated. . . . They are still found in the mountainous and wooded parts of the State and we believe are most numerous in St. Lawrence and the adjacent counties" (De Kay, J. E., 1842: 43).

De Kay's comments, particularly concerning St. Lawrence County, received later confirmation, for it is in this section that some of the last wolves were bountied in the late nineties.

Of the wolf in New York, Lanman relates a story of John Cheney, Adirondack hunter, as follows:

"Another animal, that we sometimes find pretty plenty in these woods, is the big grey wolf; they are savage fellows and dangerous to meet when angry. On getting up early one winter morning, I noticed in the back part of my garden, what I thought to be a wolf track. I got my gun, called for the dogs, and started on the hunt. I found the fellow in his den among the mountains. I kindled a fire and smoked him out. I then chased him about two miles, when he came to bay. He was a big fellow and my dogs were afraid to clinch in;—dogs hate a wolf worse than any other animal. . . . I fired at the creature but my gun missed fire. The wolf then attacked me, and in striking him with my gun, I broke it all to pieces. I was in a pretty bad fix, I tell you, but immediately threw myself on my back, with my snow shoes above me, when the wolf jumped right on to my body, and probably would have killed me if it had not been for my dog, Buck, who worried the wolf so badly, that the devil left me to fight the dog. While they were fighting with all their might, I jumped up, took the barrell of my gun, and settled it right into the brain of the savage animal. That was the largest wolf I ever killed in this wilderness" (Lanman, C., 1848: 90).

NORTH DAKOTA

Catlin, while among the Mandan Villages of the Upper Missouri River about 1835, recorded:

"There are several varieties of the wolf species in this country, the most formidable and most numerous of which are white, often sneaking about in gangs or families of 50 or 60 in number, appearing in distance, on the green prairies nothing but a flock of sheep. Many of these animals grow to a very great size, I should think being quite a match for the largest Newfoundland dog" (Catlin, G., 1913: 286).

On wolves in this State Bradbury says in his notes:

"I remarked this day that the wolves were more numerous and more daring than in any former part of our voyage. Within the last week we frequently saw a few every day, but now some of them were almost constantly in sight, and so fearless, as to stand at no great distance to gaze. For the present they were protected by their worthlessness, their skins being out of season. It appears that in a natural state the wolf is a diurnal animal; but in the neighborhood of condensed and stationary population its habits change and it becomes *nocturnal*.

"Footnote: [Pertaining to the Missouri Valley near southern boundary of North Dakota] During the autumn whilst the Indians are employed in killing game for their winter's stock, the wolves associate in flocks, and follow them at a distance to feed on the refuse of the carcasses; and will often sit within view waiting until the Indians have taken what they chuse, and abandoned the rest" (Bradbury, J., 1904: 118).

OHIO

Suggestive of the long period of time that wolves inhabited present-day Ohio is the finding of skeletal remains of wolves in several of the Mound Builder sites. From one of these, known as the Baum Mound, the skull of a female wolf (*Canis lupus lycaon*) was removed by H. L. Reynolds in 1888 for the Bureau of American Ethnology. This site is located in Ross County, on Paint Creek, 12 miles west of Chillicothe.

Wolves seem to have existed in most of Ohio. According to Schaff, ring hunts were employed to decrease the number of black bear, and in a hunt conducted between 1823 and 1825, three wolves were among the mammals taken (Schaff, M., 1905: 151).

Hill mentions a bounty of $4 being paid for the scalp of a large wolf, according to the record of the Lincoln County commissioners (Hill, N. N., Jr., 1881: 176).

In his history of Fairfield and Prairie Counties, A. A. Graham mentions the taking of a den of young wolves in 1815 in Hopewell Township, Prairie County (Graham, A. A., 1883:201).

In his report of 1839 Sager lists the wolf in his partial report on the mammalia of Ohio, but does not indicate in any way the portions of the State it occurred (Sager, A., 1839: 4).

According to a narrative from an early pioneer of 1816, transmitted by Sterling, relating to the first settlement on the "Western Reserve," in the northeastern part of Ohio, bordering on the south shore of Lake Erie, wolves were numerous. They are described as the "common gray wolf . . . , a grizzly gray on the back, a yellowish gray or dirty white below, a bushy tail fifteen to twenty inches long . . . ." (Sterling, E., 1883: 348).

Bole and Moulthrop mention a wolf specimen "shot in 1810 on the present site of the Cleveland Museum of Natural History" (Bole, B. P., Jr., and Moulthrop, P. N., 1942: 120).

OREGON

Suckley, quoting Gibbs, records the wolf as occurring in earlier times at the mouth of the Columbia River: "The Gray Wolf occurs on Clatsop Plains, near the mouth of the Columbia, and also upon Nisqually Plains, Puget Sound. It attains a very large size, and is too much for any single dog. It is called by the Chinooks Ieakhum, and is the Spilyer of the Yakimas" (Suckley, G., and Gibbs., G., 1860: 110).

This author further noted:

"They are exceedingly numerous in Oregon and Washington Territories, from the Cascades to the Rocky Mountain divide, and probably extend much further north, east, and south. They are sparingly found west of the Cascades, occurring, according to Gibbs, on the Clatsop Plains, and have been obtained by me from the elevated plateau at the western base of the Cascade mountains, upon which Muckleshoot prairie is situated" (Ibid., p. 111).

Of the wolves observed during the years 1805-06 near Fort Clatsop, near the mouth of the Columbia River, Lewis and Clark note that seven elk killed by their hunters were "untouched by the wolves, of which indeed there are but few in this country; . . ." (Lewis, M., and Clark, W., 1904-1905: vol. 3, p. 340).

The Clatsop Indians, who resided on the south side of the lower Columbia River, knew the wolf inhabiting this region by the name of "Lalo," and in the Chinook jargon was spelled "Leloo," which is derived from the French "le loup" (Lee, D., and Frost, J. H., 1844: 344).

In a conversation on February 19, 1940, with Frank Ellis Brallier, then in his 74th year, who had homesteaded on Cannon Beach and the Elk Creek and Ecola sections in 1890, the writer further verified the presence of wolves in this part of Oregon during earlier days. He recalled seeing in 1887 a wolf on Clatsop Plains, 6 miles north of Seaside, Oreg., approximately 1 mile from the Pacific Ocean at this point.

Mr. Brallier further recalled having heard the howl of a wolf about a mile below Arch Cape in Clatsop County on the Oregon coast, while he was assisting in holding a small herd of cattle at this point during 1888. These coastal wolves used elk trails as their travelways. Such trails, Mr. Brallier asserted, interspersed in all directions through the Clatsop forests.

From these recordings by Brallier, it appears that the wolf on the northwest coast of Oregon held on some 80 years after the visit of Lewis and Clark.

On the national forests of Oregon the annual game census of the Forest Service for 1929 showed a total of 90 wolves on five national forests.

PENNSYLVANIA

According to Rhoads, native wolves apparently existed in Pennsylvania as late as 1890. . . . (Rhoads, S. N., 1903: 5).

Rhoads further states:

"Wolves were once commonly and uniformly distributed over the entire limits of the two States. . . . They were approximately exterminated in New Jersey in the early decades of the 19th century" (Ibid., p. 149).

As will be later observed, Pennsylvania contained many wolves within its borders, and was among the foremost colonies to use the bounty against them.

In the vicinity of Philadelphia, William Penn observed:

"The Creatures for Profit only by Skinn or Fur, and that are natural to these parts, are the Wild Cat, Panther, Otter, Wolf, Fox, Fisher, Minx, Musk-Rat, . . ." (Myers, A. C., 1912: 229).

THE PRAIRIE STATES

So far as the prairie region of the United States is concerned, the observations of animal life noted by the two intrepid explorers, Lewis and Clark, and by a member of their expedition, Sgt. Gass, probably represent the first accounts of the occurrence of the wolf. In the journal of Gass, dated June 26, 1804, is the entry:

"We encamped on the south side of a point at the confluence of the Canzan or Kanzas River with the Missouri. It was agreed to remain here during the 27th and 28th where we pitched our tents and built bowers in front of them. Our hunters killed 4 deer and a young wolf, and caught another alive" (Gass, P., 1904: 10).

From the journals of Lewis and Clark, dated June 30, 1804, we note:

"Set out verry early this morning, a very large wolf came down to the bank and looked at us this morning. . . ." (On the Missouri River ten miles above the Kansas River, western border of Missouri.) (Lewis, M., and Clark, W., 1904-05, vol. 1, p. 62.)

On July 1, 1804:

". . . . great many wolves about us this evening." (Near the mouth of the Platte River.) (Ibid., p. 87.)

On April 3, 1805:

". . . we are all day engaged packing up Sundery articles to be sent to the President of the U. S. . . . . Box No. 1, contains the following articles i.e. In package No. 3 . . . . No. 12, The bones and Skelton of a Small burrowing wolf of the Praries the Skin being lost by accedent." (From the Mandan village, N. Dak.) (Ibid., p. 280.) This was undoubtedly a coyote.

April 17, 1805:

". . . . saw immence quantities of game in every direction . . . herds of Buffalo, Elk, and Antelopes with some deer and woolves." (Western North Dakota.) (Ibid., p. 317.)

". . . . saw . . . small parties of antelopes large herds of Elk, Some white wolves. . . ." (Western North Dakota.) (Ibid., p. 319.)

May 14, 1805:

"I felt an inclination to eat some veal and walked on shore and killed a very fine buffalo calf and a large woolf, much the whitest I had seen, it was so white as the wool of the common sheep." (140 miles west of the junction of the Missouri and Yellowstone Rivers, northwestern Montana.) (Ibid., v. 2, p. 33.)

May 29, 1805:

"We saw a great many wolves in the neighborhood of these mangled carcases [buffalo driven over a precipice by Indians] they were very fat and gentle, Capt. C. who was on shore killed one of them with his espontoon." (At the mouth of the Judith River, north central Montana.) (Ibid., p. 93.)

Feb. 20, 1806:

"The large brown woolf is like that of the Atlantic States and are found only in the woody country on the Pacific Ocean imbracing the mountains which pass the Columbia between the great falls and the rapids of the same. The large and small woolves of the plains are the inhabitants principally of the open country and the woodlands on their borders and resemble in their habits and appearance those of the plains of the Missouri precisely. They are not abundant in the plains of Columbia because there is but little game on which for them to subsist." (At Fort Clatsop near the mouth of the Columbia River.) (Ibid., v. 4, p. 90.)

July 14, 1806:

". . . . the hunters killed a couple of wolves, the buffaloe have almost entirely disappeared. . . . . the wolves are in great numbers loling about in the plains in view at the distance of two or three hundred yards. I counted 27 about the carcase of a buffalo, which lies in the water at the upper point of the large island. These are generally of the large kind." (Sun River, western Montana.) (Ibid., v. 5, p. 201.)

Coues, in his history of the Lewis and Clark expedition, quotes from their record of September 18, 1804:

"We saw goats, elk, buffalo, and black-tailed deer; the large wolves too are very numerous; they have long hair with coarse fur, and are of a light color. A small species of wolf about the size of a gray fox, was also killed, and proved to be the animal which we had hitherto mistaken for a fox." (Near the "Big Bend" of the Missouri River.) (Coues, E., vol. 1, 1893, p. 121.)

From Pike's Arkansaw Journal, under date of August 7, 1806:

". . . . saw a bear and a wolf swimming in the river." (Central Kansas.) (Pike, Z., 1932: 31).

October 15, 1806:

"Killed two buffalo and left part of our clothing with them to scare away the wolves."

October 16, 1806:

". . . . at twelve o'clock crossed to our two buffaloes; found a great many wolves at them, notwithstanding the precaution to keep them off.")(Central Kansas.) (Ibid., p. 97.)

November 7, 1806:

"The herbage being very poor, concluded to lay by on the morrow, in order to recruit our horses. Killed three cow buffalo, one calf, two wolves, one brelaw. . . ." (Kearny County, western Kansas.) (Ibid., p. 115.)

Professor Knox, of Baker University, records the following with respect to Kansas:

". . . . Gray or Timber Wolf—not uncommon in all parts of the State. Many are taken on the plains every winter for their splendid fur that is used for muffling robes. . . . C. lupus seem to be getting more common in older parts of the State." (Knox, M. V. B., 1875: 19.)

In the course of his expedition during the late summer and fall of 1845 from Bents Fort over Raton Pass, striking the headwaters of the Canadian River and thence continuing eastward along its course to its junction with the Arkansas, Lieutenant J. W. Abert recounts observation of the "large gray wolf" along the Canadian, which is now in Oklahoma. This shows undoubtedly that the large grey wolves of the plains were to be found in the same habitat as the red wolf (*Canis niger rufus* and *Canis frustror* Woodhouse)—the latter, a coyote, being described from 100 miles west of Fort Gibson which Lt. Abert reached with his expedition October 21, 1845.

Referring to *Canis nubilus* as The Dusky Wolf, Woodhouse recorded it as "Very common throughout Indian territory, Texas, and New Mexico." (Woodhouse, S. W., 1853: 45.)

According to these records the range of the wolf in the prairie region extended into every one of the present so-called prairie states. The animal also occurred to the international border in North Dakota and Montana, and far northward into the Canadian prairie provinces. Now few, if any, wolves remain in this vast territory. A gray wolf killed in the Killdeer Mountains of North Dakota in March of 1938 provided one of the latest records of wolf occurrence in the prairie country.

THE ROCKY MOUNTAIN STATES

Wolves occurred in great numbers throughout all of the Rocky Mountain States: Montana, Idaho, Wyoming, Utah, and Colorado. In Colorado they were on both sides of the continental divide, extending well onto the eastern plains section of the State. This was true also of Montana and Wyoming. In Idaho most of the wolves were confined to the eastern and southeastern sections. The wolves formerly found in Utah were restricted to the eastern and extreme southern areas of that State. Wolves were trapped in some of these States at elevations of from 9,000 to 10,500 feet above sea level.

TENNESSEE

Wood, in writing of the first recorded English exploring expedition from Virginia to the Tennessee Valley, says:

". . . as they travell still towards the sun setting great store of game, all along as turkes, deere, elkes, beare, woolfe . . . ." (Wood, A., 1928: 27).

In earlier days, D'Artaguette states:

"Two of our Frenchmen went ashore (while we continued our journey) to look for the cow they had killed yesterday, but they found that it had been entirely devoured by the wolves" (D'Artaguette, D., 1928: 75).

And Du Pratz found:

"As in all this country, ... we find numbers of buffaloes, elk, deer and other game; so we find numbers of wolves, some tiger, cat-a-mounts (Pichous), and carrion-crows . . . ." (Du Pratz, L., 1928: 110).

Miles, writing from Brownsville, Tenn., near the close of the 19th century, says:

". . . . There are several of us who would like an answer through your columns as to whence comes a species of large gray wolf which in the last four years has taken possession of our river bottoms and seems to have gone to permanent housekeeping. Twenty-five years since the small black wolf was exterminated, and now, as though dropping from the sky, comes this gray monster that none of our dogs can successfully tackle; in fact, for a dog to leave the pack for a few yards in a chase is always fatal. This creature has little fear of man and renders his range useless for a place to raise stock or hogs. Perhaps some correspondent can tell us what he is, whence he comes, and what of him, and why he has waited for this late day to make his appearance, for until very recent years we knew him not" (Miles, B. C., 1895a: 182).

TEXAS

In earlier days Texas was very heavily infested with grey wolves. The so-called No. 4½ wolf trap was developed in Texas as a means of curbing wolf depredations.

In describing the species of wolves taken by him near Fort Vancouver, Wash., in September of 1836, Dr. John K. Townsend quotes from a letter addressed to Dr. S. G. Morton by Dr. J. K. Barnes of the U. S. Army, who was stationed for many years in various parts of Texas, which conveys some idea of the characteristics of the so-called buffalo wolf of that State:

"The Buffalo wolf of the Texas frontier is found remote from civilization, in the usual ranges of the Buffalo, and is distinguished from other wolves by peculiarities of form, size, color and habits. Most commonly they are seen in pairs, or singly. The greatest number I have seen together being two pairs, which had approached to within two miles of the settlements during the extremely cold weather of December, 1848. Their color in Texas is a dusky or smoky white; hair thick, long and coarse about the head, neck and shoulders, shorter and wiry on the back, rump and legs. The tail is shorter, straighter and less bushy than that of the common wolf. In form the buffalo wolf approaches nearer to the St. Bernard mastiff, and having recently had an opportunity of seeing some of the finest dogs of this and the Newfoundland breeds, that the full-grown male buffalo-wolf is equal in size and superior in strength to the majority of them.

"The appearance of this wolf is, to the hunter, a certain indication of the proximity of buffalo, as they follow closely the movements of these animals, and seize upon the infirm and crippled and upon the calves, which become separated from the herd. I have been assured that they will attack and hamstring the largest buffalo, which thus becomes an easy prey.

"Their gait is a long steady trot, or quick and vigorous run, very different from the slouching gallop of the common wolf. The tail is carried straight, and at a slight angle from the body, much as we observe it in a pointer dog when hunting.

"The cranium will be found to present a resemblance to that of the Newfoundland or mastiff dog, in the great comparative size of its posterior superior portion" (Townsend, J. K., 1850: 75).

Besides the large grey wolf which occurred mainly in west Texas, there also occurred at this time the so-called Texan red wolf. Its range was and is still mainly confined to east Texas, where it occurs today in goodly numbers.

VIRGINIA

Wolves were common throughout most of Virginia, particularly in the mountains. The early records of attempts made by the settlers to extirpate the animals attest to the large numbers of wolves present. Virginia was the second colony to adopt the bounty scheme for wolf control.

Wolves were an object of sport for some of the aristocratic young Virginians near the close of the 17th and the beginning of the 18th centuries. The chase held a prominent place in the lives of these early sons of the Old Dominion who were practically born to the saddle and to the use of firearms (Randall, H. S., 1858, vol. 1, p. 5). According to Beverly, an early historian of Virginia, it was not an uncommon thing to see these hard riders come dashing into a Virginia hamlet dragging attached by their horses' tails live wolves that had been run down in the chase (Beverly, R., 1707: 417).

WEST VIRGINIA

In the early days of settlement in this State, McWhorter tells:

"Of the carnivora of West Virginia, the common or Black Bear, the Grey or Timber Wolf and the Panther were the principal: and the last two by far the most ferocious. . . . The panther is still met with in certain remote regions, but the wolf is practically extinct. A few are said to haunt the more obscure wilds and the gloomy recesses of the Gauley Mountains. . . . In September, 1902, Mr. William E. Connelly heard them one dark night in the deep forest between Buffalo Creek and Gauley River, in Nicholas County. The last one seen on the waters of Hacker's Creek, was about 1854, by Mr. Thomas Boram, on the farm where I was raised on Buckhannon River. . . .

"The settler pursued the wolf with rifle, trap and poison; but Doddridge claims that the rabies was the prime factor in their extermination. But some of them, at least, escaped all enemies and died of old age. When the Hurst family was residing on the Cheat River, the children going to the spring one morning found a wolf lying dead nearby. An examination revealed that it did not have a tooth in its head, and that it had succumbed to the ravages of hunger and senile decay.

"Owing to the crafty nature of the wolf, comparatively few of them fell before the hunter's aim. The strategy by which they secure their prey enabled them to flourish in vast numbers throughout this uninhabited wilderness teeming with game. Their cunning has always been proverbial. . . .

"Singly the wolf is cowardly, but when driven by extreme hunger it is then very bold. . . .

". . . They overran the entire Trans-Allegheny. No one was safe alone in the woods at night, or at any time during the winter when the wolves were often in a starving condition" (McWhorter, L. V., 1915: 342).

According to Richard Ernest Brooks, who wrote on the mammals of West Virginia in 1911, the last record for the wolf in West Virginia is of one that was killed, January, 1900, in Randolph County.

WISCONSIN

In earlier times wolves occurred in practically every county of Wisconsin. Today they are confined mainly to the isolated and rugged north-northeastern portion of the State.

In 1908 Jackson reported them as common in the extreme northern counties and apparently increasing in numbers (Jackson, H. H. T., 1908: 27).

Wolf bounty has long been paid in Wisconsin, but according to a recent communication received from Aldo Leopold, Professor of Game Management at the University of Wisconsin, the bounty at present has been repealed in view of the impending crisis in excess deer.

Schorger opines with regard to the Great Lakes region that "the timber wolf exists in sufficient numbers that there is no immediate danger of extinction. Cessation of trapping could increase the population readily. Fortunately it is possible to exercise control on the national forests. Elsewhere, where there is damage to stock, the coyote and timber wolf decline together. Deer are sufficiently numerous so that only under exceptional conditions will it be necessary to control the timber wolf on this account, should the point be reached when its existence is endangered" (Schorger, A. W., 1942: 24).

PRESENT DISTRIBUTION OF WOLVES IN NORTH AMERICA

Wolves now occur throughout most of northern Mexico; sparsely so in the western United States, including Minnesota, Wisconsin and Michigan; Alaska and the Canadian Northwest Territories. They are likewise found on Vancouver Island and in the northern interior of British Columbia, particularly the Peace River country. In this area:

"All trappers and game wardens we spoke to agreed that in the areas more remote from settlement timber wolves were abundant. . . . During the winter of 1937-38 wolves were reported by Ted Morton as abundant along the Halfway River. Here in September a large black individual was shot by a member of a hunting party returning from the Prophet River region. Late in the same winter a pair of wolves were reported to have passed through the Tupper Creek area coming from the direction of Peavine Lake" (Cowan, I. M., 1939: 76).

In Alaska the wolves definitely appear to have increased in the past five years. In 1940 the number was estimated at 7,000 in this Territory. They occur only in very sparse numbers in the Canadian prairie provinces and in far eastern Canada. Ontario has probably the largest representation of wolves in its region. According to Cahn, we note that:

"In spite of statements to the contrary, timber wolves are still common both in the Quetico and in the Superior National Forest to the south, and they cross back and forth freely between the two areas" (Cahn, A. R., 1937: 25).

Clarke estimates that the migratory caribou herds of northern Canada range over some 600,000 square miles. In this area he believes that there may be 6 wolves to 100 square miles and estimates the present day population of wolves at 36,000 in the so-called Canadian barrens (Clarke, C. H. D., 1940: 108).

In the United States wolves still occur in Oregon, possibly in Washington; in northern Minnesota, where they were reported by G. E. Gilbertson, Game Warden stationed at Buyck, to be on the increase during 1942 within the Superior National Forest; Wisconsin, and Michigan; in southeastern Oklahoma, southern Missouri, eastern Texas, western and north central Arkansas, and southwestern, northern, and northeastern Louisiana; and in Arizona and New Mexico, particularly along their southern borders, where wolves continually enter from the states of Sonora, Chihuahua, and Coahuila in Mexico. The latter country probably has one of the widest and largest distributions of wolves of any portion of North America at the present time, the animals still occurring over the greater part of their original range from the middle tableland northward to the Mexican-United States border. Little effort has been made by the Mexican people toward their elimination.

Most of the wolves occurring in the United States at the present time are on the national forests. With respect to those occurring in Oregon within the Cascade Mountains forests, Jewett states:

"I am of the firm opinion that the Cascade timber wolf has about held its own in numbers in Oregon for the past twenty years. In other words, there has been no great increase or decrease in their numbers in Oregon. The only strays from the main Cascade Range are one from Bear Valley, Grant County, and the well known 'Sycan Wolf' in Lake County."[5]

Since the receipt of Jewett's summary, a later compilation made by Robert Rowe, of the Fish and Wildlife Service, tends to show that the range of the wolf, which formerly included all of the Cascade Mountains, is shrinking perceptibly. Jackson, Douglas, and Lane Counties appear to be the only areas from which wolves have been taken recently. An investigation of all of the State to the northward—formerly a part of the Oregon wolf range, including the regions where they were observed by Lewis and Clark, Douglas and Townsend—leads to the opinion that the animal is either extinct or becoming extremely rare.

In the national forests by regions, the Forest Service estimates (1939) that wolves still exist in the following numbers:

---

[5]Letter of Stanley G. Jewett to the Fish and Wildlife Service, March 25, 1939.

		No. of Wolves
Region 1		
Montana		
Cabinet	Forest	1
Deerlodge	„	12
Flathead	„	2
Gallatin	„	3
Lolo	„	1
Lewis and Clark	„	7
Kootenai	„	1
Bitterroot	„	1
Idaho		
Nezperce	„	10
Coeur D'Alene	„	2
Bitterroot	„	1
Region 2		
Wyoming		
Shoshone	„	1
Region 3		
Arizona		
Coronado	„	10
Crook	„	2
Kaibab	„	1
Prescott	„	2
Tonto	„	10
New Mexico		
Apache	„	2
Carson	„	6
Cibola	„	5
Coronado	„	10
Gila	„	5
Lincoln	„	2
Region 4		
Idaho		
Salmon	„	5
Boise	„	5
Challis	„	10
Targhee	„	10
Weiser	„	5
Nevada		
Humboldt	„	10
Utah		
Cache	„	10
Manti	„	5
Wyoming		
Wyoming	„	5
Region 5		
California		
Lassen	„	16
Tahoe	„	4
Eldorado	„	12
Stanislaus	„	6
Angeles	„	5

		No. of Wolves
Region 6		
Oregon		
Deschutes	Forest	5
Mt. Hood	„	20
Rogue River	„	5
Siskiyou	„	10
Umpqua	„	60
Willamette	„	30
Washington		
Columbia	„	10
California		
Rogue River	„	5
Region 7		
(According to the Forest Service, there are no wolves in this region at this time.)		
Region 8		
Arkansas		
Ouachita	Forest	20
Ozark	„	37
Louisiana		
Kisatchie	„	95
Oklahoma		
Ouachita	„	50
South Carolina		
Sumter	„	2
Texas		
Angelina	„	10
Davy Crockett	„	200
Sabine	„	2
Sam Houston	„	25
Region 9		
Michigan		
Ottawa	„	100
Huron	„	10
Upper Michigan	„	30
Minnesota		
Superior	„	550
Chippewa	„	60
Missouri		
Gardner	„	100
Clark	„	350
Wisconsin		
Chequamegon	„	130
Nicolet	„	100
Region 10		
Alaska		
Chugach	„	85
Tongass	„	1,025

TABLE 1.—*Estimate by regions of wolves occurring on the national forests for period 1927-38 inclusive.*

Region	1927	1928	1929	1930	1931	1932	1933	1934	1935	1936	1937	1938
1	271	77	42	41	40	35	34	37	—	—	14	41
2	528	347	18	20	20	17	19	11	10	12	8	1
3	152	11	92	83	96	42	66	63	75	34	28	55
4	147	74	126	102	89	91	75	93	68	29	81	65
5	—	—	—	—	—	—	82	—	28	—	—	—
6	220	429	191	137	153	233	242	180	144	186	148	145
7	375	275	{ 438	128	325	238	283	—	—	—	—	—
			{					335	183	316	382	441
			—	320	587	572	545	552	—	—	1,280	1,430
10 Alaska	800	1,330	1,600	1,500	2,500	2,600	650	925	925	1,075	1,100	1,110
Total	2,493	2,543	2,508	2,331	3,810	3,828	1,996	2,196	1,433	1,652	3,041	3,288
Total U.S.	1,693	1,213	908	831	1,310	1,228	1,346	1,271	508	577	1,941	2,178

Region 9 starts in 1930.

At the present time, 5 years later, it is questionable whether any wolves now occur in South Carolina, Montana, Idaho, California, Nevada, Utah, or Wyoming. However, a large old male wolf measuring 6 feet from the tip of its nose to the tip of its tail and 33 inches at shoulder height, and weighing 106 pounds, was shot and killed on April 27, 1941, near Three Forks, Mont. This wolf is believed to have drifted into this part of Montana from southern Canada.

The late Charles Poole, long connected with the economic work of the Fish and Wildlife Service in California, stated:

"Infrequent reports of the presence of wolves, . . . have come to me during the period of some 19 years in this District; but in all except two or three cases, upon investigation by myself, these reports have proved to be without foundation. There is a possibility that there may be a limited alternating drift from Oregon on the north and Arizona on the south, but this is undoubtedly infrequent."[6]

The Aguila wolf captured by Charles Gillham and the one killed by Mark E. Musgrave near Truxton (south of Kingman), Ariz., in the early 1920's are the two most westerly Arizona wolves taken by the Fish and Wildlife Service. The Aguila wolf was taken approximately 76 miles air line from California line, and Musgrave's Truxton wolf about 57 miles air line from Colorado

---

[6]Letter from Charles Poole to Fish and Wildlife Service dated March 20, 1939. In files of Fish and Wildlife Service.

River boundary. These animals probably ranged at times near if not across the California border.

Poole continued:

"The last authentic case of timber wolves being present in the state was in the vicinity of Cow Head Lake, in northern Modoc County, practically on the Oregon-Calif. line. I investigated the case myself and determined beyond doubt that there were 5 present; but within a very short time after my investigation, they disappeared and have never been heard of since. Without doubt they went into Oregon and remained there.

"The wolf caught by Fay Clark in July 1922 was taken in Modoc County—a drift from Oregon.

"A timber wolf was caught by former Hunter Frank W. Kochler on Standish Mountain in Lassen County, near Litchfield, in June 1924" (Ibid.).

The Service has a record of a wolf trapped in Santa Barbara County by Hunter John A. Johnson in November 1920, but on closer investigation it is felt that this is not an authentic record of a wolf, the hunter who took the animal having probably confused it with a large coyote. This leaves but two records for wolves in California, so far as the Fish and Wildlife Service data are concerned.

Grinnell, Dixon, and Linsdale speak of a wolf obtained in San Bernardino County. They state:

"Information concerning this animal was furnished by Mr. A. B. Montgomery of Long Beach, who was on the ground at the time. A Mr. Watson, homesteader in the vicinity, trapped the wolf on December 14, 1922, at the old Barnett mine, in the Providence Mountains some twelve miles west of Lanfair (about fifty miles west-northwest of Needles). According to Montgomery, the animal, an old male, was 'caught by two toes on the left front foot in coyote trap, size No. 3, weighted by a plow share and a pick ax.' The tracks showed that it 'got into the trap by accident while pursuing a mountain sheep.' . . . The animal was thought to weigh 'about 100 pounds.' The pelt was 'mounted' and at last account was privately owned. The skull, however, together with photograph of the animal taken while it was alive and tied, came into possession of the Museum of Vertebrate Zoology" (Grinnell, J., Dixon, J. S., and Linsdale, J. M., 1937: 531, 532).

As noted previously, wolves were apparently always scarce in California. The Providence Mountains record appears to be the first authenticated report of the wolf's occurrence anywhere in southern California.

With reference to wolves in the national parks, Mount McKinley National Park in Alaska appears to be the only one now containing wolves. Of these, Cahalane states:

"The census report for Mount McKinley National Park for 1938 shows an estimated total of 105 wolves in the park. Census figures for Glacier Bay and Katmai National Monuments are not available and it is therefore impossible to give you an estimate of the number of wolves inhabiting these areas."[7]

In the United States, with the exception of northern Wisconsin and Michigan, all wolves have been extirpated east of the Mississippi River. They have also disappeared from most of eastern Canada, and all of Newfoundland.

---

[7]Letter from Victor H. Cahalane to Stanley P. Young, April 24, 1939.

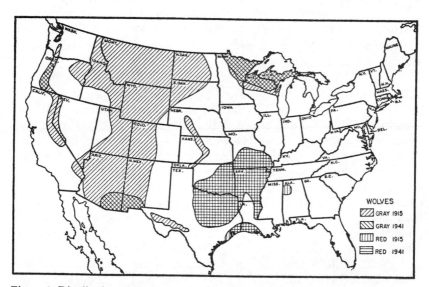

Figure 3. Distribution of gray and red wolves in the United States in 1915 and 1941

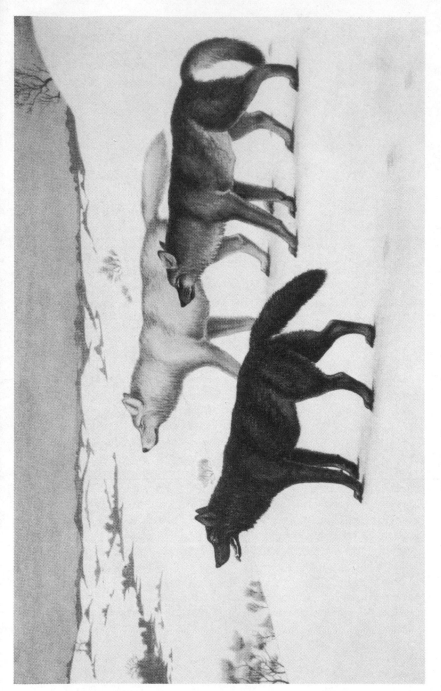

Plate 16. Common color phases of northern gray wolves

III

HABITS AND CHARACTERISTICS

COLORATION

THE COLOR of North American wolves, according to both earlier and later authorities, varies greatly, so much so that it is relatively unimportant for scientific description of the animals.

Commenting generally on the color of all the American wolves seen by him up to that time (1867), Elliott Coues noted that they may vary "from nearly white to pure black, through every gradation of gray, rufous, and dusky; these divers colors exist in such varying proportion, and present such an unbroken chain from one extreme to the other, that it seems impossible to consider them as indicating more than remarkable variations to which a single species may be subject, arising from differences in food, climate, and other circumstances" (Coues, E., 1867: 288).

This was corroborated in1876 by J. A. Allen, who wrote:

"The common Gray Wolf of the northern hemisphere presents a range of individual variation in color exceeded by but few known species of mammals; gray, white, and black individuals, with various intermediate stages of coloration, occurring with greater or less frequency wherever the species abounds, several of these varieties sometimes occurring in the same litter. Black and white wolves seem to occur more frequently at some localities than others, but gray is generally everywhere the prevailing color. Cream-colored and rufous varieties are also said to have a wide prevalence over some parts of the great plains of the interior. To what extent these variations in color are to be considered as geographic is not yet well established" (Allen, J. A., 1876c: 313).

To organize the references that have been made to the coloration of wolves, they are arranged according to localities, in north to south sequence, proceeding from Alaska to California, and then from west to east, the regions being named more or less in column form as seen on the map.

E. W. Nelson, commenting on the wolves of interior Alaska in 1887, wrote: "Among several thousand wolf skins brought into Saint Michaels during my residence there only a single albino was seen and this was a beautiful snow-white skin. Large numbers of the black or melanistic variety were brought in, and it is a noteworthy fact that the headwaters of the Yukon yielded a large majority of these black skins, and that from the same district come nearly all of the black-fox skins obtained in northern Alaska. These dark skins vary in endless gradations from the ordinary gray to a glossy coal-black. As a rule the black skins are considerably smaller than the gray ones and the fur is shorter upon them. . . . The black and gray wolves hunt in the same packs, and are distributed over the same range" (Nelson, E. W., 1888: 238).

In British Columbia, Canada, wolves also were reported as varying "greatly in colour from almost entire black to grizzly grey, and from brindled brown to yellow" (British Columbia, Province of: 1910: 27).

In northern California, Gibbs stated that "a black wolf was seen by me in the mountains between Scott's and Shasta Valleys . . . . in 1851. Several were together." And in Washington near the coast, he mentions, "A black wolf, perhaps the same, perhaps the *C. nubilus*, or 'dusky wolf,' is found on the Nisqually Plains, Puget Sound. Some skins are grizzled" (Suckley, G., and Gibbs, G., 1860: 110).

This northwest coastal region is one of heavy rainfall and at the time of the writing quoted was densely forested. Numerous dark races or subspecies of birds are known from there and their obscure coloration is attributed to the humidity and associated environmental conditions.

Much has been recorded about the color of wolves of the Arctic, from which the following comment is cited. A noted early Arctic explorer, Sir John Richardson, said:

"In some of the districts which we traversed, the wolves were very numerous, and varied greatly in the colour of their fur, some being white, others totally black, but the greater number were mixed gray and white, more or less tinged in parts with brown" (Richardson, J., 1829: 61).

While in the country between Gordon Bay and Ellis River in the Canadian Arctic, French observed:

"At this point we were molested continually by bands of wolves; these same animals are the biggest species of wolf I have ever seen. They are dark brown and rangy, and bigger than a timber wolf" (Police, Royal Northwest Mounted, 1919: 40).

Speaking of the observations made in the far northern Thelon Game Sanctuary in the years of 1936-37, Clarke found the wolves therein to be ". . . quite white, still more are largely white, and some are brindled, black, or even yellowish" (Clarke, C. H. D., 1940: 36).

While on his journey up the Missouri River Audubon noted: "The diversity of their size and colour is quite remarkable, no two being quite alike" (Audubon, J. J., and Bachman, J., 1851-54, vol. 2, p. 159).

Again, Dr. F. V. Hayden wrote:

"This animal varies so much in color that the traders on the upper Missouri suppose there are four or five species. I have seen them differing in color from an almost snowy whiteness to a dark brown or black, and was at first inclined to attribute this difference to age and sex, but Mr. Zephyr, an intelligent trader, informed me that he had noticed the same variations of color in all ages" (Hayden, F. V., 1863: 141).

While working among the trading posts of the Upper Mississippi and Missouri Rivers, Kurz had many opportunities to note wolf pelts. Speaking of their color, he says:

"Caught a wolf. Brought him in to serve as model for a study. There are wolves here of great size and also prairie wolves, which are smaller; the latter appear to be half fox. Of the large species there are many different colors, varying according to age and season of the year: black, brown, yellow, gray, mixed, snow white" (Kurz, R. F., 1937: 212, 213).

In a litter of seven wolves a few months old that I took from a wolf den southeast of Pueblo, Colo., in the spring of 1921, two were grey, one grayish-black, two nearly white, one grayish-buff, and the other brownish-black. Adult wolves in this same general area showed about the same variations mentioned. One noted male white wolf was dubbed "Old Whitey" because of the striking whiteness of his pelt, which was very noticeable whenever this wolf was seen on the open range. Later, upon his capture, the pelt was found comparable in whiteness to those of the pure white wolves of the Arctic. Similarly other wolf dens containing young in other parts of Colorado have shown wide color variations among whelps in the same family.

Lt. J. W. Abert, while at Bent's Fort, southern Colorado, during the summer of 1846, made at this time many natural history observations. He mentions examining "some skins of the grey and white wolves; and from all I can learn, these animals are one and the same kind, as the grey wolf becomes whiter as it advances in age. Some of the skins were white, some grey, and others in a transition stage" (Abert, J. W., 1848: 424).

Elliott Coues wrote that the wolves observed by him in early-day Arizona "were of the grizzled grayish-white variety. In winter they are very light colored, appearing from a distance almost white; but along the middle of the back, and down the shoulders and flanks, the light color is mixed with slaty or grayish-black. I met with no winter skins showing any brownish or tawny. At this season their pelages were thick and heavy, and a good many of the animals were killed with poison for the sake of the fur, which made very beautiful robes" (Coues, E., 1867: 288).

Speaking of the northern prairie wolves, Isaac Cowie, a Hudson's Bay Company employee during the years 1867-74, states:

"There were two kinds of wolves, the smaller being those known today by the familiar name of coyote, and then called 'togony,' an abbreviation of the longer Cree word. The others were the real big prairie wolf, 'Me-hin-gen' in Cree, which, fattening on the bison and as scavengers on the field of slaughter, often attained an immense size. These were of various shades, from white to grey, with occasional patches of black, and were esteemed good eating by the Indians" (Cowie, I., 1913: 250).

In his observation of the occurrence of wolves in the vicinity of Grand River, then referred to as Dakota Territory in the early 1870's, Hoffman noted that "The coloration varies greatly, in fact, so much so that different local names are applied to the same species on that account." This observation was apparently based on the wolves that then occurred in the present-day county of Corson as well as adjacent counties of northern South Dakota (Hoffman, W. J., 1878: 95).

Relating to the Dakota territory also is the comment of Maximilian, Prince of Wied, who in the early 1830's wrote:

"I obtained many wolves from the quite white to the perfectly grey, common variety" (Maximilian, Prince of Wied, 1906: vol. 22, p. 44).

While along the Platte River in eastern Nebraska, on the 25th of of May, 1852, Turnbull stated ". . . While eating breakfast a large black wolf passed about 20 rod from us . . . ." (Turnbull, T., 1913: 164).

Gregg commented:

"Though the color of this wolf [with reference to the plains wolf] is generally a dirty gray, it is sometimes met with nearly white. I am of the opinion, however, that the diversity of color originates chiefly from the different ages of the hair, and the age and condition of the animal itself. The few white wolves I have seen, have been lean, long-haired, and apparently very old" (Gregg, Josiah, 1905: 272).

Castaneda, from whom most of our knowledge of the Coronado Expedition is derived, was probably the first writer to comment upon the color of the North American plains wolves. When this expedition had advanced far out onto the plains of present-day Kansas, he recorded:

"There are very great numbers of wolves on these plains, which go around with the cows [buffaloes]. They have white skins" (Winship, G. P., 1896: 528).

James O. Pattie, while near the Republican River in western Kansas in 1824, noted:

"The following morning we took a S.S.W. course which led us

from the stream during this day's journey. Nothing occurred worthy of mention except that we saw a great number of wolves, which had surrounded a small herd of buffalo cows and calves, and killed and eaten several. We dispersed them by firing on them. We judged that there were at least a thousand. They were large and as white as sheep" (Pattie, J. O., 1905: 56).

Further, with respect to the color of the gray wolf of the prairies Dr. Thomas Flint notes in his journal on July 1, 1853: "Large white prairie wolves numerous and bold yet it is difficult to get a good shot at them" (Flint, T., 1924: 82).

Speaking of the Louisiana red wolf, Stanley C. Arthur states:

"In Louisiana we very frequently find a wholly black wolf, pupped in a litter with ordinary gray brothers and sisters, which proves this phase to be merely a color variation and does not make the animal a separate species. In the Audubon Park Zoo, New Orleans, a male black wolf with a gray bitch from the same litter taken in Evangeline parish, and kept in captivity for a number of years, bred three times, and in each litter there were black pups as well as gray. The first litter was composed of five, three of the young being black and the other two taking the pelage of the mother. The second and third litters consisted of four young each, there being two black and two gray pups in each litter. The coloration did not follow the sex, as in the first litter, the blacks being bitches and the grays were dogs. . . . .

"The black Louisiana wolf is not wholly black, as it usually has a light-gray breast patch that appears pure white in contrast with rest of the pelage" (Arthur, S. C., 1928: 146).

In the fall of 1934 a wolf was trapped in Madison Parish, La., whose gray coat was comparable to that of the gray wolf formerly occurring in the Dakotas.

Returning again to the north, almost Arctic again, we find that the wolves found on Southampton were of a rather uniform color at least at the season when they were observed by Sutton and Hamilton. The latter says:

"I am not in position to say whether the Southampton Island wolf varies in color with the seasons. The only specimens I saw were of a creamy or pale buffy white color generally speaking; some of the longer hairs tipped with grayish and whitish, giving some areas of the body a frosted appearance" (Sutton, G. M., and Hamilton, W. J., Jr., 1932: 36).

Reeks found the wolves of Newfoundland to vary greatly in color. With apparently but one race of the animal ever existent there, he nevertheless states, "It would be difficult to find two skins, even in the same litter of whelps, marked exactly alike; so great is the variation in the shades or degrees of coloring—from pure black to almost clear white" (Reeks, H., 1870: 2033).

Thomas Morton, referring to New England wolves, wrote in 1637, "The wolfes are divers coloures: some sandy coloured, some griselled, and some black. . . ." (Morton, T., 1637: 79).

Black wolves were taken in New England during the first several decades of colonization, and were considered a real prize, "fit for a prince," indicating that this color phase was not common.

Kalm, who spent parts of the years 1748-51 in exploring and observing conditions in the eastern portion of North America, said of the wolves in Pennsylvania:

"There are two varieties of wolves here, which however seem to be of the same species. For some of them are yellowish, or almost pale gray, and others are black or dark brown" (Benson, A. B., 1937: 150).

Audubon noted for the more southern Atlantic seaboard:

"All packs of American wolves usually consist of various shades of colour and varieties, nearly black, have occasionally been found in every part of the United States. . . . in Florida, the prevailing colour of the wolves is black. . . . There is a specimen in the Museum of the Philosophical Society of Charleston (S. C.), obtained on Goose Creek, a few years ago, that is several shades darker than the specimen from which our drawing was made; and in a gang of seventeen wolves, which existed in Colleton District, S. C., a few years ago (sixteen of which were killed by the hunters in eighteen months), we were informed that about one fifth were black and the others of every shade of colour—from black to dusty grey and yellowish white" (Audubon, J. J., and Bachman, J., 1851-54, vol. 2, p. 130).

And Bartram observed in Florida:

"The wolves of Florida are larger than a dog, and are perfectly black, except the females, which have a white spot on the breast; but they are not so large as the wolves of Canada and Pennsylvania, which are of a yellowish brown colour.

"I have been credibly informed that the wolves here are frequently seen pied, black, and white, and of other mixed colours" (Bartram, W., 1928: 173).

Thus it appears that variability was almost everywhere the rule. It was as evident in the very whelps from the den as among the adults. The phenomenon in a Colorado litter has already been cited (p. 62) and Rhoads recorded for Tennessee that of a brood of seven, three were gray and four black (Rhoads, S. N., 1896: 200).

To sum up, observations reveal that there is hardly a part of the North American wolf's range where color may be said to be uniform. Gray is the most prevalent color, but even in the Arctic regions where white seems to predominate, variations to almost jet black are found. Farther south in the higher mountains and plateaus as in middle eastern Wyoming dark gray is the rule; but here, again, the wolves show a diversity of color from dun to blackish brown, and nearly pure black. Southward in Oklahoma, Arkansas, Louisiana, Florida, and Texas, while the coloration of the red wolf tends more toward red and buff, variations to brownish black, grayish black, and even approaching pure black occur.

The opinion is held by some that the great variation in color found among the wolves in North America may be caused by varying intensities of light in their respective habitats. This possibility, coupled with the effect of varying degrees of humidity and temperature, may account for the diverse colors of wolves, especially for whiteness in Arctic regions.

With respect to the white pelage of many of the Arctic wolves and other mammals of this region, Darwin felt that in these perpetually snow-laden regions the animals "have been rendered white to protect them from their enemies, or to favor their stealing on their prey" (Darwin, C., 1874: 619).

WEIGHTS AND MEASUREMENTS

Records of weights are arranged geographically, as were those for color, except that statements including measurements even if they also mention weights have been segregated in a following section.

Northern wolves tend to be heavier, as shown by these Alaskan records:

A male killed during September 1937 near the head of Gold Creek, a tributary of the Suasitna River above Curry, weighed 100

Plate 17. The wolf in full cry. (Photo courtesy Leo D. Harris, Killdeer, N. Dak.)

Plate 18. A young wolf wading a stream, Mount McKinley National Park, Alaska

Plate 19. A. Approach to water-hole in Turkey Creek at northern terminus of scouting course. The trail is used by pumas, jaguars, peccaries, deer, and livestock, besides wolves

B. The water-hole, Turkey Creek, where the main wolf-run joins the scouting course

pounds, and one shot in the Savage River drainage, Alaska, on January 23, 1934, weighed 157 pounds.

A very large male collected by Frank S. Glaser, July 12, 1939, on 70-Mile River, approximately 50 miles from its mouth in extreme east central Alaska, weighed 175 pounds. It was the heaviest that has been taken by any of the personnel of the Fish and Wildlife Service.

Another male wolf killed on January 4, 1920, in the Olympic Mountains on Elwha River, 22 miles south of Port Angeles, Wash., weighed 86 pounds.

After a night in a wolf trap, the weight of a male specimen of *baileyi* captured in southern Arizona was found to be 98 pounds, while the weight of its mate was 65 pounds. A specimen of *youngi*, taken near Eagle, Colo., after a long trip across country dragging a wolf trap, weighed 125 pounds. This specimen was one of the largest wolves taken by the Fish and Wildlife Service in the course of wolf control operations in the Rocky Mountains.

The wolf (termed *Canis variabilis*) was discoursed upon by Prince Maximilian in 1841; he says in part, regarding the "varying wolf" of the Upper Missouri, "A specimen of this wolf killed at Fort Clark, and reduced by hunger, weighed 58 pounds" (From Maximilian, Reise in das inner Nord-America, II, 1841: 95; also Baird, S. F., 1857: 111).

Andy Kay, an employee of the Fish and Wildlife Service who has long been familiar with wolves in Arkansas (*Canis niger gregoryi*) and who has trapped these animals for many years, states that individuals weigh between 45 and 65 pounds.[8]

Thompson says of the early-day Vermont wolves: "The largest wolves killed in Vermont have weighed from 90 to 100 pounds" (Thompson, Z., 1853: 34).

Apparently from other old records, the weight given by Thompson appeared to be the average for New England wolves.

In summary it may be said that the weight of fully matured gray wolves varies between 60 to 175 pounds, the latter weight being that attained in Alaska and in the Mackenzie River district of Canada.

---

[8]Letter to Fish and Wildlife Service from Hamilton, Ga., dated July 20, 1939; in files of Fish and Wildlife Service.

The smallest of the North American wolves, *Canis niger rufus,* averages between 30 and 35 pounds in weight. Occasionally specimens of this species will be found weighing between 70 to 80 pounds, but these are invariably males. This wolf is rather greyhoundish in appearance, with long, somewhat spindly legs, a build which seems better fitted for long-distance running than is that of its relative of the western plains, the coyote. Wolves also are more prone to travel constantly, which activity is not conducive to accumulating fat.

The measurements of wolves, like the weight, vary considerably, even in fully matured animals. The height at the shoulder is known to range from 26 to 38 inches in the gray wolf alone.. Information on measurements (as well as in some instances on weight) is given in succeeding paragraphs. The arrangement of items again is geographical.

Joseph S. Dixon, while Field Naturalist of the National Park Service, took measurements of a male wolf killed in Mount McKinley National Park, Alaska, near the main highway on Teklanika River flat on October 13, 1938, as follows:

a. Length along the upper side from tip of nose to end of tail, exclusive of hair_____ 59 inches
b. Length of tail from base to tip, exclusive of hair_____ 17   ”
c. Length of hind foot from end of longest claw to tip of hock_____ 5   ”
d. Weight _____ 140 pounds

A young female captured on March 4, 1938, at the mouth of the Matanuska River, Alaska, weighed 64 pounds. Its total length was 5 feet, 6½ inches, the tail comprising 18 inches of this. The shoulder height was 29¾ inches.

Frank S. Glaser reported the measurements of a black wolf snared near Mount Hayes, Alaska, on October 21, 1939, as 69 inches from tip to tip, and 38 inches high at the shoulders. It weighed 135 pounds. A gray wolf trapped on October 24, 1939, in the same vicinity measured 69 inches in length and 37 inches at the shoulders, and weighed 125 pounds.[9]

A male wolf taken on Jannuary 4, 1912, by H. V. Radford near Schultz Lake, Northwest Territories, Canada, weighed 101 pounds;

---

[9]Glaser, Frank S., Itinerary Reports of August-November, 1939. In files of Fish and Wildlife Service.

its total length was 1,720 mm. (67.7 inches), of which the tail length was 519 mm. (20.4 inches).

Dellinger and Black record for Arkansas:

"Two black wolves [*Canis niger gregoryi*], a male (length 58½ inches) and a female (length 42¾ inches) were taken by Game Warden Bland in the Big Woods Game Refuge, Howard Co., in September, 1939" (Dellinger, S. C., and Black, J. D., 1940: 189).

A male red wolf captured on the Aransas Migratory Waterfowl Refuge in southeastern Texas on March 22, 1940, weighed 50 pounds, its total length was 52¼ inches, its tail 14½ inches, its ear from notch 4 inches, and its height at the shoulder 21¼ inches.[10]

David Thompson, in discoursing on the wolf noted by him in the so-called Muskrat Country of northern Canada (at present pierced by the Hudson Bay Railroad in its course from The Pas on the Saskatchewan River to the mouth of the Nelson River), says:

"Of the three species of wolf [probably only one, *Canis occidentalis*], only one is found in this stony region that I have described, and this species appears peculiar to this region; it is the largest of them, and by the way of convenience is called the Wood, or Forest wolf, as it is not found elsewhere; its form and color (is) much the same as the others if a dark grey, the hair, though not course cannot be called soft and fine, it is in plenty, and with the skin make warm clothing. It is a solitary animal. Two are seldom seen together except when in chase of some animal of the Deer species. . . . they are very rarely caught in a trap, but redily (sic) take the bait of a set Gun and (are) killed" (Thompson, David, 1916: 75).

Some conception of the size of these wolves is given by Thompson when he says:

"The cased skin of one of these wolves, came with ease over a man of six feet, two inches in height dressed in his winter clothing, and was ten inches above his head. . . ." (Ibid.).

Under date of March 23, 1940, W. J. Breckenridge, of the University of Minnesota Museum of Natural History, Minneapolis, gives the following information with respect to the weight and length of 9 wolves taken in northern Minnesota during 1938 and 1939:

---

[10]Letter to Fish and Wildlife Service signed by James O. Stevenson, Assistant Refuge Manager, dated March 30, 1940, Aransas Refuge, Austwell, Tex.; in files of Fish and Wildlife Service.

Specimen number	Sex	Date	Locality	Weight	Total length	Tail
				(pounds)	(inches)	(inches)
1271	Male	Mar. 6, 1938	Superior National Forest	76	66	17
1282	Do.	Mar. 4, 1938	Do.	80	60½	17½
1260	Do.	Mar. 16, 1938	Baudette, Minn.	75	60½	16½
1349	Do.	Jan. 21, 1939	Superior National Forest	85	61	17
1360	Female	Feb. 28, 1939	Do.	68	59	17
1361	Male	Do.	Do.	77	62	17
1362	Do.	Feb. 11, 1939	Do.	74	60½	16½
1350	Do.	Jan. 24, 1939	Do.	58	59½	17
——	Do.	Feb. ?, 1939	Do.	96	60½	12½

A male wolf [probably *Canis lupus lycaon*] killed 20 miles west of Merrill, Wis., in November, 1907, measured 5 feet, 10 inches in length, 33 inches at the shoulders, and weighed 100 pounds (Breck, L., 1908: 297).

According to Donald B. MacMillan, the wolves occurring on the eastern coast of Greenland "seem to run small." The following measurements submitted by MacMillan are of three wolves shot by members of the Denmark Expedition in the Arctic region between 75° and 83° 10′ N.:

1. Length from muzzle to root of tail .... 108 cm. (42.5 in.)
   Total length of tail .... 42 cm. (16.5 in.)
   Head from neck to muzzle .... 30 cm. (11.4 in.)
   Length of the ear .... 10 cm. (3.9 in.)
   Breadth of the ear .... 10 cm. (3.9 in.)
   Height from shoulder .... 76 cm. (29.9 in.)
   Tail .... 46 cm. (18.1 in.)
   Circumference of chest .... 75 cm. (29.5 in.)
   Weight .... 63.8 lbs.
2. Length from muzzle to root of tail .... 109 cm. (42.9 in.)
   Tail .... 44 cm. (17.3 in.)
   Height .... 73 cm. (28.7 in.)
   Circumference of chest .... 67 cm. (26.3 in.)
   Weight .... 45.10 lbs.
3. Length .... 114 cm. (45.2 in.)
   Tail .... 41 cm. (16.1 in.)
   Circumference .... 79 cm. (31.1 in.)
   Weight .... 55 lbs.

MacMillan further states that a wolf shot at Repulse Harbor "by John Rae, northern part of Hudson Bay, was 5 feet 9 inches in length, tail 1 foot 7 inches, and height at shoulder 2 feet 8 inches."[11]

---

[11]Letter from Donald B. MacMillan, Provincetown, Mass., to E. A. Goldman, Washington, D. C., dated April 11, 1941. In files of Fish and Wildlife Service.

SCENT GLANDS

Like most mammals, the wolf has a special scent gland. It is bluish black in color and is located on the upper side near the base of the tail. This gland appears to function when wolves meet, as the tail is thrown straight up almost at right angles to the backbone, held stiffly for a moment, when the animal's friend or foe each takes a sniff.

The urine carries a strong and, to wolves apparently, an identifying odor for each individual. Field observations have shown that urine taken from a strange wolf and exposed on a runway causes the greatest excitement to the wolf or group of wolves using that run. Much scratching and kicking up of dirt, and often excessive deposits of excreta, are to be noted when such urine is applied to the scent posts. The great interest led to the use of urine as a lure in trapping wolves.

The wolves, and particularly males, when angry, or sometimes when smelling wolf scent, bristle the long hair on the nape, so that often it appears as a mane.

Success in causing a red wolf (*Canis niger gregoryi*) to take its own picture by flashlight was accomplished in Louisiana during the fall of 1934, by the use of scent and urine taken from a wolf from western Arkansas. (Gregory, T., 1935: 68 p.)

STRENGTH, SPEED, AND ENDURANCE

Occasionally, wolves that have been trapped have been known to lunge with such bodily force as to straighten a prong of a drag-hook attached to the trap chain. The usual drag-hook, of wrought iron and approximately one quarter-inch in diameter, is used to impede a trapped animal's progress. As it is dragged over the ground it leaves a tell-tale mark which enables the captor to trace the catch.

A female wolf trapped in Santa Cruz County in southern Arizona near the Mexican border in November 1917 succeeded in escaping with a wolf trap, to which was attached 8 feet of quarter-inch linked chain, and a steel stake pin, made of gas pipe, which was 18 inches long and 1 inch in diameter. The capture took place in a very rugged canyon, densely forested on its sides with oak, pine, and juniper. When two hounds were put on this wolf's trail, it was jumped approximately 200 yards from the place the trap was set, where it apparently had lain down in a small but heavily benched thicket. From this point the wolf scrambled nearly 500 feet to the top of the watershed divide, turned south into Cherry Creek, and finally came to the edge of the eastern side of the San Rafael Valley south of Canelo Pass. The trailing dogs were followed by three horsemen. The chase led to this point through almost impassable country for about 5 miles, with the wolf well in advance. As the running wolf reached the edge of the valley, the horsemen were able to see it with the dogs not far behind. Every time the wolf leaped, the steel stake pin would swing around and whack it on the hind quarters. The chase continued well out on the valley floor, where the wolf was dispatched by a bullet from a .38 Colt revolver. The weight of the trap, chain, and stake pin approximated nearly 7 pounds, and the chase extended more than 6 miles. With this encumbrance, the wolf was able to keep well ahead of the pursuing dogs while in the dense thickets before reaching the valley floor, and on the latter was able to fight off the two dogs as they caught up with it.

McFarlane records the remarkable endurance displayed by a wolf which had escaped with a trap on its foot as follows:

"In the sketch of Western America (1868), Archbishop Tache of St. Boniface, Manitoba, recounts a remarkable instance of persevering fortitude exhibited by a large dark wolf caught in a steel trap at Isle a la Crosse many years ago. A month afterwards, it was killed near Green Lake, 90 miles distant, with the trap and connecting wood block still attached to one of its hind legs. It had evidently dragged both around in the snow for many a mile, during a period of intense cold, and it was therefore not surprising that he was a 'walking skeleton' when finally secured" (MacFarlane, R. R., 1905: 693).

The speed of the wolf has been clocked at 28 miles per hour for a distance of 200 yards. It is believed, however, that the pace of a wolf over a long run would not average more than 22 to 24 miles per hour, and that for the first mile or two, when it would be reduced, probably as much as 50 percent. This rate of running is much slower than that of other large four-footed mammals, and might cause wonderment as to how a wolf overtakes swifter prey. The explanation lies in the wolf's great endurance. It can keep up its loping gait mile after mile, the whole night through if necessary; seldom is full speed resorted to except when the prey is to be pounced upon.

The hunting technique of wolves is based on the exhaustion of their prey. Their greater endurance over that of most, if not all, of the big game animals, is one of their main assets in overcoming prey.

On wolf speed, Ralph Lomen, writing to his brother Carl from Nome, Alaska, mentions the taking of a large wolf, stating:

"Bill Munz came in the other day and sold us a seven foot black wolf hide which he had picked up a few days before at the head of Aurora or Bonanza Creek, Noxapaga, about 25 mi. east of Harris Dome. . . . After sighting it, he started chasing it by plane and for 45 mi. kept him on the go. Bill said that he could throttle down to 50 mi. an hour when going into a stiff wind and that the wolf was making no less than 40 per. Finally the wolf became so tired that he could hardly navigate so Bill landed his plane and took a shot at considerably less than a hundred yards."[12]

Whether the wolf was going 40 miles per hour would seem problematical, but this airplane chase gives some measure of the endurance of the wolf.

The wolf is a great traveler. All of the old-time range men attest to this trait of the wolf; so do the professional private "wolfers" of earlier days on the plains, as well as the wolf trappers of the Fish and Wildlife Service.

In the studies that are being conducted by the Service with relation to the natural drift of the larger predators, some interesting facts are being developed that give some conception of their migratory movements. These studies have been facilitated by ear-tagging and releasing the animals. One record was obtained of a red wolf in southeastern Oklahoma, which in two weeks had traveled a distance of 125 miles, crossing four mountain ranges.

Isaac Cowie touches on the wolf's traveling ability in writing of the feat of one Thomas Manitou Keesik employed as livestock guard at early Fort Pelly who was noted "for his pre-eminence as a long-distance runner in a country remarkable for wonderful feats on foot." Cowie states further: "Thomas made a specialty for special reward in the form of rum, which had become a luxury placed quite beyond the reach of an Indian there except under most extraordinary circumstances. . . . This specialty of Thomas was in running down on

---

[12]Letter from Ralph Lomen to Carl Lomen dated April 17, 1939, Nome, Alaska, in files of Fish and Wildlife Service.

foot and clubbing the wolf to death. I am informed by Mr. William Phillips, now a farmer of good repute at Clandeboye, in Manitoba, that when he was stationed at Fort Pelly in 1865 Thomas Keesik (his middle name was generally dropped in conversation) ran a wolf down all the way from Fort Pelly to near Touchwood hills (a distance of probably one hundred miles), till both the pursued and the pursuer fell down together exhausted, Thomas tripping and falling on the wolf. Both lay as they fell together for some time completely spent, till Thomas, sooner recovering, gave the wolf the final coup, and added it to this long record of such feats" (Cowie, I., 1913: 369).

The remarkable elusiveness and endurance of the wolf are further brought to light in Shiras' description of the tracking of a wolf on Grand Island in the Lake Superior region. After being trailed by a dozen expert rifle shots during the daytime for four days, it was finally slightly wounded. This apparently only caused the animal to increase its endeavors. "At the end of nearly two weeks, with relays following it all day and sometimes at night with lanterns, the wolf was finally killed. With the wages paid and the loss of deer destroyed by this single animal, the cost was estimated at $1,500" (Shiras, G., III, 1921: 165).

THE VOICE OF THE WOLF

Many stockmen, when describing a wolf-howl to the author, have made statements to much the same effect as the following:

"The cry of the lobo is entirely unlike that made by any other living creature; it is a prolonged, deep, wailing howl, and perhaps the most dismal sound ever heard by human ear. Anyone who has heard it when the land was covered with a blanket of snow and elusively lighted by shimmering moonlight, never will forget this strange, trembling wolf cry that came to him through the cold and stillness of the dead of a winter night on the range" (National Livestock Historical Association, 1905: 720).

Henderson, quoting from Bishop Spangenberg, an early colonial minister of the gospel, says of the wolf and its howl in northwest North Carolina during 1752: "The wolves wh. are not like those in Germany, Poland, and Lifland (because they fear men and don't come near) give us such music of six different cornets the like of wh. I have never heard in my life" (Henderson, A., 1920: 36).

A much later writer at least agreed with Spangenberg as to the variety of wolf sounds. Keim says of wolves partaking of a meal from a buffalo carcass, that "A wolf feast over the carcass of a buffalo is one of those sharp toned entertainments, which could only be compared to an old fashioned tea-party, composed of snappish octogenarian, paralytic, and generally debilitated characters of both sexes, with a fair sprinkle of shriveled virginity, and a few used up celibates of the masculine gender. Each one guzzling to his heart's content, and growling, and finding fault with his neighbor" (Keim, DeB. R., 1924: 294).

So far as present studies reveal, the wolf utters five distinct vocal sounds, each with a different significance. The first in our classification is a high, though soft, and plaintive sound similar to the whine of a puppy dog, and is used mostly at or near the opening of the wolf den, particularly when the young whelps are out playing around. It seems to indicate solicitude for the offspring, and is made mostly by the adult female. As the pitch of this whines varies so much, it seems ventriloquial.

The second is a loud, throaty howl, seemingly a call of loneliness. It is best heard in zoological parks where either the male or the female wolf is confined alone; and when a sudden loud noise such as the sound of a whistle, a clap of thunder, or the clang of a fire-bell causes the animal to give voice. This long, lonesome-sounding howl is also uttered during the breeding season (December, January, and February).

The third sound is a loud, deep, guttural, though not harsh, howl, apparently the call of the chase, that generally is given by an adult male and is answered by other wolves on the hunt for food. It might be termed a call for assembling a group of wolves of the same vicinity. This guttural howl may at times be followed by a loud bark or two similar to that of a Newfoundland dog.

The fourth call is that of the chase, made after starting prey, as a deer or moose. This utterance is not quite so throaty or guttural as the third, and consists of several short, deep, barking sounds rapidly made, very similar to that of a pack of hounds on a very hot scent.

The fifth call is that of the kill. A bulldog of the heavier breed makes a similar sound when in hard combat with a rival. It is a deep snarl produced by exhaust of air through the wolf's partially opened mouth as it hangs on with teeth sunken into the flesh of its victim.

The howl or lonesome call of the wolf is generally given early in the evening, or again in the morning shortly before break of day. During even the coldest winter nights, wolf howling may be quite common. Bartram, in his observations of the wolf then occurring along the Atlantic seaboard, stated:

"They assemble in companies in the night time, howl and bark all together, especialy in cold winter nights, which is terrifying to the wandering bewildered traveller" (Bartram, W., 1928: 173).

Through varying the tone thus producing a ventriloquial effect, one howling wolf can easily confuse the hearer as to the number of wolves present. This is not so common, however, as with the coyote. Also, the red wolf of Texas does this more than the larger species of the mountains and plains.

Speaking of the wolf howl, Rudolph Friederich Kurz, while on the western prairies and among the Indians on the Mississippi River and the Upper Missouri River during the years 1846 to 1852, states:

"Their speech is a howl, which varies according to the motive that actuates the beast. When the wolf is hungry or gets the scent of something he dares not tackle he sends forth a prolonged, dismal howl; when he is in pursuit of wild beasts a much more quick, angry note that is yet not the same as the yelp of a dog. Perhaps I might more clearly indicate the difference in sound by saying that wolves use head tones only, no chest tones. By brisk, insistent howls they invite fresh wolves continually to aid in the pursuit; constantly call in new forces. When those that first began the chase become tired and out of breath they lie down to rest until their victims come back that way, for at every turn the quarry pursued finds enemies anew, called thither by the howling of its pursuers, and finally driven back again to its pasture ground, falls exhausted into the jaws of the beasts waiting there" (Kurz, R. F., 1937: 298, 299).

Shoemaker records of the wolf of the Alleghenies that:

"Another Susquehana County wolfer has this to say concerning this howl: 'I wish I could describe this howl, but the best comparison I can give would be to take a dozen railroad whistles, braid them together and then let one strand after another drop off, the last peal so frightfully piercing as to go through your heart and soul; you would feel as though your hair stood straight on end if it was ever so long.' " . . . (Shoemaker, H. W., 1917-19, vol. 2, p. 29).

Some wolf hunters and other woodsmen become adept at imitating the various calls of the wolf. Many instances are on record of wolves having been called up to within shooting range of the hunter. Some of the Eskimos in northern Alaska, who are proficient in wolf-calling, are reported as often succeeding in thus enticing near enough to kill wolves depredating on reindeer herds.

THE WOLF AS A SWIMMER

Numerous observations prove that the wolf is not at all averse to getting into water. In southeastern Alaska wolves frequent the beaches at low tide, and are captured in the so-called salt water or tidewater wolf-set which necessitates its wading into water from 6 inches to a foot in depth.

At times wolves seem not averse to feeding in water. This is interestingly reported by Johnson as observed by him within the Superior National Forest in Minnesota, where he saw a wolf feeding upon the floating carcass of an adult cow moose that "lay in a pool about six or seven feet deep . . . and was held in place by a long pole lying crosswise in the current" of the stream. It was noted that the wolf apparently was treading water and at the same time "taking savage bites" at the moose's carcass (Johnson, C. E., 1921: 11).

While he does not specifically say that wolves swim in pursuit of prey, Dr. F. V. Hayden so implies when he notes: "Descending the Yellowstone River in an open boat, in the summer of 1854, we passed an old bull (buffalo) lying upon the bank, and evidently alive, surrounded with wolves, who had already deprived him of his nose and tail. He had evidently yielded to his fate, but pitying the poor animal, we halloed and fired a charge of shot among the wolves, which dispersed them. The old bull revived, started down the bank, and swam across the river to a sand bar, where he fell exhausted. Before we were out of sight, the wolves had surrounded him again" (Hayden, F. V., 1863: 141).

Our observations indicate that wolves are good swimmers, and Joseph N. Neal, of Meeker, Colo., stated in a personal conversation with me that "Water was no barrier to the wolf. Wolves would swim the White River of northwestern Colorado at any place if they desired to cross at that point to reach the opposite bank in travelling over a runway."

At the time of the capture of the female wolf known locally as "Three Toes," which is discussed later, it was proved that this animal had no aversion to entering the Apishapa River in southern Colorado. In the course of an attempt to rid herself of a four-pound wolf trap on her front paw, she zigzagged in and out of the river, which necessitated some swimming at times. This was successfully accomplished, despite the impediment on her paw.

Ligon recorded of the wolf as a swimmer in southeastern Alaska:

". . . we have one instance of fishermen who killed a wolf and deer swimming in one of the channels, more than a mile from the nearest land. The wolf was close behind the deer, but what would have happened had it overtaken the deer, so far out, is a guess." . . . (Ligon, J. S., 1926: 158).

It seems to have been common for wolves to take to water whenever necessary in chasing deer. On this point, Dickson is quoted in Billing's "Natural History of the Wolf," as follows:

"The wolves are very destructive upon the deer, and hunt them singly or in packs, both in summer and winter. If water be near, the deer when hunted, makes for it, as he has a better chance of escape from being able to swim faster and with more ease than the wolf, as it generally loses some time before it strikes the deer track, where he again takes to the land, as he almost invariably swims either up or down the river instead of crossing direct; indeed, he will sometimes come on shore on the same side, thereby throwing the wolf off the track; and, if there happen to be weeds or brush about the bank, the deer will often sink himself so that nothing but part of his head will be above water. . . . but in the winter season when deer goes upon the ice the wolf makes a short chase of it, as the deer slips and falls down every bound he makes upon the glare ice. But if the deer take to a rapid, sufficiently deep to sweep the wolf off its feet, and not so deep but that the deer can stand or walk, the chances then are that a strong buck may kill the wolf by striking him with his fore hoofs. I have lost several good dogs in the same manner. In these cases the deer shows great tact in either striking his enemy, or leaping aside and allowing the wolf to be swept past by the current." (Billings, E., 1856: 211.)

USE OF RUNWAYS

The wolf runway or circuit, correctly referred to also as a hunting route, is a travelway giving access to the territory of a given pair or family. It generally runs through more or less open country. It may consist in part of trails of game, cattle, or sheep, old wood roads, or even highways in thinly settled areas; it may traverse dry washes and canyons, and cross low watershed divides or swamps. In cold countries, frozen lakes may become part of a winter runway. Wolves have been known to use runways covering a circuit of considerably more than a hundred miles.

The width of the run as used may be from a few feet, as where it coincides with a cow, horse, or game trail, to a mile or more where the animals are hunting. Along the runway one often finds that high points are used as vantages for observation. The wolves also employ these sites for playing or resting.

On these runways wolves have what are commonly referred to as "scent posts," or places where they come to urinate or defecate. These are found on or near the bases of bunch grasses, on bushes, or on an old weathered carcass. These scent posts may be recognized by the scratches made on the ground near them by the wolf after it has relieved itself. This habit of having scent posts and of scratching near them is similar to that noted in dogs. The scratching by the wolf after defecating or urinating is possibly the vestige of a former habit of burying the dung or urine. As wolves pass over their runways, they stop at these posts, invariably voiding urine, and often feces as well. As with the dog, the excreta contain much hair and bones which serve to indicate the food.

The shape of the runway is generally an irregular circle, the diameter of which may be between 20 and 60 miles. Its extent depends on the amount of food available. If in an area heavily stocked with game, cattle, or sheep, the runway is relatively small, but where food is scarce it is proportionately larger. Occasionally, one may find what might be termed scouting courses, where wolves make short detours from the main runway. These eventually join the main runway again, and are apparently deviations made in search of prey.

While traveling their runways, which they generally do counterclockwise, wolves move with a slow, regular trot, as they do on cross-country travel. They often take advantage of sandy arroyos, washes, or soft dirt, possibly because of the lesser wear and tear on their footpads. In snow, where the going is difficult, wolves step in each other's tracks, so exactly that it often is impossible to tell how many of the animals are traveling together. Sutton and Hamilton say of a wolf's track in the snow of Southampton Island, Hudson's Bay:

"Traps set in the most ingenious way failed to catch them [wolves]. One man had set many traps about a well-baited fox trap, and the wolf had stolen the bait, making his way off from the trap by putting his feet in the prints he had made coming in. In this part of the North Country it is the wolf, not the fox, apparently, that is the symbol of cunning" (Sutton, G. M., and Hamilton, W. J., 1932: 34).

In the early fall of 1917 an opportunity was afforded for thoroughly tracing out of a well established wolf runway. As used by two wolves at that time, the starting point was approximately 20 miles south of Parker Canyon P. O., Santa Cruz County, Ariz. This point is about 14 miles south of the Mexican boundary in the State of Sonora. The wolves traveled northward and out of Mexico, a little west of Parker Canyon, crossing the San Rafael Valley to the foot of the Canelo (sometimes spelled Canela or Canille) Hills. At this point they swung into a deep canyon and headed for the crossing of the Canelo Hills, known as Cherry Creek Pass. Going through this pass, they ran along the divide of the Canelo Hills, which bore a well defined trail used by livestock and cowboys, until they reached the head of Turkey Creek. There they swung northward through the narrow valley of Turkey Creek, a distance of approximately 4 miles, turned west, again crossed the Canelo Hills, and headed toward the Patagonia Mountains; when about 12 miles west of the Canelo Hills, they turned south once again toward the Mexican boundary, which they crossed some 10 miles farther west than on the northward stretch. These wolves passed Cherry Creek Pass and the Divide with regularity every nine days. Their circuitous route totaled about 70 miles, made up as follows:

1. 14 miles to Mexican Boundary.
2. 2 miles to Parker Canyon.
3. 10 miles to Canelo Hills.
4. 2 miles on Cherry Creek Divide.
5. 4 miles down Turkey Creek Canyon.
6. 12 miles west, crossing Canelo Hills and toward Red Rock in Patagonia Mountains.
7. 14 miles down south and crossing the Mexican boundary again.
8. 12 miles allowed for scouting deviations from runway.

Returning to this area 23 years later in February, 1940, I found that wolves were still using this runway.

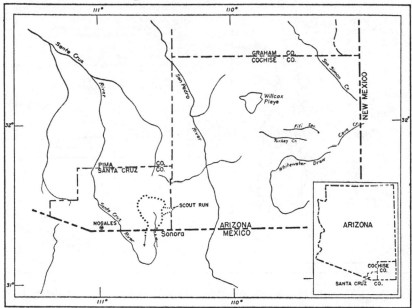

Figure 4. Canelo Hills wolf runway, Santa Cruz County, Arizona

A second well-established runway that wolves have long used in passing between the United States and Mexico is located in southwestern New Mexico, west of the Whitewater Mountains. Wolves cross the international boundary by coming north from Chihuahua. This, in addition to the Canelo Hills run and the Meeker run mentioned below are fully illustrated (Figs. 4 and 5) and need not be further described.

Another wolf runway in Rio Blanco County (Fig. 6), northwestern Colorado, was of elliptical shape and at least 100 miles long. It was located within a wolf range near Meeker that continued west to the Utah line, south to the Colorado River, and thence eastward again to the Meeker ranges. A part of the Piceance Creek drainage known as Dry Fork formed a portion of this wolf run. On it was situated a large stock ranch, which the wolves visited regularly every nine or ten days.

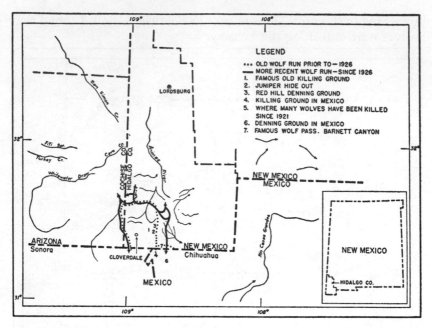

Figure 5. Wolf runway, Cloverdale-Whitewater Mountains area, Southwest New Mexico.

It is of interest to note that meat-eating birds, as the magpie and raven, may be occasionally observed flying along a wolf runway, apparently biding the time when a wolf will have departed after taking a meal from a fresh kill, so that they may in turn feast thereon. Dr. Adolph Murie was fortunate in obtaining a motion picture of magpies thus following wolves in 1939 while he was engaged on wildlife studies in Mount McKinley National Park, Alaska.

REPRODUCTION

Wolves do not breed until between 2 and 3 years of age. They couple much as dogs do but can more readily separate. In captivity oestrum has been noted to continue from three to five days; the female has stood for the male over a period of five days, and then rejected further advances; not until the vulva became noticeably swollen would the female stand. The period of discharge of blood from its start in late December until the swelling of the vulva and

Plate 20. A. Main wolf-run leading north down Turkey Creek from water-hole

B. Main wolf-run following juniper wood road

SCENES TYPICAL OF A WOLF RUNWAY IN CANELO HILLS, SANTA CRUZ COUNTY, ARIZONA

Plate 21. A. Canelo Hills in distance, through which wolves cross after turning west from Turkey Creek toward Red Rock Canyon in Patagonia Mountains

B. Red Rock Canyon, Patagonia Mountains, most northernly point on Canelo Hills wolf runway

Plate 22. A. Red Hill area, an old wolf denning ground

B. Looking southwest from Red Hill

Plate 23. A. Animas Mountains—Red Hill denning area in middle foreground

B. Juniper Forest wolf hideout, eight miles north of Mexican border. Often
driven by cowboys, who dislodged one to fifteen wolves at a time

Plate 24. A. North view of juniper wolf hideout. Peloncillo Mountains in background

B. Further close-up of juniper wolf hideout

Plate 25. A. Remains of two-year old heifer killed by wolves, January, 1940, near Juniper Forest hideout

B. A wolf crossing off from Barnett Canyon, three miles north of Mexican boundary

Plate 26. A. Espuela Mountains, Mexico, through which wolves pass to enter United
States. Cloverdale-Whitewater area, New Mexico

B. Animas Valley, looking northeast—the scene of many wolf killings of livestock

Plate 27. A. North end of Animas Valley, showing Animas Peak

B. Looking up Bear Canyon, Animas Peak in distance. Many wolves have been killed
in this canyon

Plate 28. A. Trail leading up Bear Canyon, used extensively by wolves

B. Wolf-hunters' camp, which has been used as a base for many years on Cloverdale-Whitewater wolf runway

Plate 29. U. S. Government Hunter W. C. Eckols, who has worked the Cloverdale-Whitewater wolf runway since 1921, capturing many wolves

the final copulation for five females averaged 45 days. The female wolf has ten teats in two rows, one each side of the belly.

The mating of wolves seems to be for life. As with the dog, the gestation period is 60 to 63 days. Brown, commenting on the gestation periods of the wolves in the Philadelphia Zoo, gives the period as "9 weeks" for *Canis lupus lycaon* (Brown, C. E., 1936: 12).

In the Gardens of the Zoological Society of London, Flower records: "about one hundred and fifty-five Wolves are recorded as having been born in the Gardens. Of these eighty-six (86) were probably of European parentage, 1829-1921, and were all born in the month of May with the exceptions of one litter on 1 June, 1848, and one on 4 April, 1921. Fourteen were *C. niger*, 1869-1873, only one of these being reared, and fifty-five were *C. occidentalis* 1903-1914" (Flower, S. S., 1929: 114).

These records for the European wolf and wolves in captivity, as well as field observations upon wolves in North America, would appear to show that wolves usually give birth to their young during the months of April, May, and June.

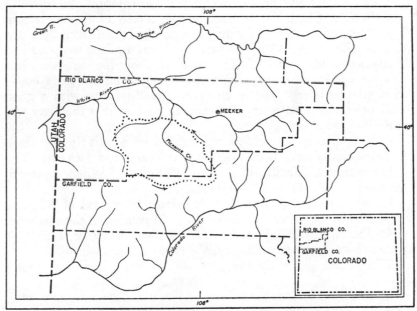

Figure 6. The Meeker wolf runway in Rio Blanco County, Colorado

Ligon's observations on sex ratio and the season of the birth of wolves trapped in February 1916 in New Mexico are embodied in the following statement:

"It is interesting to note that the wolves, as to sex, were divided equally, 34 males and 34 females. Of the whelps taken, 10 were males and 5 females. It seems that the wolf whelps come in this district rather regularly, from about March 20 to April 5. There is little variation in time, except possibly in Southern Arizona and Southwest New Mexico, where the Mexican subspecies (*Canis lupus baileyi*) occurs, and the young are brought forth earlier in some cases. Bert Smith took from a hole in a rock cliff, in the extreme southwest part of New Mexico, in the Peloncillo Mts. at about 6,500 feet, 6 whelps on March 22. These whelps did not have their eyes open. Very likely in this region the young are born any time from the 10th of March to the 1st of April" (Ligon, J. S., 1917).

The size of the wolf litter varies. Whelps have been noted in numbers ranging from 5 to 8 and from 8 to 14 in individual wolf families. The average appears to be about 7. Charles Burdick, Special Representative of the Secretary of the Interior, observed:

"While at Chatinika, Alaska, on the Steese Highway, late in May 1939, I saw a litter of wolf pups that had been taken by a den hunter. There were 13 in the pen and I was advised that one had already been given away. . . . They were all about the same size, just a few days old, and were being fed evaporated milk from a bottle and nipple. All appeared to be strong, healthy pups with a good chance of reaching maturity. It seems to me now that the litter was evenly divided in sexes."[13]

A female wolf whose den was robbed consecutively for three years produced a total of 21 whelps, or an average of 7 a year. The locality was near Fruita, in western Colorado. When captured, December, 1923, she bore 7 embryos.

Bailey records that 4 wolf dens containing a total of 32 pups were found in the Green River Valley of Wyoming in the spring of 1906. During the spring of 1907 in this same valley he records 47 wolf whelps from 6 dens (Bailey, V., 1908: 2, 3).

Whelps are generally sooty brown at birth; however, young

---

[13]Letter from Charles G. Burdick to Stanley P. Young, dated August 5, 1940, in files of Fish and Wildlife Service, Washington, D. C.

Plate 30. Mother and young leaving den. (*Canis lupus irremotus*)

wolves in the Arctic, where the white color phase of parent wolves predominates, are often a light blue, as in that color designated as Maltese, or dull slate. The pelt of a young wolf becomes rough with the development of its teeth, makes a gradual transition into the first winter's coat, and then a complete change to the summer pelage when the animal is approximately a year old. Compared with the coyote whelp, the wolf whelp is stockier, has a larger head, and a blunt muzzle.

The eyes of wolf puppies open within 5 to 9 days. They are blue, and very tender in expression until approximately two months after birth. They are well grown at 18 months, and the males are fully matured in 3 years. The females seem to mature somewhat earlier, at approximately 2 years.

DENNING AND REARING

Wolves use dens when bringing forth and rearing their young. These dens are generally located near a runway or travel route. They may be established in an eroded sandstone or limestone bluff, or under a shelf of such rocks and are usually located so as to give a commanding view of the surrounding terrain. They may likewise be located in the decomposing stump of a tree, in enlarged badger or rabbit holes, or in holes purposely dug in dry cut-banks or sagebrush hillsides, and occasionally even in abandoned beaver dams. Wolves prefer, however, high den locations that permit a good view of the surrounding country.

The female wolf, up until shortly before the birth of the whelps, may clean out or dig several holes besides the one to be first occupied. These dens may be from 5 to 10 miles distant, or again, they may be but a few hundred yards apart. The male at times assists the female in establishing these holes. The dens may have one or several entrances in use, and several passages may branch from the main one. They are of sufficient size to allow the adults to slip into them with ease; but are seldom large enough to permit the wolves to enter upright. The animals generally must enter in a sprawling posture, but once inside find more room, in some dens sufficient to permit the wolf to assume a nearly upright position, but this is not common with holes dug by the wolves themselves. Some tunnels have been found to run 30 feet from the entrance back to where the whelps are bedded. Also some burrows have been found to continue from the entrance back through a narrow passage for from 4 to 6 feet and from that point to enlarge so as to permit two adult wolves to pass. This type of den would seem to be more easily protected from intruders. When digging den holes, the wolves generally claw out the dirt in one direction from the mouth of the den, where it forms a mound, although some dens have no such mound.

The interior of a wolf den generally receives no special preparation, the floor being simply dry earth, the compactness which depends upon the nature of the local soil. In adobe country, it is likely to be quite compact; but elsewhere it is generally loose and dusty. Occasionally some hair will be found lining the bottom and sides of the den entrance, but this accumulates merely through rubbing off from the bodies of the parents as they enter and leave. Some hair also comes from around each teat of the female, where it sloughs off at time the young are born. Then, too, at this period the spring molt is on, beginning with the underfur. A late den will thus have more hair in it than one used earlier. Before the whelps leave the den permanently, the skin of the older wolves usually becomes shaggy, and unkempt. Many dens that have been examined have yielded no traces of feces or urine. It is believed that both these excretions are voided mainly outside the den. Sometimes they are greatly in evidence near the den entrance.

A female wolf in captivity with young was noted to eat the excreta of the whelps until the nursing period was over.

After the dens are completed, the female stays in fairly close proximity to the first den to be occupied, generally about three weeks until the birth of the whelps. However, observations are also on record which tend to show that birth of the young sometimes occurred before the female wolf could return to the den. When the young are whelped away from the intended home, the mother seeks the shelter of cedars, junipers, or other trees, or sometimes thickets, where accumulated litter forms an attractive bed. However, when this happens the young are moved in a short time to the den. The female wolf, in moving her whelps, may hold them in her mouth so that the head and tail project on each side of her face, or she may take them by the nape of the neck. When thus transporting the young the wolf travels in almost a beeline with each until the task is completed. This mode of transport is abandoned as soon as the young are large enough to travel under their own powers.

The male may tend to the young when misfortune overtakes his mate. For instance, Twitchell states that: "In riding out trap lines July 6th [1916], we found a mother wolf in a trap. Shortly after this we located the den about three quarters of a mile away. We set some traps on trails leading to the den and caught two pups. After this disturbance the male wolf moved the remainder of the pups and we were unable to locate any of them."[14]

Speaking of the den of the eastern wolf in northwest Maryland, Meshach Browning, a trapper of the late 1700's and early 1800's, says:

"Wolves always seek the most hidden places in the wilderness in which to make their den, when they raise their young. They sometimes penetrate to a great distance underground, but they always go under far enough to shelter themselves from all storms. While the female is unable to seek food for herself, and even after she brings forth her litter, the male attends to her wants, and will travel ten or fifteen miles in search of food for her and her whelps. If the distance is great, he will swallow large pieces, until he is stuffed full; when he will return home, and disgorge it for the use of his family" (Browning, M., 1928: 272).

This account by an early Maryland trapper applies very well to the denning habits of the wolf in most parts of North America.

Twitchell, in commenting upon wolf dens and how they are chosen, mentions the appropriation of a beaver den by wolves in Idaho:

"This den was found by Grady Quinn and myself on July 6, 1916, approximately twenty-five miles east of Blackfoot, Idaho, on Wood Creek. This location is on the Fort Hall Indian Reservation about three miles south of the Blackfoot River.

"An old beaver dam had been washed out leaving the entrance to the beaver den well above the water level of the creek. At this point the hill rose rather abruptly from the creek bank. A pair of wolves had enlarged the beaver den, and here their pups were born."[15]

After the whelps arrive, the parent wolves seem to have no set

---

[14]Letter from Leo Twitchell, of the Fish and Wildlife Service, to Stanley P. Young, from Pocatello, Idaho, April 9, 1940; in files of Fish and Wildlife Service.
[15]Letter from Leo Twitchell to Stanley P. Young, Pocatello, Idaho, April 9, 1940; in files of Fish and Wildlife Service.

time for being at home, but may by chance be found there at almost any hour. They both forage for food to feed the young after weaning. The nursing period seldom extends beyond 6 to 8 weeks' time, after which the young are fed almost exclusively on meat. The adults may range as far as from 15 to 20 miles from the den. Dixon records a female wolf in Mount McKinley National Park, Alaska, carrying food for her young a distance of 12 miles (Dixon, J. S., 1934: 158).

When they make a kill at such a great distance from the den, wolves will cram themselves with fresh meat, return, and disgorge it in small piles around the entrance of the den for the whelps to feed from. The female does this more than the male. However, at this time wolves do not seem to gorge themselves so extensively on fresh meat as they do when hunting under conditions of greater freedom.

As much as 150 pounds in the aggregate of disgorged beef was noted at the entrance of a wolf den near Thatcher, in southern Colorado, in the late spring of 1921. The weather being warm, and flies in abundance, much of the meat was rather putrid, and its stench offensive. It is believed that such a messy condition at the den, together with an abundance of fleas within may cause the parent wolves to abandon the burrow and move to a new one. Wolves appear to harbor fewer fleas than coyotes. Moving for sanitary reasons seems to be a trait not uncommon in the wolf, for evidence has been found of as many as four different dens having been used during the same season by the one pair of wolves and their whelps.

Slaughtering to provide a supply of food ahead of the whelping season has been observed in cold countries. Thus Frank Glaser reported to the Alaska Game Commission on March 15, 1938, from Fairbanks, that: "The main slaughter of sheep, caribou, and moose is from the middle of February to the first of April. At the time breeding starts with the wolves, I have seen as many as three families in one pack, have watched them through my binoculars and just at dark they would surround a band of caribou and start to howl. The next morning I have found as many as twelve dead caribou on the flats where they had surrounded the caribou the night before. It always seemed when these big killings were made that nothing but the tongues of the caribou were eaten. This goes on from the latter part of February until the 25th of March.

"It was over five years before I finally found out what this slaughter was all about. I am now sure that the wolves are smart enough to make these killings so there will be a supply of meat on hand when the pups are born so that the dog wolf will have a good supply of meat on hand in case the caribou have moved. . . .

"A wolf den that I found last spring, the 15th of May (1937), provided another example. The snow was about four feet deep around the den, and cached in the snow I found the remains of about five sheep. In May the sheep venture a long ways from the cliffs to find food, and they being thin and weak, are easy prey for wolves. . . ."

While wolf-hunting on snowshoes at the head of Lemhi Valley near the divide between Idaho and Montana, a Service hunter saw a pair of wolves traveling down a snowy gulch. He followed them and soon located their den. Snow was about 4 feet deep on the level, but these wolves had dug about 8 feet through a drift to the mouth of the den. Excavating the burrow for 30 feet, the hunter got 7 whelps about 12 days old. Meanwhile, the old wolves kept about uneasily, out of rifle shot, until toward evening, when the male came nearer and was killed.

A beaten trail led from the den about 200 yards to a place where an early snowfall had caught 11 horses and forced them to form a winter "yard,"—a not uncommon happening in that part of the West. This pair of wolves had already killed and eaten 8 of the horses, 3 remaining alive and in fairly good condition. Near the mouth of the den were large pieces of horse meat torn from the carcasses and dragged where they could be more conveniently fed upon. It was apparent that these wolves had killed the horses one by one as they were needed, and the 3 survivors would have taken the family through to the coming of the open season. In late spring or summer a pair of wolves finding 11 horses in a small enclosure, would in a single night kill or maim all of them. In this instance foresight apparently was used and with a family coming the wolves safeguarded their food supply.

Besides raw meat, bones and small freshly-killed rodents and rabbits are often carried to the whelps. The bones carried to the pups generally come from wolf kills. Transport of bones such as neck vertebrae and bones of the shoulder, as well as legs, to the den from a distance of from 3 to 4 miles has been observed. Apparently these bones are used by the whelps for aiding the growth of their teeth, for they gnaw them constantly.

Wolf dens are not necessarily located near sources of water, for the young whelps seemingly survive nicely for not less than a month without water, receiving sufficient liquid from the mother's milk. When being moved from an old to a new den, the whelps may have their first opportunity of obtaining water. The manner of drinking water is the same in wolves as with the domestic dog, though the laps seem to be louder, and more water is seemingly taken at each lap.

At first the whelps keep closely to the interior of the den, not venturing out until about 3 weeks old. From this time onward until the den is abandoned, they romp and play, similarly in every respect to domestic puppies. They are very alert, however, and the main defenses of the wolf, eyesight, acute smell, and alert hearing, develop rapidly in the young. The least unusual sound sends them scampering into the den, from which they cautiously emerge only when there appears to be no danger.

The wolf whelps, while maturing, develop most rapidly as to the pasterns, feet, and jaws. This produces some ungainliness of actions until the whelps are nearly half-grown, when the remainder of the body begins to develop in proportion to the limbs.

At times, while the whelps are maturing, there are indications that severe fighting takes place among members of the litter, for occasionally half-grown wolves have been captured having bobtails that seem to have become bobbed by the bitings of their fellows. Often in wolf litters are to be found one or two whelps more vicious than the others, a characteristic that becomes even more marked as they mature. Males have been noted to be more vicious than females from the same den.

While foraging for food for the young in the den, the parent wolves seldom deviate more than a few hundred yards from a direct line even in a distance of several miles. This directness of travel to and from the den seemingly denotes full knowledge of food possibilities, and that no time is lost in going to the hunting grounds. Thus that part of the runway fairly near the whelping den becomes, during the period of rearing the young, the scene of severe depredations. It has been noted that a female with a den of whelps will almost invariably clean up her kill, if it is not molested, even if numerous trips to it are required. If it is disturbed, a new kill is made. The trait of visiting a kill and eating from it more than once at this period is at variance with the usual custom of wolves at other times.

Seldom does the male wolf use the den in the daytime. When at home, his place is generally at some higher point or lookout, where he acts as sentinel. Here he alternately dozes and watches for threats of danger. Any alarm is soon communicated to the family, which if outside of the den, immediately retreats to it. The male wolf in such instances has been observed to scamper away from his lookout and the immediate vicinity of the den, and by voicing a succession of howls to attempt to distract the attention of the intruder, especially if a human, so that the den will not be discovered. In doing this he has been known to go away from the den a number of miles, letting himself be seen, and howling at intervals. Such lookout points are often well marked, because traces of the male's having laid down there are much in evidence; numerous scats also may be present.

The foraging for food that both wolves partake in is generally started at early twilight and continues until prey has been obtained. Some hunting is done shortly before the break of day, but generally, however, the intensity of the prowl for food for the whelps is during the cooler hours following sunset. Consequently, in late forenoon and most of the afternoon both parents usually are near or in the den. These traits make the wolf mainly a nocturnal animal during the season of rearing the young. At this time of the year they have little fat owing to their strenuous efforts in foraging for food.

The den or dens are abandoned when the whelps are approximately 2½ to 3 months old, from which time on they are continually in the company of their parents. At this time, much hunting takes place over the runway, but use is made of what may be termed loafing spots. At these points the whelps seem to frolic and play and sleep for several days at a time, while the parent wolves forage the surrounding country. Returning to these points, the wolves feed their offspring, travel another stage and resume hunting. It is probable that these "loafing spots" represent points along a runway where the parents have made a kill and have taken the growing whelps to feed upon it. At this stage of their life, the whelps have permanently left the den; the old wolves no longer carry food to them but make a kill and move the young to it. Thus, the young may stay several days feasting and playing at a "loafing point."

When the teeth of the young are well developed, the parent wolves start training them to kill. This generally takes place in August and September, depending upon the time in the spring when the young were whelped.

S. K. McClure says that " 'they have either learned from the cowboy how to round up cattle, or they have taught him how to do so.' They often work in pairs in killing stock, one going to the animal's head and the other to his heels. . . . It is the general belief among cattlemen that these wolves would put their young through a period of training in the methods of killing stock. John Arnot says that the loboes would often take their pups out in the spring and early summer and teach them how to kill young calves. Often, he says, when the pups were first beginning, they would catch hold of the calf's tail and . . . . pull the tail off . . . ." (Sheffy, L. F., 1929: 94).

Occasionally it has been observed that parent wolves, when rearing young, will permit the occupancy of the den at the same time by the young of the previous year. Consequently, when in a wolf denning habitat, one might see wolves of different sizes emerge from the same den. This sociability of the wolf family probably carries on until the final separation of the young at the age of full breeding maturity. However, no instances of two female wolves rearing their young in the same den have come under observation, although this has been observed on the part of female coyotes.

INDIVIDUAL AND FAMILY TRAITS

When domestic animals are brought into their range, wolves promptly learn that these new beasts and fowls are easier to capture than wild life. Then following the line of least resistance in gaining a livelihood, they wreak havoc upon the slower and less suspicious farm animals. The apparently wanton killing of more sheep or other livestock than needed by them for food considered so outrageous by the stock owner, apparently is to the wolf but a form of sport. Mass killings of sheep or cattle by wolves appears to result from sheer physical exuberance of this predator in the height of vigor, and becomes a form of recreation.

Sheffy referred to this in his article on the lobo, saying:
". . . . They ate nothing but fresh, fat meats and only that which they killed themselves. They never returned to a carcass for a second meal, and, unless they were very hungry, they never ate more than the ham and loins and the kidney fat of the stock which they killed. . . . They would even kill calves for the sport of it, this being one of their forms of play. . . ." (Sheffy, L. F., 1929: 94).

While a single wolf can kill a full-grown animal such as a deer, elk, moose, or cow, generally two or more wolves work together in subduing prey. Usually this is accomplished by one wolf's snapping and tearing at the animal's head, while the other attacks the hindquarters or flanks severely lacerating them and often hamstringing the victim, causing it to fall. This front and rear mode of attack enables wolves to strike at the two most vulnerable parts of their intended victim whose flanks may not only be gashed to the extent of disemboweling, but whose head may have been bitten so severely that the nose is completely removed or one or both eyes are blinded.

When a pair of wolves on the hunt have singled out such prey, as a domestic cow or steer, the female of the pair invariably approaches the head of the animal. By attracting its attention through various antics, but not closing in, it avoids any charge. The male wolf, at the same time, works from the rear and attempts at every opportunity to hamstring the prey. These actions of the female were referred to on the open western prairie ranges as "loafing" in front of the prey; hence, the term "loafer wolf" became commonly adopted and was used in western range parlance as the name of the plains wolf.

Numerous instances of cooperative effort of wolves in conquering prey are described in following sections on the food of wolves.

Often one hears the term "lone wolf." The lone wolf in the wild is generally an old male, but sometimes an old female that has lost its mate. When this occurs, old males or females seldom mate again or participate in group hunting forays. Such wolves hunt singly and stay much by themselves. Occasionally an individual becomes a lone wolf because great wear of its teeth prevent it from joining in teamwork with other wolves in obtaining food.

There is as previously noted a distinct variation as to intelligence, disposition, timidity, boldness, viciousness, strength, and size among young wolf whelps even of the same litter. This individuality shows up strongly when the animals are raised in captivity. Some are kindly and affectionate from the beginning, while others are sulky and vicious, and never respond to efforts at taming. This occurs even among wolves taken so young that their eyes are still closed. In one instance an attempt was made to raise a female and a male whelp in a specially-made kennel and wired runway, at Louviers, some 20 miles south of Denver, Colo. They were about one month old when captured, and remained exceedingly wild, though handled every day during the first five months of their captivity. When 1½ years old, they broke out of their kennel one day, killed some 60 ducks and chickens in the farmyard where they had been located, and proceeded to drive the lady of the premises back into the house as she rushed out to ascertain the reason for the commotion amongst the barnyard flock. She hastily called for aid from one of the farmhands on another part of the place, and he quickly dispatched both wolves with a shotgun, but not until they had threatened him as well.

On the assumption that some of these characteristics become more pronounced with maturity in the wild, we can better under-stand the outstanding individual traits that were manifested by some of the last of the noted stock-killing wolves. To remove these animals from the ranges of South Dakota, Wyoming, Oregon, Colo-rado, and Arizona required extreme effort, and all of the ingenuity of the expert wolf trappers of the Federal Government. The cun-ning of many of these wolves and their ability to avoid capture at times caused the greatest wonderment. Many of the hunters were prone to consider these wolves as possessed of near human intelli-gence. Each of them became known by some distinctive trait, which was as marked in its way as the differences between human indi-viduals.

Unless one has had an opportunity to observe wolves while making a kill, it is almost impossible to comprehend the great power of their bite. A wolf can snap off the tail of a long yearling, a full-grown cow, or steer with the cleanness of cut as that of a scythe on maturing hay. It can with similar ease bite clear through the hide of a cow and lacerate it in a terrible manner. In other words, a wolf seldom bites into its victim without removing some of the flesh.

Peale, one of the naturalists with the Charles Wilkes exploring expedition while in the vicinity of Puget Sound during the year 1841 records the killing "of a calf by a single bite [of a wolf] which had divided its spine . . . ." (Cassin, J., 1858: 16).

An old male wolf captured in the Canelo Hills of southern Arizona severed with one bite a dried, knotty juniper limb that was 2 inches in diameter. This occurred when a wolf hunter, attempting to give the wolf some water as it lay prone on the ground, used the stick to push a can of water towards the animal's head. Like a striking rattlesnake, it suddenly lunged its head forward, with wide-open jaws, and snapped the limb in two—apparently without effort.

A shearing effect is obtained by the action of the carnassial teeth (or the last premolar and first molar on each side) and tearing is probably done mostly by the canine teeth (eye teeth or tusks). Just as a floating iceberg has its greater portion immersed beneath the water, so the wolf's canine tooth is imbedded nearly two-thirds of its total length in the gum and jaw bone. Measurements of the right lower canine tooth of a typical specimen of *Canis lupus youngi*, second largest wolf in the United States, show a total length of 56.1 mm., or 2-3/16 inches:

Length of crown (posterior)	22.0 mm., equals ⅞ inch
Length of crown (anterior)	21.0 mm., equals ¾ inch
Length of root (posterior)	34.0 mm., equals 1⅜ inches
Length of root (anterior)	50.3 mm., equals 1¹³⁄₁₆ inches
Greatest diameter (longitudinal)	15.6 mm., equals ¾ inch
Greatest thickness of tooth	9.4 mm., equals ⅜ inch

The snap of a wolf's teeth resembles the noise made by suddenly clapping together two pieces of flooring board. This sound is often made by a trapped wolf when it is approached.

Wolves approaching what might be termed old age, that is, from 10, 12, to 14 years old, are likely to have much-worn teeth, including broken incisors. Often this condition of the teeth makes it difficult for the wolf to kill its prey with the same dexterity as of old. Hence it may resort to strangulation of its victims. Such wolves have been known to grab prey by the throat, and though not possessing sufficiently sharp teeth to penetrate the hide or flesh, still have tremendous power of jaw by which they choke their victims to death.

Often, too, a wolf with teeth in this condition becomes more of a scavenger and is more likely to revisit a carcass than it did during its younger years. Trappers refer to such a wolf as a "gummer," or occasionally as a "smooth-mouthed wolf." The so-called "gummer wolf" corresponds to a similar description used by the

sheep men in speaking of broken-mouthed ewes, which are called
"gummer ewes" by them.

Mead, who had much experience with wolves on the Kansas
and surrounding prairies, stated that he had "killed numbers whose
teeth were entirely gone, except a few black stumps. Such could not
kill game for themselves, but ate that killed by others" (Mead,
J. R., 1899: 280).

Loss of toes or a foot, or other crippling by traps, appears to
cause a wolf to prey to a greater extent on domestic stock doubtless
because it is more easily caught and subdued than is wild game.
While no study of the stomach contents of the peg-leg wolves has
been possible, as with the peg-leg coyotes, it is known that some of
the most severe depredations on western ranges were by wolves
with crippled toes or a stubbed foot. It is reasonable to assume that
the same handicap which increases the depredations on livestock by
the coyote would have a similar effect in wolves (Sperry, C. C.,
1939: 190).

One conspicuous instance occurred in Stephens County, Tex.,
during the fiscal year 1939. Here, after 75 days of persistent effort,
a federal hunter captured a crippled red wolf that had killed $1,000
worth of sheep and goats on one ranch. When caught, the animal
had one fore foot and two toes of one hind foot missing, and the
other hind foot broken.

The power of observation in some adult wolves is exceedingly
keen. This has been proved time and again when a hunter, in placing traps on a runway, may have inadvertently moved some natural
object out of place. When this happens, the wolf, the next time it
passes that point, is more than apt to shy away.

When a new den is occupied by the wolf family, and the whelps
need not be carried, the move, if a long one, affords the parent
wolves opportunity to teach the whelps to keep close together while
traveling cross country. The whelps are never out of hearing of the
whimpering call of the female. One Colorado hunter on horseback
came unexpectedly on a family of wolves en route to a new den,
and because of their close grouping he was able to kill five of the
whelps with a revolver while sitting in the saddle. In this instance,
also, the old female, on seeing the hunter shortly before he shot,
gave a loud whine as a warning, and the whelps endeavored to scatter in all the directions. She then quickly ran to the top of a small

sagebrush knoll, but out of gun range, and set up a series of howls apparently meant to distract the hunter's attention, so that the whelps might be afforded an opportunity to escape. If one stalks a wolf den while the young whelps are playing around the entrance, and is observed by the female, she utters a warning whine, and the pups scatter widely so that it is difficult to find them again.

Affection and sociability continue until the whelps become fully adult. This is shown by the never-failing return of relatives to a trap set after one of the wolves of the family has been caught and dispatched. All of the members of whole families of wolves, numbering from five to seven, have been taken one after another in one or two traps set at or near where the first one was captured. Wolf tracks left leading to and around these spots leave unmistakable evidence that the remaining members of the wolf family have been seeking the lost member.

A male wolf was trapped on November 1, 1917, near the northern end of its runway in the Canelo Hills of Santa Cruz County in southern Arizona. It had been observed that but one other wolf accompanied it, and judging from the smaller size of the tracks, it was a female. From the evidence of its tracks, this female, following the capture of the male, showed much bewilderment and gave every indication of being on a hunt for her lost mate. She never missed a night in covering this part of the runway. Sixteen days later, she was trapped within 20 yards of the set that took her mate.

Strong affection sometimes displayed in a wolf family is described also by Freuchen, who while camped north of Berthic Harbour, near Wager Inlet north of Hudson Bay, observed the actions of two old white wolves and three whelps. He states:

"As soon as we came ashore we heard the howling of wolves quite close, about a hundred metres away. We went out to look for them and saw five, two old white wolves and three cubs that were nearly as large as their parents, but grey. They were sitting on the ground, noses in the air and howling, but sprung up when they saw us and fled. Shortly afterwards we caught sight of a fourth cub, grey like the others, caught in a steel trap close by. . . . The others had made great efforts to set it free by overturning large stones from the cache at which it had been caught, and they had scratched at the frozen ground around the stone to which the chain

was made fast; the trapped wolf could not have done it, for it was
caught by the forelegs. . . . next morning their tracks told that they
had been to the place where the others had been trapped, and also
within ten metres of our sledge and camp" (Freuchen, P., 1935b:
120).

Glaser recounts a most interesting observation made of a wolf
family at a den in Mount McKinley National Park, Alaska. In this
instance, the firm bond within the wolf family was shown, not only
against the intrusions of a strange wolf but also against those of
grizzly bears. Early in June of 1940 Glaser records:

"Yesterday Ranger Herning and I started out to drive to the
Toklat River to look for wolf dens. When we were about three
miles from a den located on the East Fork of the Toklat, we saw
four grizzlies, a female and three yearlings, traveling toward it.

"On May 31st we witnessed a fight at this den that was interesting. While we lay on a ridge about 700 yards distant a gray wolf,
apparently a stranger, approached. One of the wolves at the den, a
large gray, ran up to it and seemed as though it were very friendly.
They wagged their tails. Soon, what we took to be the mother wolf,
came full speed and knocked the stranger down, then three more
wolves came at full speed from the vicinity of the den and all
jumped the strange wolf. We could hear the noise plainly. Then
without any apparent cause, they stopped fighting and just chased
the strange wolf down to the river bar. Then the five wolves went
back to the den; one crawled in, the other four lay down around the
den. From where we were located, Herning, Murie, and I could
see the wolf that had been attacked. Its hind parts were covered
with blood and it looked as though it could not live long. Apparently the small brownish wolf was the mother of the pups in the
den, the large black wolf the father, and another black and two extra
large grays last year's whelps.

"Well, to go back to the bears. Yesterday Herning and I made
up our minds to go over to the lookout and watch the den, in the
hope that we would see what would happen if the four bears should
cross downwind of this wolf family. I knew that the wolves would
have an abundant supply of caribou and sheep meat buried around
the den and that would be a great attraction to the bears. When we
were in a position to leave the car and go on foot to the den, Chief
Ranger Corbly drove up and asked Herning to do some other work

Plate 31. A. Wolf den at base of tree near snow-bank, Toklat River, Alaska, May 15, 1937

B. Wolf den dug through snow and into a cutbank, Alaska. (Photo courtesy *Alaska Sportsman*)

Plate 32. A. Typical wolf-denning country, Wind River Mountains, Wyoming

B. Entrance to a wolf den, Wyoming

112

Plate 33. A. A litter of nine wolf whelps in front of den, Big Piney, Wyoming

B. A Wyoming wolf with litter of 11 whelps

Plate 34. A. Wolf-denning country, Big Piney, Wyoming

B. Wolf den, Sacramento Mountains, New Mexico

Plate 34 (Continued). C. Wolf den, Arizona

D. Wolf denning country, Colorado

Plate 35. Wolf whelps approximately 8 weeks old

Plate 36. The wolf's manner of drinking water is the same as that of the domestic dog. The laps taken sound louder and more water is seemingly taken with each

Plate 37. A. Surroundings of wolf den near Kenton, Michigan, 1932

Plate 37 (continued). B. Trail approaching the den

C. Den established in hollow log

so he did not go. Murie and I went and soon located the four grizzlies asleep about a mile from the den. At the wolf den we saw two
black and one brown wolf. After about an hour, the four bears
started down the slope toward the wolf den. Finally one of the
bears got the scent of the rotten meat around the den. The four
bears keeping close together were within, I would say, about 30 feet
of the den when with a sudden rush the three wolves were on them.
The first rush confused the bears and they ran, which was a mistake,
for the wolves got home some severe slashes. The bears bunched
up closely out in the open. The wolves rushed them repeatedly and
slashed them. The bears retreated down to the knoll, where the
den was located, and started to dig up pieces of meat. The wolves
rushed the bears steadily several times, it looked as though a bear
had a wolf under him, the way they would leap at the wolves.
Finally, one of the absent gray wolves came into the fight. He was
desperate and rushed up to sink his fangs into a bear. Several times,
the female grizzly almost had this wolf.. The mother wolf stayed
as close to the entrance of her den as possible. The other three
wolves tried time and again to coax one of the yearlings away from
the mother bear. One of the wolves would rush a yearling bear,
bite it and then when the yearling would charge this wolf the other
two wolves would grab the yearling from the rear; then the female
bear would come to the rescue. This battle went on for over three
hours. When the gray wolf came into the fight, it made just too
many wolves for the bears. One could see that they wanted to leave
but the wolves were on all sides of them. When the bears turned
their backs to the wolves, the wolves were at them inflicting punishment. It seemed as though there was no limit to the wolves' endurance. Finally the bears retreated down the hill to the river bar.
The wolves stayed around the den for a short time, then two of them
started down to where the bears were. The last we saw of the bears,
they seemed to be quite angry. They would stop and look back
toward the den. One of the yearling bears sat down in the river for
a while; it appeared to be hurt."[16]

Large numbers of wolves traveling together are called a "pack."

[16]Report from Frank S. Glaser, Alaska Game Commission, to Mr. Frank Dufresne, dated June 6, 1940, at Mount McKinley National Park. In files of Fish
and Wildlife Service, Washington, D. C.

The pack is generally a pair of wolves and their yearling or two-year-old offspring. At times, however, there will be an intermingling of several wolf families to form a large pack; but the duration of such bands is short. The myth of the permanency of the wolf pack dates apparently from the early Greeks, as to be noted in Homer's Iliad, Xenophon's Hepparch, and other early Greek writers.

An ancient description of their cooperation was related by Xenophon: "Even wild creatures less intelligent than man, such as hawks will grab unguarded plunder and get away to a place of safety before they can be caught: wolves, again, prey on anything unprotected and steal things lying in holes and corners; and if a dog does pursue and overtake him, the wolf, if stronger than the dog, attacks him, or if weaker, snatches away the prize and makes off. Moreover, when a pack of wolves feels no fear of a convoy, they arrange themselves so that some shall drive off the convoy, and others seize the plunder; and thus they get their food" (Xenophon, 1925: 265).

GORGING

Of all the members of the canine family, the wolf, when in its prime, can be most irregular in its feeding habits. Equipped with abundant power to kill, the preference is for large prey in order to sustain its large body. When large prey is not available, long intervals between meals may be endured rather than spend time and energy in quest of small animals. Then when opportunity again occurs the animals fill themselves to repletion.

Wolf hunters refer to the results of gorging as a "meat drunk." Observations have been made of wolves which, after gorging, traveled but a short distance, took cover and slept for several days. The apparent stupefaction that the gorging causes was noted in earlier days on the plains when it was found that after gorging on a newly-killed buffalo carcass a wolf was readily approached by the hunter, who could kill the animal with the butt of his rifle or a club.

Long ago Edward Umfreville observed:

"The Indians likewise shoot them in the following manner: A buffalo being killed, and cut in pieces over night, the Indians appear at the place the next morning on horseback, when they find the wolves so over-gorged with eating as to be incapable of retreating, so that they become an easy prey to the hunters" (Umfreville, E., 1790: 169.

Ten male wolves (*Canis lupus youngi*) held in captivity by the author and fed well from early puppyhood until three years old, were found to weigh at this time an average of 90 pounds each. These animals were then killed and pelted when the skins had primed. Before they were killed, however, trial was made to learn how much food a wolf would consume at a single meal. Allowing each animal all it could eat after two days of starvation, the food consisting of fresh horse meat, beef, and fat, I found the weight of the stomach after gorging to be nearly one-fifth of the body weight (18 pounds).

A full-grown adult male wolf whose age approximated seven years was captured in Colorado. For a week it refused all offers of food, but drank water moderately on three different occasions. On the eighth day, however, it ate ravenously, and gorged on fresh horse meat and fat to the point of stupefaction. It refused water following this gorging of food. This wolf, on completion of its meal and before it was killed, weighed 110 pounds, 8 ounces. After it was killed, the stomach, greatly distended, was found to weigh 19 pounds, 3 ounces. The horse meat and fat eaten were but little masticated, being crunched only enough by the molars so that it could be gulped. In these gorging experiments, it was observed that the wolf stomach is capable of stretching to large proportions, assuming at length a shape not unlike that of an elongated watermelon.

Dr. E. H. McCleery, of Kane, Pa., began keeping and studying grey wolves obtained in the western portion of the United States in 1920. In 1940 he informed me that the 34 wolves he then had in his kennels, which were nearly all adults of both sexes, would, after a few days of starvation, completely consume in two days' time all edible portions of a 1,500-pound horse.

A characteristic trait of the wolf when gorged with raw meat is the passage of large quantities of exceedingly loose excreta of the consistency and color of melted licorice.

FEAR OF MAN

An animal that sometimes attacks and kills man certainly is not ruled by fear of man. It may avoid man, at most times, as a policy, being indifferent to him except when there is a conflict of interests. Under primitive conditions, there was a period when wolves were not well enough acquainted with man to keep away from him. Such a condition prevailed in this country when it was still very sparsely populated.

In his "Natural History of the Wolf," which describes, among other wolf traits, that of fear of man, Billings quotes from A. Dickson, Esq., of Kingston, Ontario:

"The Canadian Wolf is a cruel, savage, cowardly animal, with such a disposition that he will kill a whole flock of sheep merely for the sake of gratifying his thirst for blood, when one or two would have been sufficient for his wants. I have always found them the most cowardly of animals,—when caught in a trap, or wounded by a gun, or when cornered up so that they could not escape, I invariably killed them with a club or tomahawk, and I never met with any resistance. It is true I have seen them show some boldness if a number of them had run down a deer when I attempted to drive them away, yet have always seen them give way if a shot were fired amongst them" (Billings, E., 1856: 211).

With reference to some of his experiences with wolves while in the employ of the Hudson Bay Company for the years 1867-1874, Isaac Cowie, who at the time was accompanying a dog team and party in January 1868 from Fort Ou'Appelle to Wood Mountain, states: "I had, of course, read many a terrible tale of travellers in the snow being pursued by packs of ferocious wolves, and when I saw them abounding along our route I was surprised to see the perfect indifference of my companions.

"Instead of men being afraid of wolves, the wolves were afraid of men. I was told of their wonderful intelligence in keeping out of the range of gunshot, and afterwards when repeating long range rifles came into use they soon learnt to keep out of range of them too" (Cowie, I., 1913: 250).

As to the habit of a wolf's taking a broken or used trail made by man or beast, particularly in snow, Cowie vividly describes the Indians' belief that wolves could count to seven. He comments: "During after years several different Indians at different times and places assured me that wolves could count up to seven, and the way it was proven was this: They have a habit of following in a trail beaten by travellers, and on a rolling prairie or mounting a rise over which the party they were following had disappeared, the wolves would halt till they got clear sight of them again. Then, if one of a party of seven men had forked off to watch the trail to get a shot at the wolves following it, as they passed the place he had concealed himself, the animals would stop and follow no further on that trail. But if the number exceeded seven men, then one might detach himself from the party and not be missed by the wolves. I am sure that my informants believed this story of the wolf's ability to count, and I know that a band following us would stand for a while on the top of a knoll before coming on again after us. . . . The only time the wolves were ever considered dangerous on the plains was in the month of March, when an occasional old male went mad, so mad in fact as to come within range or striking distance of hunting people, who courted the opportunity to get the hide. It may be said the wolves on the prairie of which I am speaking were not the same animals as those found in the woods. But they were exactly the same, and I have seen thousands of them alive, and handled thousands of their skins, and in the very much smaller number of timber wolves I have seen, 'on the hoof' or in the hide, I have noticed no difference except that those reared in the woods were darker in color and on an average not so large as those who feasted on the buffalo. The difference between them in any desire to attack mankind or to leave him severely alone was occasioned by the one in the woods being famished and the other on the buffalo plains being well fed as a class; while the latter's greater familiarity with the power of hunting men inspired him and his with a wholesome dread not experienced by his kind beyond the seas in Europe and Asia, and even in the forests of North America" (Ibid.).

Further commenting on the wolf's fear of man, he continues:

"Even when the buffalo had migrated afar and food could not have been plentiful, the wolves never plucked up courage to attack people in the way described in tales of other countries. . . ." (Ibid., p. 252).

Stanley C. Arthur mentions what was represented as an attack of red wolves on an alligator hunter, Dave Moore, in Louisiana in the summer of 1926. Arthur states, however: "The probabilities are that the wolf pack was attracted by the odor of blood from alligators Moore had been skinning and that the members of the wolf pack had no intention of attacking the aged and experienced hunter, as the Louisiana wolf is, as are the wolves elsewhere, cowardly to the extreme" (Arthur, S. C., 1928: 149).

Through recorded history, certain happenings between man and wolf in the wilds incline one to the belief, at times, that what was presumed to be an attack upon an intended victim might have been, instead, attempted theft of food.   In this connection, Bartram records a hair-raising account of the wolf's visit to his camp in early day Florida: "When awake I started at the heavy tread of some animal; . . . close shrubby thickets part and bend under him as he rushes off. . . .

"When looking up I find my fish carried off, though I had thought them safe on the shrubs, just over my head; but their scent, carried to a great distance by the damp nocturnal breezes, I suppose were too powerful attraction to resist.

"Perhaps it may not be time lost to . . . reflect on the . . . unaccountable incident which, however, pointed out to me an extraordinary deliverance or protection of my life from the rapacious wolf that stole my fish from over my head.

"How much easier and more eligible it might have been for him to have leaped upon my breast in the dead of sleep, and torn my throat, which would have instantly deprived me of life, and then glutted his stomach for the present with my warm blood, and dragged off my body, which would have made a feast afterwards for him and his howling associates!   I say, would this not have been a wiser step than to have made protracted and circular approaches, and then after, by chance, espying the fish over my head, with the greatest caution and silence rear up, and take them off the snags one by one, then make off with them, and that so cunningly as not to waken me until he had fairly accomplished his purpose?" (Bartram, W., 1928: 144).

Wolves of North America, particularly those of the western plains, while in their maximum abundance, seemed at first to have had but little fear of man.   Verification of this is provided by some of the journals of the explorers, hunters, and trappers.   Lack of fear of man on the part of the western plains wolf in the later days of the western "wolfer," who resorted to strychnine for killing wolves, is depicted by George Bird Grinnell.   In describing the poisoning by the "wolfer" of a buffalo carcass used as a bait, he states: "Often while this is being done, the wolfer would be surrounded by a circle of ten or a dozen or more wolves, waiting patiently for him to complete his operations and go away, so that their meal might begin.   In those days wolves had no fear of man.   They were very seldom shot at, and knew of the gun chiefly as an implement to call them to a feast." (Grinnell, G. B., 1897b: 161.)

Again, Grinnell, in quoting Joseph Kipp, a half-breed Mandan, gives a further hint on the non-fearing wolf of the plains. He continues: "One day we ran a large herd of buffalo, which we found a mile or two north of where Cutbank Stream joins the Marias. I had a splendid horse, but as soon as I killed a cow I stopped, for that was all the meat I wanted, and more too. I had reached the herd some time before the Indians did, and when they saw me dismount one of them asked me to exchange horses with him, as he wanted to make a big killing. I let him have it, and tying his horse to the horns of the buffalo, I proceeded to skin it. In less than five minutes the wolves began to gather about me. It was the running season, and each bitch was surrounded by a number of dog wolves playing and fawning about her, and quarreling with each other just like a lot of dogs. The wolves kept about 50 or 60 yards from me, but one coyote came up quite close, and a couple of Kit foxes ventured up within eight or ten feet. I felt a little uneasy to be surrounded by such a big pack, and considered for some time whether to fire at them or not. I had only four balls left and rather wanted to keep them. Finally, however, I did shoot at a big white wolf, and not only killed him, but another one beyond. The rest of them, however, didn't pay any attention. Well, I only took the depouille and bossribs of the cow, and tying them to my saddle, I rode off about fifty yards. The wolves immediately ran up to the carcass, and such snapping and clicking of teeth you never heard. In a very few minutes the cow was eaten up, and the bare bones were dragged and scattered about. The wolves, as soon as the carcass began to be fairly well picked, commenced striking out toward the northeast, and finally all of them went off in that direction, leaving only the Kit foxes to keep me company" (Ibid.).

Townsend observed: "I have often been surprised at the perseverance and tenacity with which these animals will sometimes follow the hunter for a whole day, to feed upon the carcass he may leave behind him. When an animal is killed, they seem to mark the operation, and stand still at a most respectful distance with drooping tail and ears, as though perfectly indifferent to the matter in progress. Thus will they stand until the game is butchered, the meat placed upon the saddle, and the hunter is mounted and on his way; then, if he glances behind him, he will see the wily forager stealthily crawling and prowling along towards the smoking remains, and pouncing upon it, and tearing it with tooth and nail, immediately he gets out of reach.

"During the day, the wolves are shy, and rarely permit an approach to within gun-shot; but at night (where game is abundant), they are so fearless as to come quite within the purlieus of the camp, and there sit, a dozen together, and howl hideously for hours" (Townsend, J. K., 1839: 118).

It will be recalled that through a period of many years thousands of buffalos were killed for no other portions of the carcass than the fat, tongue, or tenderloin, the remainder of the carcass being left to be consumed by wolves and other carnivores. This practice, doubtless, was a large factor in causing the plains wolf at times to show but little fear of man. The wolves learned that every time a rifle cracked a meal was in the offing.

Luttig says of the loss of buffalos killed by members of his party while on a journey on the Upper Missouri River in October 1812: "Late last Evening the Boat and hunters arrived with a fine Chanoe of Meat they had Killed 19 Cows and 4 Elk, but lost the meat of 7 Cows by the Wolves, there are incredible quantities of Wolves in this parts, they go in gangs of 3 to 400 and at Nights the Prairies echo with their howling. . . ." (Luttig, J. C., 1920: 85).

Horace Greeley, in his comments on the wolf of the prairies which he observed first-hand during his trip across country in 1859, stated:

"It is very common for these wolves to follow at night a man travelling the road on a mule, not making any belligerent demonstration, but waiting for whatever may turn up. Sometimes the express wagons have been followed in this way, but I think that unusual. But this creature is up to anything wherein there is a chance for game" (Greeley, H., 1860: 93).

He further noted, while on this journey, "Of some twenty of them that I have seen within the last two days, I think not six have really run from us" (Ibid.).

While in command of the Bathurst Inlet Patrol in the Canadian Arctic, Inspector F. H. French recorded that "Wolves seemed very numerous from time to time on the trip and several times our camp was attacked by them and a general melee would ensue among the dogs. On March 24, when nearing Schultz lake, a pack of wolves came around our igloo and it was not before we had killed two of them that they went away.

"A similar occurrence took place on Back's river. These wolves were much larger than those previously seen and we shot one out of this band. At periods these wolves would follow us for days, evidently being hungry, and looking forward to the time when we left camp, when they would come up and clean up anything left behind. They were our constant companions across the Barrens to Bathurst inlet, where we appeared to lose them" (Police, Royal Northwest Mounted, 1919: 13).

Lt. J. W. Abert comments in his journal of January 31, 1847, on wolves following man. He states, after meeting on the trail with a party of men going westward to Santa Fe, that "Shortly after passing these people, we encountered some wolves following their trail. So intent were the wolves in their employment that they came quite close to us, holding their heads near the ground as they scented the tracks of the men, when one of my party levelled his rifle and killed the foremost. The animals have become very daring; . . ." (Abert, J. W., 1848: 530).

Toward the close of his journey eastward, Lt. Abert and his expedition, while some miles west of Fort Leavenworth and after days of struggling among snowdrifts and other vicissitudes of the trail, had one of his men temporarily blinded by snow. He was left alone in camp while Abert and his men sought better quarters a short distance eastward. The new camp being established, and protected for the time being from the elements, he dispatched some men back to the old camp site to bring on his snow-blinded member. States Abert: "In the evening, some of the men led Brown into Camp. He said that, while lying near old old camp fires, listening to the bickering of the ravens and magpies, which were contending for the scraps we had left, he felt something give his buffalo robe a jerk, and looking around, he saw several wolves; they ran off a few steps, seeming to have but little fear of him; his eyes pained him so much that he did not attempt to shoot" (Ibid., p. 533).

MacMillan writes of a wolf that followed his exploring party in the Arctic during 1914 "from Axel Heiberg Land to Etah, a distance of 200 miles, where it was shot by one of my men in front of our door."[17]

Hoffman states:

"It is frequently the case that a pedestrian will meet these animals along the coulees, and on firing at them, if they are not hit, they will remain in one position until their curiosity is satisfied, when they will walk off deliberately and slowly. This, however, is not the case when they are hungry, at which time they become extremely fierce and bold. They have been known to enter the Indian villages at night and attack the dogs" (Hoffman, W. J., 1878: 95).

Apparently even as late as the 1870's wolves were still undisturbed by the reports of a rifle shot. Fear of man came about gradually as the animal was subjected to every possible weapon in the hands of those seeking its extirpation. As a result of this experience, the North American wolf at the beginning of the 20th century was more timid, wary, and cautious, avoiding direct meeting with humans.

It remained able to prey upon man, however, under certain circumstances, and there is some evidence that it did so. In Europe the period of confidence in man is buried in antiquity but there are numerous records of attacks upon humans. The evidence for such forays in both continents is reviewed in the following section.

ATTACKS ON MAN

European comments of earlier times regarding unprovoked attacks on humans are numerous, while those relating to North America are much fewer. Whether these stories are products of the fertile imaginations, or are truth, is difficult to determine. There are so many Old Country accounts of such attacks that the old saying "Where there is so much smoke, there must be some fire," leads the student to believe that these European stories of wolves attacking humans cannot all be untruths. The following are illustrative. During the reign of James VI of Scotland in 1577 when, it appears, wolves were very numerous throughout a large part of the Scottish highlands and very destructive to sheep, Harting says: "It was necessary to provide houses, or 'spittals' as they were termed, to afford lodgings to travellers who might be overtaken by night where there was no place of shelter. Hence the origin of the Spittal of Glen

---

[17]Letter from Donald B. MacMillan, Provincetown, Mass., to E. A. Goldman, Washington, D. C., dated April 11, 1941. In files of the Fish and Wildlife Service.

Shae, and similar appellations in other places" (Harting, J. E., 1880: 166, 167).

The so-called spittals were meant to guard the traveler from wolf attacks. Harting quotes from Camden's *Brittania* of 1586 on the danger to cattle and humans from wolves, as follows:

"Wolves, which, to the great damage of the country, not only furiously set upon cattle, but even upon the owners themselves, to the manifest danger of their lives" (Ibid., p. 167).

Mivart relates:

In 1875 one hundred and sixty-one persons fell victims to wolves in Russia . . . . (Mivart, St. George, 1890: 5, 9).

Again, speaking of the wolves of India, he says:

"A large number of Indian children are carried off each year by them. Their depredations are facilitated by the superstition of the people, who are very averse to killing a wolf, thinking its blood injures the bearing of their fields" (Ibid.).

Thornton, in a discourse on "Wolf-Hunting in France," states:

"The chase of the wolf has this advantage over all others that while it is of itself extremely sporting, it is at the same time very useful, and often even necessary; nothing being more destructive than those animals which have frequently desolated the country, either by surprizing the flocks, or by attacking children, whom they carry off and devour" (Thornton, T., 1806: 21).

Paderewski describes what was believed to have been an attack from wolves at night while in the course of a long sleigh journey with Baron Horoch. Baron Horoch was returning the then youthful Paderewski to his home from Kiev, Ukraine, South Russia, using two sleighs, one of which was burned in conjunction with straw stacks obtained from a field near their sleigh road as a frightening measure to ward off the unprovoked wolf attack against the party (Paderewski, I. J., and Lawton, Mary, 1938: 29).

Cox observed:

"Although the wolves of North America are the most daring of all the beasts of prey on that continent, they are by no means so courageous or ferocious as those of Europe, particularly in Spain or the South of France, in which countries they commit dreadful ravages both on man and beast; whereas an American wolf, except forced by desperation, will seldom or never attack a human being; . . . ." (Cox, R., 1831: vol. 2, p. 89).

In a footnote concerning the foregoing, Cox, still speaking of the European wolf, notes that:

"During the late Peninsular War, the Duke of Wellington had occasion to send dispatches by a mounted dragoon, to a general of division not quite a day's march distant from headquarters. The answer not having arrived at the period it was expected, His Grace despatched three others to ascertain the cause. They found the mangled remains of their unfortunate comrade lying beside those of his horse, and the greater portion of the flesh eaten off their bodies. His sword was firmly grasped in his mutilated hand, and the carcasses of seven or eight wolves which lay about him exhibited strong marks of the sabre, and of the desperation with which he fought before he was overpowered by numbers" (Ibid.).

Douglas, in writing of wolves in *Old Calabria,* says:

"Fortunately, human beings are seldom attacked, a dog or a pig being generally forthcoming when the usual prey is not to be found. Yet not long ago a sad affair occurred: a she-wolf attacked a small boy before the eyes of his parents, who pursued him, powerless to help—the head and arms had already been torn off before a shot from a neighbour despatched the monster. . . . Milo of Croton, the famous athlete, is the most renowned victim of these Sila wolves. Tradition has it that, relying on his great strength, he tried to rend asunder a mighty log of wood which closed, however, and caught his arms in its grips; thus helpless, he was devoured alive by them" (Douglas, N., 1938: 315).

In North America, the records of the early trappers, explorers, and traders are not lacking in accounts of the wolves attacking man. Few of them, however, assert that persons were actually killed by wolves in unprovoked attacks. An attempt has been made to bring together here the most pertinent discussions of wolf molestation, actual or fancied, during the early occupancy of North America. It may be said in comment that in the 25 years that the Fish and Wildlife Service has aided in cooperative wolf control, no incidents have come to the notice of the Service or of any of its personnel indicating unprovoked attack upon man.

While traveling between Fort Des Prairies and an Assiniboine Indian village southwest of that point in southern Canada, and when nearly out of food, Alexander Henry noted in his journal:

"For breakfast, the next morning, I put the last square of chocolate into the kettle; and our meal finished, we began our march, in but very indifferent spirits. We were surrounded by large herds of wolves, which sometimes came close upon us, and who knew, as we were prone to think, the extremity in which we were, and marked as for their prey, but I carried a gun, and this was our protection. I fired several times, but unfortunately missed at each; for a morsel of wolf's flesh would have afforded us a banquet" (Henry, Alexander, 1901: 273).

Still under the threat of starvation, Henry continues: "Our misery, nevertheless, was still nearer its end than we imagined; and the event was such as to give one of the innumerable proofs that despair is not made for man. Before sunset, we discovered on the ice, some remains of the bones of an elk, left there by the wolves. Having instantly gathered them, we encamped; and, filling our kettle, prepared ourselves a meal of strong excellent soup. The greater part of the night was passed in boiling and regaling on our booty, and early in the morning we felt ourselves strong enough to proceed" (Ibid.).

As to possible attack on man by wolves, mentioned by Henry, a comparable account in this connection also comes from Pennsylvania in the early part of the 19th century, for we read of one Dr. Thornton, "Becoming lost in this region on his way to visit a patient, was beset by wolves but fortunately defeated them after a two-day skirmish by the use of ammonia, with which he saturated one of his leggings and struck the animals as they came near, the mysterious character of his defense getting the better of their rapacity more on account of its invisible nature than its physical effects" (Rhoads, S. N., 1903: 151).

Henderson records an early account of wolf attack involving one of our famous frontiersmen:

"In the late autumn of 1761, Daniel Boone and Nathaniel Gist, the son of Washington's famous guide, who were both serving under Waddell, temporarily detached themselves from his command and led a small party on a 'long hunt' in the Valley of the Holston. While encamping near the site of Black's Fort, subsequently built, they were violently assailed by a pack of fierce wolves which they had considerable difficulty in beating off; and from this incident the locality became known as Wolf Hills (Now Abingdon, Virginia)" (Henderson, A., 1920: 134).

In writing of the early Swedish settlement along the Atlantic seaboard and particularly of the Delaware Bay section and adjacent areas, Kalm states that smallpox broke out among the Indians: "This disease they got from the Europeans, for they knew nothing of it before. It killed many hundreds of them, and most of the Indians of the section, then called New Sweden, died of it. The wolves then came, attracted by the stench of so many corpses, in such great numbers that they devoured them all, and even attacked the poor sick Indians in their huts, so that the few healthy ones had enough to do to drive them away" (Benson, A. B., 1937: 150).

This recording is similar to that made by David Thompson with reference to wolf attacks on the Chipeways and the Sioux approximately 30 years later.

According to Mark Catesby:

"The wolves in America are like those of Europe in shape and colour, but are somewhat smaller; they are more timorous and not so voracious as those of Europe; a drove of them will flie from a single man; yet in very severe weather there has been some instances to the contrary" (Catesby, M., 1771: 26).

While en route across the country through a portion of the old Oregon Territory, Ross Cox, while lost from his party of trappers in the Walla Walla Indian country of that portion of the early-day Northwest, during August of 1812, vividly portrays his troubles with wolves in his fatigued, starving condition. During the course of his confused wanderings he observed:

"About dusk an immense-sized wolf rushed out of a thick copse a short distance from the pathway, planted himself directly before me, in a threatening position, and appeared determined to dispute my passage. He was not more than twenty feet from me. My situation was desperate, and as I knew that the least symptom of fear would be the signal for attack, I presented my stick, and shouted as loud as my weak voice would permit. He appeared somewhat startled, and retreated a few steps, still keeping his piercing eyes firmly fixed on me. I advanced a little, when he commenced howling in a most appalling manner; and supposing his intention was to collect a few of his comrades to assist in making an afternoon repast on my half-famished carcass, I redoubled my cries, until I had almost lost the power of utterance, at the same time calling out various names, thinking I might make it appear I was not alone. . . . The wolf remained about fifteen minutes in the same position; but whether my wild and fearful exclamations deterred any others from joining him, I cannot say. Finding at length my determination not to flinch, and that no assistance was likely to come, he retreated into the wood, and disappeared in the surrounding gloom" (Cox, R., 1831, vol. 1, p. 155).

Again, Cox relates the heart-rending trials of the Indian widow of Pierre Dorrien, the famous guide and trapper. In endeavoring to elude massacring Indians and to protect her two babies while seeking aid and succor in the Walla Walla River country in 1813, she encountered a "band of prairie wolves," feeding on the bodies of her white friends but recently massacred. "The sound of her voice scared them, and they fled." Previous to viewing this scene, this Indian woman had cached her two babies in the woods some distance away.

"Fearful that they [the wolves] might find their way to the spot in which she had deposited her previous charge, she hastened thither, and arrived just in time to save her children from three of those ferocious animals which were then approaching them" (Ibid., p. 254).

Commenting on the wolf as noted by him in the Columbia River drainage, Alexander Ross said:

"No wild animal in this country stands less in awe of man than the wolf, nor is there any animal we know that is so fierce. The bear, on most occasions, tries to fly from man, and is only bold and ferocious when actually attacked, wounded or in defense of her young. The wild buffaloes are the same; but the wolf, on the contrary, has often been known to attack man; and at certain seasons of the year—the spring for instance—it is man's wisdom to fly from him. Some time ago, a band of seventeen wolves forced two of our men to take shelter for several hours in a tree, and although they had shot two of the most forward of them before they got to the tree for protection, the others, instead of dispersing, kept close at their heels" (Ross, A., 1855; vol. 1, p. 62).

Dr. Elijah White, famed in early Oregon territorial history, records an incident of being treed by wolves in the Willamette Valley, near Wheatland, in present Marion County. Among the trials of the early Oregon settlers of this region, it is recorded one of "their greatest annoyances was the howling of wolves about the house during the nights." To Dr. White and his wife "This seemed particularly frightful, as they were in rather a lonely situation, being at a mile's distance from any habitation, and the doctor was often absent." While thus absent ministering succor and help to his friend Mr. Sheperd, who was ill, he was followed by wolves, one of which "came within six feet of him, and by its call gathered others to the pursuit." Dropping a stick he was carrying for protection, he then "plied his heels with admirable dexterity till the tree offered its friendly shelter, when he hallooed for help with all the force of his lungs." Mrs. White, on hearing the howling wolves, "fancying she also heard a faint cry" of her husband, set out with "a long pair of cooper's compasses . . . accompanied by the men [two men that were hired help around the White homestead] armed with rifles." With this formidable array, this narrative indicates, the wolves were dispersed, and Dr. White climbed down to safety and returned home (White, E., 1850: 88).

Bancroft also speaks of this instance of Elijah White's being "driven in a tree by wolves, and of being rescued by his wife and hired man." White was at the time a leading citizen of early territorial Oregon, spending a decade in the Willamette Valley region and surroundings between the late 1830's and 1840's (Bancroft, H. T., 1882-90, vol. 29, p. 300).

At a much later date, Webster recounts the treeing of Charles Morgenroth, of Port Angeles, Wash., by wolves of the same subspecies as encountered by Elijah White. This incident took place in the Olympic Mountains area of western Washington. After being treed twice, Morganroth finally resorted to the use of a stout club when again gaining the ground. "Just why they [the wolves] did not rush him [at the first encounter] as he came up out of the canyon, Mr. Morganroth cannot imagine. Doubtless they had reached the point where hunger and fear hung in the balance; certainly they were waiting to study mankind at close range and learn the limit of his ability to defend himself" (Webster, E. B., 1920: 81).

While south of Fort Laramie in the late spring of 1850, Steele records: "Presently a large whitish wolf made its appearance; then two more; their howls were answered by others, until the gulches echoed in one continuous roar. As the day faded they became more bold, coming nearer, until I found it would be impossible to keep them at bay during the night without a fire. It was a moonless night

Plate 38. A. As the early writers and illustrators pictured a homesteader besieged by a wolf pack. The picture suggests several hundred beasts, whereas wolves never form such large groups. (Illustration courtesy Robson Black, *Forest and Outdoors*, Montreal, Canada)

B. As our grandfathers understood the terror of wolves. This old print depicts the hounding down of horses by swarms of killers in a forest clearing. (Illustration courtesy Robson Black, *Forest and Outdoors*, Montreal, Canada)

Plate 39. The familiar
story of Russian travellers
dashing over frozen roads
with a wolf pack about to
catch them. (Illustration
courtesy Robson Black,
Forest and Outdoors,
Montreal, Canada)

but the stars shone out, and turning my back on the constellation of Ursa Major, I started for camp.

"I cannot say that the wolves followed me; they were on all sides. . . . the infernal chorus grew awfully discordant at a near approach. I would then fire my rifle and pistols among them, reloading as I ran. At the report they would scatter, and for a while keep a greater distance; but always there was a bitter fight among them after a shot, and I believe that the wounded were at once devoured.

"In the open ground it was not difficult to keep them at bay; but in the deep gullies as I looked up into their glaring eyes and saw how easily they might spring upon me, I realized that, like David, there was but a step between me and death. However, I kept in the open ground as much as possible; but at best, it was a terrible night, and O, how I longed for the morning.

"Toward morning, while following a long, high ridge, most of my pursuers left me" (Steele, J., 1930: 52).

Captain James R. McClure records that while taking the census for the 7th and 8th districts, "which embraced all the territory west of Ft. Riley and south of the Kansas and Smoky Hill rivers, and extended east to the Wakarusa in the year 1855," he was pursued by wolves near the present city of Topeka, while walking in advance of his teams shortly after 4 a.m. He says: "I will never forget the terrible ordeal I passed through that morning, and the relief I felt when I found myself safe from their attacks" (McClure, J. R., 1904: 243).

John K. Townsend, while in the vicinity of Fort Vancouver, on the Columbia River in 1835, states:

"Yesterday one of the Canadians took an enormous wolf in a beaver trap. It is probably a distinct species from the common one (*lupus*), much larger and stronger, and of a yellowish cinerous color. The man states that he found considerable difficulty in capturing him, even after the trap had been fastened on his foot. Unlike the *lupus* (which is cowardly and cringing when made prisoner), he showed fight, and seizing the pole in his teeth, with which the man attempted to despatch him, with one backward jerk, threw his assailant to the ground, and darted at him, until checked by the trap and chain. He was finally shot, and I obtained his skin, which I have preserved" (Townsend, J. K., 1905: 336).

Luttig mentions his "Cart man was attacked by 5 Wolves, but

cleared himself . . . ," in the fall of 1812 while on the Upper Missouri River, but gives no details of the wolf attack (Luttig, J. C., 1920: 85).

It is difficult to determine whether Eskimo accounts of unprovoked wolf attacks are fables handed down from one generation to another, and whether one should question the veracity of some of their accounts. Mathiassen, in speaking of the caribou country, says: "There are extremely large numbers of wolves in the caribou district, where they roam about singly or in packs of ten to twenty and are a source of great embarrassment to the Eskimos; it not infrequently happened that the younger men returned from caribou hunting as they dared not proceed on account of the boldness of the wolves" (Mathiassen, T., 1931: 27).

Freuchen reports meeting an Eskimo woman at Iglulik in Greenland "who had several severe scars in her head and shoulder, said to be from a wolf which once attacked her when on her way to visit some neighbors two or three kilometres from where she lived. The wolf sprang up and first bit her in the shoulder, after which it had bitten her so fiercely that she fainted; this, however, had scared the wolf away. The woman was unconscious when her people found her" (Freuchen, P., 1935b: 122).

Recently MacMillan wrote:

"It has been stated by a so-called authority that wolves have never been known to attack a person. It is a real danger in the North, and to me not a pleasant way of passing out.

"A half-breed Eskimo with whom I traveled a thousand miles was undoubtedly torn to pieces and eaten. There was nothing about his tent but wolf tracks and blood.

"Mr. Court, Master of the Investigator, was attacked by two wolves. One, although wounded, crouched up to within three yards of him.

"One of Severdrup's men was attacked by a band of wolves. His companions returned to save his life."[18]

And MacMillan further corroborates the statement that during one of his Arctic explorations, his party "were attacked by twelve [wolves] in 1914. Fortunately, we had our rifles and dogs" (Ibid.).

---

[18]Letter from Donald B. MacMillan, Provincetown, Mass., to E. A. Goldman, Washington, D. C., dated April 11, 1941. In files of Fish and Wildlife Service.

However, Grenfell says that

"The Labrador wolf has never been known to kill a man. Yet on several occasions single men have fallen in with them. One man told me that a pack followed him almost to his own door, that they stopped when he stopped, and came as close as ten yards. He had no gun and no means of defence, yet they never touched him" (Grenfell, W. T., and others; 1913: 279).

It will be recalled that David Thompson comments upon wolves eating Indians dying of smallpox during the height of this disease among the Indians of the Plains and parts of the country controlled by the Hudson Bay Company, during 1781 and 1782. One presumes that those Indians whom the wolves devoured had succumbed to this illness, but seemingly those that lay stricken and helpless were also attacked.

Edward Umfreville spent 11 years in the service of the Hudson's Bay Company, from 1771 to 1782, and 4 years engaged in the fur trade of Canada, apparently from 1783 to 1787. When the smallpox epidemic was at its peak (1781-1782), he wrote:

"Without the least medicinal help, or that common aid which their case demanded, a prey to hunger and defease, these forlorn Indians lay in their tents expiring, under the accumulated weight of every scourge which human nature can experience. Wolves and other wild beast infested and entered their habitations, and dragged them out, while life yet remained, to devour their miserable morbid carcases; even their faithful dogs, worn out with hunger, joined the ferocious wolves in this unnatural depredation. Heads, legs, and arms, lay indiscriminately scattered about, as food for the birds of the air and the beasts of the mountains;—and as none were buried, the very air became infectious, and tended to waft about the baneful contagion. Such has been the fate of many of the tribes inhabiting these parts, and which has nearly terminated in their extinction" (Umfreville, E., 1790: 93).

While in Alaska during the summer of 1938 I investigated a report of the killing of John Millovich, a Montenegrin, who, as a prospector and trapper, had been a resident of the Far North for 35 years.

It appears that Millovich, aged sixty, had left Fairbanks late in April 1933 for a two weeks' trapping expedition on Beaver Creek near the White Mountains, where he had a cabin located 75 miles north of Fairbanks on the Yukon River drainage. When he failed to return within a reasonable time, two of his friends, Messrs. George Bojanich and Samuel Hjorta, started a search in the early part of July. They found the remains of Millovich near his cabin. Piecing together the story of his death from the scene surrounding what remained of the corpse, the two searchers were of the opinion that Millovich had left his cabin to obtain some water a short distance away. He was apparently surrounded and attacked by wolves within 50 feet of his domicile. Practically all of the flesh had been eaten by the wolves and his clothing was found scattered promiscuously around the premises. The searchers were of the opinion that the attack occurred on May 10, for on investigating his cabin it was found that the calendar used by Millovich had had its dates penciled off up to and including May 9, 1933.

Bojanich and Hjorta reported seeing many wolf tracks in going to and returning from Beaver Creek; in fact, as they returned home, they saw that many wolf tracks had been made along the trail which they had used in reaching Millovich's cabin. In this connection, however, while it is true that the scene surrounding the body of Millovich gave every indication of a deliberate wolf attack, no one actually saw the attack, so there remains the possibility that Millovich might have had a stroke or a heart attack which rendered him helpless or killed him outright; and the body was later found and devoured by wolves, leaving thus one more of those many unsolved mysteries of the Far North, in which any one of several conjectures might be correct.

In recording his various experiences on the Great Plains, Gregg mentions a battle he had with a charging wolf, in which he had only a club as his weapon of defense. He records the incident as follows: "I shall not soon forget an adventure with one of them, many years ago, on the frontier of Missouri. Riding near the border, I perceived one of the largest and fiercest of the gray species, which had just descended from the west, and seemed famished to desperation. I at once prepared for a chase; and, being without arms, I caught up a cudgel, which I betook me valiantly to the charge, much stronger, as I soon discovered, in my cause than in my equipment. The wolf was in no humor to flee, but boldly met me full half-way. I was soon disarmed, for my club broke upon the animal's head. He then 'laid to' my horse's legs, which, not relishing the conflict, gave a plunge and sent me whirling over his head, and made his escape, leaving me and the wolf at close quarters. I was no sooner upon my feet than my antagonist renewed the charge; but being without weapon, or any means of awakening an emotion of terror, I took off my large black hat, and using it for a shield, began to thrust it towards his gaping jaws. My ruse had the desired effect; for, after springing at me a few times, he wheeled about and trotted off several paces and stopped to gaze at me. . . . I . . . took to my heels, glad of the opportunity of making a drawn game. . . ." (Gregg, Josiah, 1905: 272).

Theodore Roosevelt, in discoursing about the Lewis and Clark expedition on the Upper Missouri River in 1805, says:

"Unlike the bears, the wolves were generally timid, and preyed only on the swarming game; but one night a wolf crept into camp and seized a sleeper by the hand; when driven off he jumped upon another man, and was shot by a third" (Roosevelt, T., 1903, vol. 6, p. 170).

Richardson, writing of wolves in the Far North, relates that

"I was told of a poor Indian woman who was strangled by a wolf, while her husband, who saw the attack, was hastening to her assistance; but this was the only instance of their [the wolves'] destroying human life that came to my knowledge" (Richardson, J., 1829: 64).

Audubon long ago wrote:

"Although Wolves are bold and savage, few instances occur in our temperate regions of their making an attack on man; and we have only had one such case come under our own notice. Two young negroes who resided near the Ohio, in the lower part of the State of Kentucky, about thirty years ago, had sweethearts living on another plantation four miles distant. After the labours of the day were over, they frequently visited the fair ladies of their choice, the nearest way to whose dwelling lay directly across a large cane brake. . . . One night, they set forth over a thin crust of snow. Prudent, to a certain degree, the lovers carried their axes on their shoulders, and walked as brisky as the narrow path would allow. Some transient glimpses of light now and then met their eyes in the more open spaces between the trees, or when the heavy drifting clouds parting at times allowing a star to peep forth on the desolate scene. Fearfully, a long and frightful howl burst upon them, and they were instantly aware that it proceeded from a troop of hungry and perhaps desperate wolves. They paused for a moment and a dismal silence succeeded. All was dark save for a few feet of the snow-covered ground immediately in front of them. They resumed their pace hastily, with their axes in their hands prepared for the attack. Suddenly the foremost man was assailed by several wolves which seized on him, and inflicted terrible wounds with their fangs on his legs and arms, and as they were followed by many others as ravenous as themselves, several sprung at the breast of his companion, and dragged him to the ground. Both struggled manfully against their foes, but in a short time one of the negroes had ceased to move; and the other, reduced in strength and perhaps despairing of aiding his unfortunate comrade or even saving his own life, threw down his axe, sprang on to the branch of a tree, and speedily gained a place of safety among the boughs. There he passed a miserable night, and the next morning the bones of his friend lay scattered around on the snow, which was stained with his blood. Three dead wolves lay near, but the rest of the pack had disappeared and Scipio, sliding to the ground, recovered the axes and returned home to relate the terrible catastrophe" (Audubon, J. J., and Bachman, J., 1851-54, vol. 2, p. 128).

J. Stokley Ligon recorded of a presumed wolf attack in south-eastern Alaska:

". . . While working on a tide flat at the head of one of the long inlets, a trapper and the writer heard wolves howl at intervals in the dense, dark timber that majestically folds in between the high tide line and the mountains that parallel the inlet to the west. Not expecting to have an opportunity to shoot a wolf, only a shotgun and five shells were carried at the time for the purpose of killing some ducks or geese for food. Two of the shells were loaded with buckshot and the others with small shot. Nevertheless, the trapper decided to make a stalk under cover of the forest, believing that their frequent howling would guide him and enable him to get in close range of the wolves, provided they did not move too rapidly during the quiet intervals, as is frequently the case. He had been gone only a few minutes when two shots in rapid succession were heard. They were followed after a short pause by three others in quick succession and then yells from the hunter. Before the writer could reach the forest wall, the hunter rushed out bare-headed, his shock of sandy hair standing erect, carrying his gun barrel in one hand and the broken stock in the other. In wild excitement he related how from under cover of small jackpine he had miraculously approached the three wolves as they were playing on the new snow in a little open muskeg. A favorable wind permitted him to get near them without warning. He shot the largest of the three with one of the buckshot loads. It fell but was up like a flash, making it necessary to use the other heavy load to kill it. He then began firing bird shot into the remaining animal—one of the three animals having made its escape by this time—with but little apparent effect as it began to charge toward him. When his gun had been emptied and the animal had not been checked, he changed ends with the gun, using the butt end for a club and killed the wolf, breaking the gun in the fight.

"This story of the unusual conduct of the wolf made the writer suspect that the hunter might have misunderstood the intentions of this animal. The scene of the conflict confirmed his suspicious. A close examination of the animal explained its actions.

"This wolf was a female young of the year, although it had attained almost its full size. Being taken unawares and in its excitement, it had unknowingly headed towards the concealed hunter, in its frantic effort to escape, after the first two shots were fired and the leader was killed. Although the bird-shot that hit the mark did not inflict instant mortal wounds, the animal had been entirely blinded. Its mouth was badly lacerated, causing the lower jaw to hang limp, thus giving it a raging, savage appearance as it charged headlong though helpless toward the hunter.

"And so originate most of our North American wolf stories—just thrilling, though unusual happenings, which gain momentum as they fly, until with increased distance they assume the form of horrible yet somewhat exciting realities" (Ligon, J. S., 1926: 158).

In an article in *Forest and Stream* we are told:

"For many years I have been looking for an authentic case where a western wolf attacked a human being. I think I have found one now in the daughter of Jim Baker, who still lives down in Colorado, on Snake River. The occurrence happened about fifteen years ago, and the attack was made not because the wolf was hungry, but because he was cross. The young girl, then eighteen years old, was going out just at dusk to drive in some milk cows; when she saw sitting just above the trail on the hillside a gray wolf. She called at it and when it did not move she picked up a stone and threw it. The animal came jumping down the hill, caught her by the shoulder, threw her down and tore her badly on the legs and arms. She screamed, and her brother, who happened to be nearby, ran up with his gun and killed the wolf. This was a young wolf barely full grown, and his act would be hard to explain. The woman still bears the scars of the encounter" (G., G. B., 1896: 511).

Regarding the same incident, George Bird Grinnell states:

"I have known of but one person being attacked by a wolf, and this attack was apparently not made because the animal was hungry, but because it was cross. The person who was injured was a daughter of old Jim Baker, one of the few old time trappers still living, who resides on Snake River, in the northwest corner of Colorado. [Grinnell probably means Little Snake River in Moffat County.] The occurrence took place about sixteen years ago, and in summer. The young girl, then eighteen years old, went out just at dusk to drive in some milk cows. As she was going toward them, she saw a gray wolf, sitting on the hillside, just above the trail. She shouted to frighten it away, and when it did not move, took up a stone and threw at it. The animal snarled at her call, and when she threw the stone, came jumping down the hill, caught her by the shoulder, threw her down, and tore her badly on the arms and legs. She screamed, and her brother, who happened to be near and had his gun, ran up and killed the wolf. It was a young animal, barely full grown" (Grinnell, G. B., 1897b: 174, 175).

For the following account of an unprovoked attack on man by wolves, we are indebted to John P. Holman, of Fairfield, Conn.:

"Under date of March 4th 1938 I received a letter from Ralph A. Edwards, a trapper friend of mine who lives on the headwaters of the Atnarko River in the Coast Range of British Columbia, telling of an experience he had with wolves. His Postoffice address is Hagensborg, B. C., Canada.

"Having made several hunting trips with Edwards I know him to be a very careful observer and I can vouch for the accuracy of the incidents he describes in his letter. They must have happened just as he told it.

"In my book *Sheep and Bear Trails* you will find under the chapter heading 'The Keeper of the Swans' a description of Edwards and his country and also some of the letters he wrote to me. I am going to publish shortly a little book containing some more letters from him under the title: 'Letters from Lonesome Lake' in which will be found this particular one from which I now quote in part as follows:

" 'I had stopped trapping for the season except for a few foot-log traps left for coyote, wolf, and cougar, and one otter trap. My three horses were at the head of Fourth Lake up valley, as the snow was not deep up there and there seemed to be plenty of grass. Even so I have to move them about from one meadow to another as ice conditions prevented their moving of their own accord. So I had to make a trip up there in February to change them and give them salt.

" 'A cold spell had caused the East Fork to flood all over its valley and out into the main valley. Green water was running on top of ten feet or more of ice and slush. It was impossible to cross on foot and too wide to fall timber across so I was forced to detour to the mouth of the East Fork and thence across the main Atnarko in order to reach the other side. I worked my way through the heavy timber and finally came out on Little Lake just north of the old foot-log.

" 'I had noticed some cougar tracks going my way in the timber and they led to the foot of a large, leaning fir tree. Naturally I looked up and there above my head was a cougar about thirty feet up. He was standing against the main trunk of the tree. I backed up and took off my pack and a couple of shots plumped him on the ground. Well, I wanted his meat for my minks, so I turned around and packed him home.

" 'On the way home I crossed some foot-logs down river and found a pair of coyotes hanging with tails in the river so I took them out of the traps and hung them up on poles out of the reach of predators, I hoped.

" 'The next day I started out again for the head of the river but I had gone only a couple of miles when I struck a fresh cougar track which led directly to one of my hung coyotes. It had been pulled down, untied from the pole and dragged off. I followed the drag trail through the worst mess of down timber imaginable to the place where he had thought it was safe to eat. He had eaten the heart out and pulled a lot of the fur off and then tried to cache the remains by scratching a little snow over them. It was mostly a case of scratching ice. . . . At any rate he then went and lay down under a log a few feet away where there was no snow. My coming had scared him out.

" 'I trailed him for a ways but the going got so bad I gave it up and went on to Little Lake, where I found an otter in the trap set for him there. I camped that night in my cabin at the head of Third Lake. In the morning I crossed Fourth Lake on the ice and found some wolf tracks, indicating that four wolves had been running around up there. They had killed a deer near the head of the lake and had eaten about two thirds of it and ravens were buzzing around the remains. There was a cold wind blowing. The wolves had made fresh beds just behind a point of land out of the wind but had left before I got there.

" 'My horses were in the meadow nearby and came running toward me when I spoke to them. I took them across the river on the ice and thence up the valley a couple of miles to a better meadow where I left them with some salt and grass and then started for home.

" 'I had seen wolf tracks all over the landscape, running in every direction, but I didn't figure that I would see any of the animals as it was so noisy underfoot. Suddenly, as I was plowing along with my head down watching the trail, something caused me to glance around and what I saw jerked me all the way around. Four black wolves abreast were leaping towards me scarce twenty-five feet away. When I whirled around to face them one gave vent to a low, fierce snarl and they deployed, one to the left and two to the right. The other one came straight on. Well, I had to stop them right then!

" 'I had my old 35 Remington Auto-loader and I fired the first shot from my hip, missing the one on the left flank, and still on they came. The next shot caught the one on the right middle in the paw and the third shot went right through the chest of the leader who was abreast of me and only a couple of gun-lengths away. The fellow with the sore paw turned up the hill and the fourth shot dropped him in his tracks. The other two whirled and dodged into the brush while the one I had shot in the chest stood on a rock pile a little ways up the hill and a bullet through his shoulders finished him.

" 'After a short look around to see if one or both of the other two had gone away with wounds I went to skinning as fast as I could. The two that had escaped soon started to howl up on the mountain but I didn't think that I could get up to them because of the noisy going so I paid no attention to them and loaded down with a couple of fine blue-black pelts I proceeded home without any more adventures.'

"So far as I have been able to find out there have been few substantiated records of unprovoked attacks on men by wolves unless they were driven to it by starvation. These wolves had just killed a deer so they did not charge Edwards for that reason. It would seem that it was just one of those happenings that do occur once in a great while which upset the rules of wild animal behavior as laid down by students of natural history.

"With this thought in mind I wrote Edwards and asked him if he had ever had a similar experience with wolves before. Under date of May 15th 1938 I received the following reply which I quote in part:

" 'In regard to the wolves—there have been packs in here ever since I came to this country some twenty-five years ago. They have been running on the lakes in winter—not every year but often. I have taken deer away from them several times and met them at other times but they always seemed to elude me. Either the trap chain broke and I saw wolf tracks with the marks of a dragged trap in the snow for about two weeks before they got rid of it. They seemed to be able to open the traps with their teeth in the same way that I would do with my hands. Sometimes I shot at them and missed either because of poor marksmanship or because my gun was out of order or because my gunsights had been knocked crooked. Anyway they all seemed to get away from one reason or another.

" 'During the winter of 1936-7 I met seven Timber wolves on Lonesome Lake and I only had a .22 rifle and three shells. That bunch was looking for trouble. I stood and watched them sweep up around me while I feverishly cocked my little rifle and waited. I knew then how a deer must feel when a wolf pack closes in on him.

" 'During my trapping trips down lake I had seen very little sign of even coyotes, let alone wolves. An old cougar had walked along the shore at one time and an occasional fox had crossed the lake— that was all. January came and it was time to take out the mink pelts and get the mail, so on the 10th I packed up and started. The lake and river were frozen over, with a little snow on the ice. The river had only recently become safe to travel on so I had to have an axe in hand to test the thickness of the ice. I was not in the habit of carrying my rifle on trips when I did not want meat so I left it behind. Just before I started, however, I bethought me of that cougar track.

He might come back and get in a trap so I decided to put my new .22 single-shot take-down in the pack.

" 'I went down the middle of the river and out onto the lake ice with a stiff wind and snowstorm in my face. Visibility was not quite zero but badly restricted. When about a mile down the lake and out in the middle of it I saw looming through the snow some gray forms running swiftly towards me. I started to count them. When I got up to five and decided at the same time that they were wolves, I quit counting and got off my pack in a hurry, took out the rifle parts and put them together.

" 'The wolves hesitated when they saw me but then the leader started on and the rest came along. As they came nearer they spread out fanwise with the big brindled leader coming ahead on the outside. I did not like the looks of the situation as I only had a few shells and they were in a little bag so I started to run at rightangles to my former course and reach the brush along the shore. As soon as I tried that a big black fellow with long legs whipped up double fast and cut me off, so I stopped and waited.

" 'With the black fellow between me and the shore the leader came up on the outside and the rest of the pack rapidly drew nearer. Finally the leader stopped broadside on about fifty yards off and I pressed the trigger of my rifle. For some reason the shell failed to explode so I threw it out and put in another. This one worked and at the shot the whole bunch turned about-face and high-tailed it down the lake and out of sight behind a point of land.

" 'I headed back home and got my .35 Auto-loader. When I returned to the scene of the encounter I found that they had come up from the Stillwater, about six miles away, in something like twenty minutes, according to the amount of snow in their tracks.

" 'Two weeks later the same pack came up and howled over across the valley from my place and then went on up the mountain and around to Little Lake, where they took a calf moose. A few days later we heard them howling again on the mountain back of the house early in the morning and by breakfast time they were out on the hillside across the valley. The snow was deep and crusty so I went down the middle of the river and waited for them behind some willows hoping to intercept them if they crossed back again but they sat tight on the hillside all day. After waiting awhile I went back to the house but returned at eventide and crossed their route once more but returned at dark without seeing them. The next morning I found that they had gone by the very place where I had waited for them the night before.

" 'The four wolves that came for me last spring ran into a man who was ready for them. My gun was in perfect working order, greased with coal oil so it would not freeze up. I had lost my right hand mitten in a tussle with a No. 4 double spring trap on a foot-log so my trigger finger was unencumbered. It all happened so quickly that I had no time for anything but action. There is nothing like an automatic for close, quick work. Bears and wolves can't stand the noise [like that] of a pneumatic riveter nor the bullets.

" 'Moose are new in this district but Wolves are perennial. The first year I trapped up valley I found a coyote that had been killed by wolves. Strangely enough every bone in its body was broken but the pelt was uninjured, and it happened within fifty yards of my trap cabin.'

"I might add for your information that the Atnarko River which drains the region where Edwards traps and has his home joins the Whitewater to form the Bella Coola River and empties into North Bentinck Arm on the British Columbia coast opposite the Queen Charlotte Islands. Mackenzie came down the Bella Coola River on his famous journey to the Pacific in 1793.

"I hope these notes on the actions of some wolves in that region may be of some use to you in compiling your work on their life histories. . . ."[19]

During the past 25 years the press has from time to time carried accounts of wolf attacks on humans particularly in the north country. These and similar tales that have been reported direct to the Fish and Wildlife Service, although investigated, have never been substantiated. According to Clifford Wilson, "a certain editor of a paper at Sault Ste. Marie, Ontario—the centre of a district that is famed for its blood-curdling wolf stories—has for the past fourteen years or so offered a prize of $100.00 to anyone who can prove he has been attacked by an unmolested wolf—and the prize is still in the editor's cash box!" (Wilson, C., 1937: 38.) However, the accounts to be found throughout the wolf literature seem to leave little doubt that wolves have at times made unprovoked attacks on humans. The extent to which this has been caused by the disease rabies, or by famine, is difficult to determine.

---

[19]Letter from John P. Holman, Fairfield, Conn., to Stanley P. Young, dated February 20, 1939. In files of Fish and Wildlife Service.

IV

NATURAL CHECKS, PARASITES, AND DISEASES

OTHER than man, the wolf has few enemies. Freuchen, speaking of the Arctic wolf, states: "The wolf is said to go in fear of the wolverine. If a wolf has killed a caribou and a wolverine approaches, it will retire and leave the caribou to the newcomer. One Eskimo told me, however, that he had witnessed a fight between a wolf and a wolverine; the wolverine was killed, but the wolf sustained a damaged foot" (Freuchen, P., 1935b: 100).

Ferris records the Rocky Mountain grizzly bears as enemies of the wolf: ". . . . they often rob wolves of their prey, and devour it at leisure" (Ferris, W. A., 1940: 315).

It gave no quarter, however, to the puma whenever a wolf met by chance this large North American cat along the plains watercourses where pumas are recorded as frequenting in the early days of settlement.

When attacking their natural prey, wolves at times suffer ill consequences from kicks or hooks inflicted by their intended victims such as moose, elks, and buffaloes. Evidence of this is found in museum specimens which show healed skull injuries. This points to the conclusion that the attacking predator did not always kill its prey. There were obviously occasions when it was forced to give up the attack because the skull or other injuries it received became too severe. John F. Stanwell-Fletcher, of Dimock, Susquehanna County, Pa., reports the finding of a crippled wolf on the north end of Takla Lake, British Columbia, on March 9, 1941. Here it was observed "underneath a pine tree, where it had dragged itself after a terrific battle with an apparently huge moose. . . . The evidence in the snow was quite plain to read. The wolf sustained broken ribs and three broken legs, as well as much internal injury. Apparently, the wolf attacked the moose where the snow was not too deep, and the latter, with his long legs, was able to find firm footing."[20]

No doubt the severe rigors of the intense prairie blizzards and cold, which often arise and swoop the level country on short notice, took its toll of the wolf family, as with other forms of wildlife. Lt. Abert, near the close of his overland journey to Fort Leavenworth from Santa Fe in the late winter of 1847, cites an observation of such a nature:

"As we approached our destined camp ground, we saw a wolf that was so badly frozen as to be unable to move. One of the men put an end to its sufferings by a bullit from his rifle" (Abert, J. W., 1848: 543).

During the memorable blizzard on the prairies in 1886, Byers records not only the death of thousands of cattle, horses, hogs, and sheep, but also that "Antelopes, and even wolves, drifted with the cattle and piled up with them" in death's struggle by freezing (Byers, O. P., 1912: 105).

Dickson is quoted in Billings' *Natural History of the Wolf* to the effect that in Canada: "In winter where there is not a crust sufficiently strong to carry the wolf, great numbers perish from hunger" (Billings, E., 1856: 211).

Among the ectoparasites of wolves, the human flea, *Pulex irritans,* has been reported. This is not surprising, however, since this parasite is found on various animals—quite frequently on dogs and related mammals. Trembley and Bishop report the wolf and also the coyote as hosts to this flea (Trembley, Helen Louise, and Bishop, F. C., 1940: 701).

Several species of ticks have been identified on wolves. The

---

[20]Letter dated November 18, 1941, to E. A. Goldman from John F. Stanwell-Fletcher. In files of Fish and Wildlife Service.

Lone Star tick (*Amblyomma americanum*) and *Ixodes kingi* have been known to parasitize these animals. The American dog tick (*Dermacentor variabilis*) frequently referred to in the Eastern States as the spotted-fever tick, is also parasitic on wolves. It is not known that all of these ticks serve as vectors of tularemia, but the last-named species has been definitely proved to do so.

From the coyote the relapsing fever tick (*Orithodoros turicata*) has been collected. Likewise, the biting louse (*Heterodoxus longitarsus*) has been found on this animal. It is probable that these two are also found on the wolf.

Like other members of the dog family, and particularly the coyote, the wolf is a sufferer from the skin mite that produces mange. Adult wolves have been observed in the field that had been entirely denuded of hair. Some of the experienced field men hold to the opinion that a nursing adult female afflicted with mange transmits it to her young which may die from the results of the scabs and sores produced by the mange mite.

In his discussion of the wolves inhabiting Hudson Bay and Baffin Land, Freuchen records the removal of "two tapeworms in the intestine of a young wolf, one of which measured at least 10 metres. . . . There were also a number of other intestinal worms" (Freuchen, P., 1935b: 121).

The sheep disease spread by dogs and wolves, known as gid and sometimes referred to as sturdy or turnsick in sheep, is caused by the larva or hydatid phase of a tapeworm. The eggs of this tapeworm are distributed in the feces of flesh-eating animals such as the wolf in open range lands. These eggs are taken on forage by grazing sheep and hatch on walls of the stomach. The embryos pierce the stomach walls and enter the blood; some reach the brain or spinal cord, developing cysts. There appears to be no cure for sheep afflicted with this disease.

According to Norman Criddle:

". . . . Another disease spread by wolves is that known as gid in sheep. This fatal affection is due to bladder-like cysts formed on the brain. It is in reality caused by the immature stage of a tapeworm found in dogs, coyotes, etc., and so far as is known it has no other means of spreading than through these animals. The chief method of distribution is brought about by carnivorous animals devouring carcasses of sheep which have died of the disease. Dr. Seymour Had-

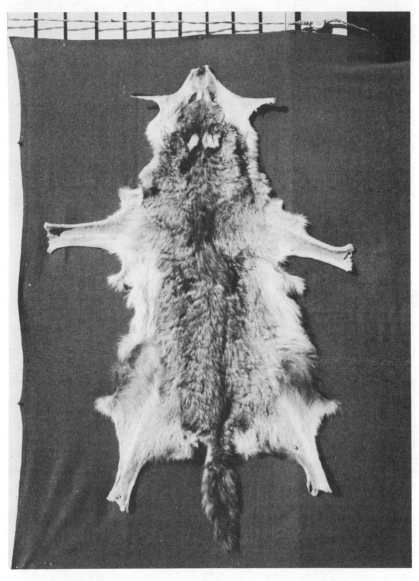

Plate 40. Wolves, when pelted for the raw fur trade, are either "cased" or taken off the animal "flat." This shows a "flat skin" properly stretched

153

Plate 41. When taken young, wolves may be raised as pets, becoming tractable and docile when with their master

Plate 42. The pet wolf of Bud Dalrymple, former Government hunter, who used it as a decoy for trapping wild wolves on their runways. Here it is howling for joy at the approach of Dalrymple after his absence from camp

wen, formerly Chief Veterinary Pathologist of the Dominion Department of Agriculture, who furnished this information states that gid in sheep is not uncommon in Montana and that it has been found in Saskatchewan" (Criddle, N., 1925: 15).

Dr. J. E. Shillinger, formerly in charge of Disease Control, Fish and Wildlife Service, adds:

"In the western great lakes region wolves have been found affected with the adult form of the fish tapeworm (*Diphyllobothrium latum*). This worm is found in the adult state in man and other carnivorous animals. An intermediate state develops in fish and, hence, the fresh water lake regions are the places where this type of infection in wolves, dogs, bears, and man would be expected to exist."[21]

From observations conducted in northern Canada, it is believed that the wolves are at times affected with encephalitis, their symptoms being the same as those of the encephalitis of dogs and foxes. This disease may be one of the main factors in keeping down wolf abundance in the caribou country of Canada.

Dr. J. E. Shillinger states further:

"In going through our available notes and other information, I find verbal records of trappers in Canada who have described wolves affected with some type of nervous derangement. The wolves appear to lose their fear of man and seemed to wander around aimlessly.

"Some of the symptoms appear to have been of a paralytic nature, which may have been ascribed to infection with rabies. No satisfactory proof of this could be procured. There is some belief that it may have been encephalitis, caused by a filterable virus which produces a similar disease in foxes. These animals are also subject to tumors, as has been demonstrated in the specimen received by Dr. Coburn from Mr. Murie; the picture of which was examined by you in my office." (Ibid.)

According to a letter from Dr. Edward L. Munson, Assistant Surgeon, United States Army, distemper appears at times to be common in the wolf:

---

[21]Memorandum dated November 15, 1939, from Dr. J. E. Shillinger, in Charge, Disease Control, Division of Wildlife Research, Fish and Wildlife Service, Department of the Interior.

"I have also heard that the introduction of dog distemper played havoc with wolves, coyotes, and Indian dogs, when it first came into the country" (Grinnell, G. B., 1904: 287).

Apparently, wolves were susceptible to smallpox. An interesting description of this probability is given by David Thompson. He mentions the onslaught of smallpox among the Canadian Indians, especially the Chipaways and the Sioux, who had become afflicted in the year 1780 because of wearing the clothing taken from some massacred whites that were down with the disease. The dead bodies of these Indians dying from smallpox were not only devoured by the Indian dogs but also by wolves in many instances. The disease apparently became widespread, for Thompson says: "From the Chipaways it extended over all the Indians of the forest to its north-ward extremity, and by the Sioux over the Indians of the Plains and crossed the Rocky Mountains . . . . All the wolves and dogs that fed on the bodies of those that died of the smallpox lost their hair especially on the sides and belly, and even for six years after many wolves were found in this condition and their fur useless. The dogs were mostly killed" (Thompson, D., 1916: 322).

Tularemia, a very prevalent disease at times among rabbits and some of the rodents, has not to date been reported in the wolf. However, since this disease has been reported in the coyote, and according to the United States Public Health Service that animal "must be considered a real source of danger in the transmission of tularemia to mankind," it is a fair assumption that the wolf was at times also affected with this disease. The wolf having disappeared from so much of its original range before the recent years of intense study of tularemia, little opportunity has remained for determining the wolf's connection with this disease or the spread of it (Kunkel, G. M., 1930: 439).

Cross reports the finding of arthritis among "the wolves being prepared as skeletal material in the Royal Ontario Museum of Zo-ology" (Cross, E. C., 1940: 2).

The specimens showing this condition were two in number, one a male captured in a snare in the Algonquin Park area of Ontario. The right leg at the elbow joint was so afflicted that Cross believes "that movement of the elbow joint must have been impeded and probably painful." (Ibid.) Likewise, he found the left hind leg to be in worse shape: "Heavy deposits of bone surround and surmount the epicondyles of the femur, and encroach on the trochlea, the inter-condylar fossa and both condyles. Patches of bone surround and surmount both condyles in the tibia, partially dislocating the joint. Marked eburnation is present on articulating surfaces of tibia and femur. The sulcus muscularis has become a jagged-edged tube. This knee joint must have caused the animal great difficulty. . . . The teeth are those of an aged animal." (Ibid.)

The other specimen, likewise a male, was taken by rifle in October 1925 in the White River area of Ontario. The hind feet of this animal, as well as the vertical column, were "markedly affected. . . . the third, fourth, fifth, sixth, and seventh costal vertebrae" were "badly encrusted. Movement of these five vertebrae must have been both difficult and painful." (Ibid.) Cross feels that "The factor responsible for the onset of arthritis in the Algonquin Park wolf would seem to be old age," while "The White River wolf, ... a younger animal . . . . arthritis in this animal was caused by injury to the left pes [foot] and severe infection which followed." (Ibid.)

A pair of wolves, taken while young from New Mexico in 1901, were presented to the Zoological Society in London. While in captivity they bred "repeatedly." The male died at the age of 9 years, and the female at approximately 15 years of age. These wolves, together with one of their whelps raised to maturity, are reported as having died of cancer (Pocock, R. I., 1935: 680).

Martin and Holland report occurrence of cancer in wolves, one in the oral cavity alone, and one in the upper respiratory and alimentary tract, in a total of 246 wild and domestic animals examined (Martin, H. E., and Holland, Beulah F., 1939: 262).

Dr. F. H. McCleery, of Kane, Pa., during his 20-odd years of observing numerous wolves that he has kept in captivity, reports cancer and also arthritis at times among his captive wolves.

Scott records carcinoma in the tonsil of a female wolf that had been held in captivity in the London Zoological Gardens for approximately 5 years. The condition of the animal made necessary the killing of it, as no one could approach it to aid it in its apparent great distress. The post mortem revealed a malignant condition that in a short time would have caused the animal's death (Scott, H. H., 1928: 43).

An extensive papilloma involving large parts of the lips and cheeks has been described in a coyote sent to the Fish and Wildlife

Service for examination. Similar conditions have been noted in the field at times among wolves. Dr. Terbert Fox, of Philadelphia, diagnosed sarcomas in the thyroid region of a prairie wolf, one of which had spread to the lungs (Fox, H., 1923: 111).

Probably one of the most prevalent diseases found in wolves is rabies; it had been known in the wolf and other members of the dog family dating from the earliest times. Harting cites an early case in Britain as follows:

"It is related in the 'Annales Cambriae' that in 1166 a rabid wolf at Caermarthen bit twenty-two persons, nearly all of whom died" (Harting, J. E., 1880: 137).

The records show this disease to be widespread and apparently, at times, very severe. The Indians were fully cognizant of the disease and greatly feared it.

An interesting account of rabies among wolves and its spread among the Plains Indians and their livestock is given by Charles Aubrey in his "Memories of an Old Buffalo Hunter." Aubrey writes as follows:

"The Indian people of the Great Plains at times suffered from hydrophobia caused by the bite of the great buffalo wolf afflicted with rabies. In their crazed condition the wolves sometimes invaded the camps of the people, snapping at them, their dogs and horses. The people thru fear shut themselves in their lodges. Any person bitten by a wolf and showing signs of the dread disease was at once bound with thongs of buffalo hide to prevent injury to patient and people" (Aubrey, C., 1908: 173).

Undoubtedly the Plains Indians must have witnessed many of their fellows afflicted with the so-called violent form of rabies; hence, the reason for binding victims with buffalo thongs. As to the treatment for rabies Aubrey says: "Treatment was given to the sick person at once. A bull [buffalo] was killed, and the naked patient was tightly bound up in the green hide,—hair side out. To each end of the hide covering him were attached stout thongs of buffalo hide by which the bundle might be lifted. Much dry grass and small dry willows were gathered on the ground, and when all was ready the great doctor offered a short prayer to the Sun God asking that he take pity on the patient, his children and his relations; that if cured he would go to war and would return with a rich offering to give to the sun.

"The Medicine Man set fire to the dry grass below the hide, the hair burning fiercely, and the patient was swung over the fire, being turned over and over as the Medicine Man directed, until the hair was burned off the hide. The patient was then freed from his confinement and was cared for by his family. The disease had been sweated out of him." (Ibid.)

He further states that "Wolves affected with rabies were most often seen in the months of March and April . . . ." (Ibid.)

Again, we find that concerning rabid wolves: "they went alone, roaming aimlessly about, lacking the motions of a hunting wolf, trotting along, at intervals making a circling movement, snapping at the tail or hind parts as they made the circle, keeping up a trot and repeating until lost sight of. When killed they showed marks of self inflicted wounds.

"The Indian dogs by their actions showed they knew mad wolves when they came into the camp by keeping from close contact with them, barking and yelping at them, closing in on them, and again retreating—herding them out of camp. (Ibid.)

Washington Irving records the following incidents concerned with an early day western fur rendezvous:

"During this season of folly and frolic there was an alarm of mad wolves in the two lower camps. One or more of these animals entered the camp three nights successively, and bit several of the people. Captain Bonneville relates the case of an Indian, who was a universal favorite in the lower camp. He had been bitten by one of these animals. Being out with a party shortly afterwards, he grew silent and gloomy, and lagged behind the rest as if he wished to leave them. They halted and urged him to move faster, but he entreated them not to approach him, and, leaping from his horse began to roll frantically on the earth gnashing his teeth and foaming at the mouth. Still he retained his senses, and warned his companions not to come near him, as he should not be able to restrain himself from biting them. They hurried off to obtain relief; but on their return he was nowhere to be found. His horse and accoutrements remained on the spot. Three or four days afterwards a solitary Indian, believed to be the same was observed crossing a valley, and pursued; but he started away into the fastness of the mountains, and was seen no more. . . . One of the men of the Rocky Mountain Fur Company had been bitten. He set out shortly afterwards, in com-

pany with two white men, on his return to the settlements. In the
course of a few days he showed symptoms of hydrophobia, and became raving towards night. At length, breaking away from his companions, he rushed into a thicket of willows, where they left him to
his fate" (Irving, W., 1895: 230).

One of the earliest accurate accounts of life among the fur
traders of the Northwest is Alexander Henry's *Journal*, a long document rich in information. Henry was a partner in the old Northwest
Company, chief competitor of the Hudson's Bay Company, and oper-
ated mostly in Canadian territory. Reference is made to this author
as Alexander Henry "the younger," because he was the nephew of
another Alexander Henry who was also a fur trader and who also
wrote a book on travels and adventures in Canada. Alexander Henry
"the younger" reports in his *Journal* on November 2, 1800, after
returning northward to Pack River Post in southern Manitoba after
a journey to northwestern Minnesota:

"Last night the wolves were very troublesome; they kept up a
terrible howling about the fort, and even attempted to enter May-
miutch's tent. A large white one came boldly to the door and was
advancing toward a young child, when he was shot dead. Some of
them are very audacious. I have known them to follow people for
several days, attempt to seize a person or a dog, and to be kept off
only by firearms. It does not appear that hunger makes them so
ferocious, as they have been known to pass carcasses of animals,
which they might have eaten to their fill, but they would not touch
flesh; their only object seeming to be that of biting. The Canadians
swear that these are mad wolves and are much afraid of them."
(Red River near Grand Forks, N. Dak.) (Henry, A., and Thompson, D., 1897: 133).

McGowan believed that the wolf is very much of a carrion eater
". . . . when there is famine in the land." And, furthermore, "At
such times mange is not uncommon and outbreaks of rabies have also
been noted by trappers and traders" (McGowan, D., 1936: 30).

Recording his observations in Greenland, as well as in Canada,
Freuchen states: "Wolves, foxes and ermines can be infected by it
(rabies) and will then attack all the dog teams they come across, or
at any rate will make no attempt to get out of the way. Until the
last moment, and then they will bite, thus transferring the infection
to the team" (Freuchen, P., 1935b: 185).

Mad wolves apparently were recognized by the early trapper-explorers of the Far West. During the fur rendezvous on Green River in 1833, Larpenteur recorded:

"A day or so later we learned that a mad wolf had got into Mr. Fontenelle's camp about five miles from us, and had bitten some of his men and horses. My mess mates, who were old hands, had heard of the like before, when men had gone mad" (Larpenteur, C., 1898, vol. 1, p. 36). At the time mentioned, the rendezvous was made up of the two camps of the American and Rocky Mountain Fur Company during midsummer of that year. Larpenteur also had one of his bulls bitten, which later "went mad," and died shortly after being bitten. As a result of the bitings, George Holmes, a member of the Rocky Mountain Fur Company, became afflicted with rabies, and died a horrible and agonizing death. (Ibid.)

According to Lt.-Col. Dodge:

"Indians say that wolves not unfrequently go mad, rush into their villages and do great damage. The following most interesting and perfectly authenticated facts are taken from the records of the hospital at Fort Larned on the Arkansas River. 'On the 5th August, at 10 P. M., a rabid wolf, of the large grey species, came into the post and charged round most furiously. He entered the hospital and attacked Corporal _____, who way lying sick in bed, biting him severely in the left hand and right arm. The left little finger was nearly taken off. The wolf next dashed into a party of ladies and gentlemen sitting in Colonel _____'s porch and bit Lieut. _____ severely in both legs. Leaving there he soon afterward attacked and bit Private _____ in two places. This all occurred in an incredibly short space of time; and, although the above-mentioned were the only parties bitten, the animal left the marks of his presence in every quarter of the garrison. He moved with great rapidity, snapping at everything within his reach, tearing tents, window-curtains, bed-clothing, etc., in every direction. The sentinel at the guard-house fired over the animal's back, while he ran between the man's legs. Finally he charged upon a sentinel at the haystack, and was killed by a well directed and most fortunate shot. He was a very large wolf, and his long jaws and teeth presented a most formidable appearance.

" 'The wounds were thoroughly cauterized with nitrate of silver, on the plan recommended by Mr. Youatt.'

"The Indians are still camped in the vicinity of the post in very large numbers. I have taken particular pains to question them as to their experience with regard to rabid wolves.

"They say that the appearance of mad wolves in their village is not infrequent; that the time of year at which they are most often seen is in the months of February and March; that, once having entered a village, the wolf will make no attempt to leave it, but will rush furiously from place to place until he is disabled; and that in no instance have any of them ever known a person to recover after having received the smallest scratch from the teeth of the rabid animal" (Dodge, R. I., 1877: 97).

Dodge, again quoting from the hospital records, makes the following entry:

" 'September 9th.—Corporal .... showed signs of commencing hydrophobia on the evening of the 6th instant. The symptoms were as usually described, were well marked and very characteristic. No treatment was attempted after the symptoms commenced. The wounds had been well cauterized with lunar caustic from time to time, and washed with alkali washes, and had he allowed the finger to be removed at first there would have been a greater probability of his recovery. A large Newfoundland dog, which had been in conflict with the wolf, has also just died with marked symptoms of hydrophobia. The wounds have healed in the other two persons, and they appear to be in perfect health.'

"The officer bitten is now (1875) in perfect health, having never experienced any ill effects beyond the ordinary pain of the wounds." (Ibid.)

Driving sheep across the plains westward, as well as from New Mexico to California, was a common occurrence beginning with the middle of the 19th century. Often these drives were made by Mexicans. They are by nature a superstitious race; thus, whenever a member of such a party became afflicted with rabies as a result of the bite of a mad wolf, his companions would seldom associate with him, believing "that all would die if they kept the man's company . . . ." (Peters, DeW. C., 1858: 403).

To what extent rabies was a factor in the elimination of wolves east of the Mississippi to the Atlantic seaboard is not definitely known. Doddridge was of the opinion that:

"The wolves formerly so numerous and destructive to the cattle are now seldom heard of in our older settlements. It may seem strange that this ferocious and cunning animal, so long the scourge of the mountain districts of Europe, should have so suddenly disappeared from an infant country" (Doddridge, J., 1824: 68).

He believed that the wolves died of hydrophobia.

Hutyra and Marek describe wolves throughout the world as being involved in the spread of rabies. They record also the transmission of glanders to carnivorous animals in zoological gardens when they are fed meat of affected horses. They state, however, that the dog kind possesses a relatively high resistance. (Hutyra, F., Marek, J., and Manninger, R., 1938: 525.)

When I was a boy living in the northwestern part of the United States (Oregon and Washington particularly), death from salmon poisoning was one of the reasons I often heard given by the early settlers, some of whom were forty-niners, for the scarcity of wolves in the coastal mountains of those states. This opinion was also voiced by others.

For instance, an outstanding trapper in this part of Oregon, Emsley Moses Houghton, who attended the public schools at Astoria, Oreg., in 1869, on February 19, 1940 (then in his 76th year) told me that elk was the chief food of the wolf in this part of Oregon, but that salmon also were taken when the runs of this fish were under way. He further said that in the year 1877, all the Clatsop County streams up which salmon ran had wolf trails on their banks. Such streams were the Young's, Necanicum, Lewis and Clark, Claskinine, and Nehalem. The salmon runs up these streams occurred from the middle of September to January. Along the banks of these streams was found an abundance of sign, indicating that the wolves fed a great deal on the salmon. Mr. Houghton stated also that he often found evidences of wolf poisoning due to their eating the salmon.

He held the opinion that salmon poisoning was the factor which held down wolf abundance in this section of Oregon. The wolves might build up to goodly numbers, but seemingly were almost wiped out during years of large salmon runs. He felt this factor was responsible for the almost total disappearance of the wolf by the early 1890's. Only occasionally he stated is the track of a lone wolf now seen in the Green and Saddle Mountain country in Clatsop County, northwestern Oregon.

David Thompson, while in the vicinity of Kettle Falls on the Columbia River in 1811, and in speaking of dead salmon found along the Columbia and tributary creeks, says:

"The Dogs that with impunity eat all other fish in a raw state, die from eating Salmon in this state, which may also be the case with other carnivorous animals, as we never saw any feeding on them; but when cooked the Dogs eat with safety" (Thompson, D., 1916: 471).

For a long period the reason for this remained unknown. However, within recent years research has established the fact that in the Pacific Northwest, there exists watercourses inhabited by trout and fresh water salmon at times infested with an intestinal parasite. A summary of these findings, the work of scientists connected with the Oregon Agricultural Experiment Station, stated among other things that ". . . the cause of so-called salmon poisoning in dogs and foxes is an intestinal fluke," and that "a cystic form of this parasite occurs in the muscles, kidney, liver, and gills of trout and fresh water salmon" (Donham, C. R., Simms, B. T., and Miller, F. W., 1926: 11).

Blue, silver, and black foxes, and also coyotes have been likewise found to be susceptible. While no experiments so far have been carried on with wolves as to their susceptibility, the opinion is held that they well might be, and that Houghton was correct in his interpretation of salmon poisoning these large predators when partaken as food by them in the area under his observations.

Finally, reality of salmon poisoning is supported by recent research on chastek paralysis in captive foxes, which has been identified as a nutritional deficiency resulting from the feeding of raw fish to the extent of 10 percent or more of the diet (Green, R. G., and Evans, C. A., 1940: 154).

V

ECONOMIC STATUS

THE SKIN OF THE WOLF, ITS USES AND VALUES

WOLF pelts provided both leather and fur utilized by man.

Billings, quoting Lawson, stated that the wolf " 'skin dressed to a parchment, makes the best drum heads, and if tanned makes the best sort of shoes for the summer countries' " (Billings, F., 1856: 209).

The coat while not in the same class with that of the high grade fur animals is thick and durable. In North America the wolf pelt is generally prime, that is the hair is thickest and in best condition from November to early April. Towards the latter part of March, generally speaking, the hair starts to come off in large patches, as the animal grows its spring and summer pelage. In that coat the guard hairs are short, often giving the animal the appearance of having been clipped.

The skin of the wolf, besides being used by man for bodily protection and adornment, and a few miscellaneous uses, was employed also as camouflage in hunting and in warfare and as insignia by some of our western Indians, as well as a medium of exchange. Harting informs us that in England:

"The fur of the wolf was formerly used for trimming robes and was employed for this purpose at least as late as the time of Elizabeth" (Harting, J. E., 1880: 157).

Strangely enough, that is about the only use of wolf pelts in the American fur trade today, i.e., in the trimming of winter garments.

Uses by whites in the past have included those for clothing and the lining of rugs and laprobes.

As noted in the section on Strychnine Poisoning, large numbers of the skins obtained by the professional wolfers were reported to make overcoats for Russian soldiers.

Kalm mentions the use of wolf skins for bedding by the Swedes who settled in the Delaware Bay section in the late 1600's (Benson, A. B., 1937, vol. 1, pp. 150, 272; vol. 2, pp. 522, 576, 596, 680, 737).

Some of the medicine men of the Blackfoot Indians used wolf skins for making couch covers which, when slept upon, were supposed to give the medicine men the strength and stamina of the wolf. The Pawnee Indians used the wolf skin as a protective blanket for their mules (Abert, J. W., 1848: 537).

Quoting from Josselyn's *New England Rarities Discovered*, Norton says: "A black Wolf's Skin is worth a Beaver Skin among the Indians, being highly esteemed for helping old Aches, in old people, worn as a Coat (Norton, A. H., 1930: 42).

The fur of the wolf was highly prized by some Indian tribes for use as robes and as trimming on the edges of a buffalo robe. Some of the far western Indians appear to have at times sheared their wolf-dog hybrids for wool and used it for weaving into blankets and rugs.

The Slave Indians of Canada utilized wolf pelts in making parts of their caps (Coues, E., 1897, vol. 2, p. 541).

Eskimos have long used the pelts of wolves for trimming the hood and other parts of their deerskin capotes or tunics. Some of the western Indians formerly used wolf teeth for arrow tips and ornaments.

The tail of a wolf was often employed by the wolf trappers of the late 19th and early 20th centuries as a duster in the final smoothing of the earth disturbed in the sinking and setting of a steel wolf trap. Into the part of the tail from which the bone had been removed was inserted a small wooden handle, to which the skin was firmly tacked. This made a ready tool comparable to a feather duster. It was supposed to have the further advantage of carrying the characteristic wolf scent and thus aiding in submerging any human odor around the trap. Very few of the old wolf trappers ever failed to carry such a duster as a part of their trapping equipment. The wolf's tail was to a real wolfer what a good saddle is to the cowboy.

The use of a wolf pelt as a camouflage when hunting the buffalo was common to nearly all of the Great Plains tribes. Catlin, who was so impressed by this ingenious device that he portrayed it in a painting, stated:

". . . . they [bison] also stand unwittingly by and behold him [the Indian] unsuspected under the skin of a white wolf insinuating himself and his fatal weapons into close company, when they are peaceably grazing on the level prairies, and shoot down before they are aware of their danger" (Catlin, G., 1913, vol. 1, p. 286).

Along this same line Alexander Ross observed that:

"During winter the men wear long detached sleeves or mittens up to their shoulders, made of the wolf or fox skins, . . . While on their hunting excursions, they also wear caps made of the skins of the wolf or bear, with the ears erect; their heads being thus metamorphosed into wolves' or bears' heads, they are enabled to approach the game with greater facility . . . the wolf is the animal they seem to imitate the best. An Indian concealed in a wolf's hide, pulls the skin of the wolf's head, with the face, eyes, and nose entire, over his own head, the ears erect, the tail in proper place, will walk, run, and frisk about on his hands and feet, so that he can scarcely be distinguished from the real animal itself" (Ross, A., 1849: 282).

Somewhat farther eastward, the Blackfoot Indians on the Upper Missouri River employed the wolf skin for camouflaging also, according to Maximilian, Prince of Wied, who states:

". . . . Wolf skins are useful to them, especially when they want to observe the enemy. They wear them across their shoulders and, when they wish to approach the enemy unperceived, they throw them over their head, and lie down behind an elevation, or rising of the ground, in such a manner as to have the appearance of a white wolf" (Maximilian, Prince of Wied, 1906, vol. 22, 119).

Another of Alexander Ross' interesting observations pertains to a heraldic use of wolf skins. He notes:

"The royal insignia of an Indian king or chief is simple, and is always known in the camp. The Oakinacken emblem is a white wolf-skin fantastically painted with rude figures of different colours —the head and tail decorated with the higua, bears' claws, and the teeth of different animals—suspended from a pole, in a conspicuous place near the chief's lodge. On our first arrival among this people, the wolf skin was always to be seen waving conspicuously from the pole, but as they began to associate and got accustomed to us, they became less particular in exhibiting the insignia of royalty" (Ross, A., 1904: 277).

Wolf skins or scalps, through a long period, were used as a medium of exchange. The Slave Indians of Canada bartered in wolf skins with some of the early fur traders, particularly Alexander Henry, of the Northwest Company, while at Fort Vermilion in 1809 (Coues, E., 1897: vol. 2, 541).

Among the early settlers of Maryland, according to Meshach Browning, "If any man wished to hire help, the parties would have an understanding as to what the wages were to be paid in. Sometimes linsey, pork, beef, honey, or corn, and at others, a calf, pig, sheep, deer skin, coon-skin, or a wolf's scalp, together with many other articles were used as substitutes for money" (Browning, M., 1928: 364). An additional reason for the usefulness of wolf scalp in exchange was that the recipient could turn it in at any time and collect the prevailing bounty. Wolf skins, from the earliest to the latest days of the frontier trading posts, were traded for the necessities of life. Storer notes that in the vicinity of Fort Benton during the early 1870's, a wolf skin was rated as worth two cups of sugar (Storer, T. I., 1931: 77). An old pioneer stockman informed me one day, however, that the cups used for measuring the sugar sometimes had false bottoms, and that it was not uncommon to find much sand mixed with the sugar.

As to the value of wolf skins, it appears that in the early years of the fur trade, following organization of the Hudson's Bay Company in 1670, it was considered of scarcely any value when compared to those of the beaver, otter, mink, and even other fur-bearers. The price each pelt brought was nominal, and so continued for more than a century and a half.

In the eight years between 1800 and 1808, while trading with the Indians in the country around the Pembina Mountains in southern Manitoba and south along the Red River to Grand Forks, N. Dak., Alexander Henry, the younger, of the Northwest Company, received approximately 2,850 wolf skins. There may have been mixed in this lot a few coyote pelts labeled as *wolf*, but it is believed that very few coyotes were traded at this time because of the predominance of the wolf in that region. The wolf skin was taken in trade for mediocre articles of the traders; in some instances very much diluted rum or wine was often exchanged, and it seems that actual outlays of strictly cash when trading were not used for the wolf skin until the middle of the 19th century, that is, from 1845 onward. However, with regard to the value of the wolf skin in the early fur trade of the Far West, Chittenden says: "The skin of the grey wolf, though gathered to some extent, was not of great value in the market, and formed an insignificant part of the fur trade" (Chittenden, H. M., 1935: 819).

Wolf skins in early shipments from North America were valued in shillings; in 1786, among the 705,000 skins, valued at £203,378, exported from Quebec, there were 12,923 of wolves valued at 10s each, or a total of $32,305 (Anonymous, 1800: 57).

Between the years 1738 and 1747, the Hudson's Bay Company sold the following numbers of wolf skins, the average price per skin being shown for each year:

Year	Number of skins	Price per skin *
1738	454	9 s 10½ d
1739	642	12 " 3 "
1740	771	13 " 6½ "
1741	680	12 " 7¼ "
1742	973	17 " 9½ "
1743	1,885	18 " 11¼ "
1744	761	16 " 6½ "
1745	1,060	14 " 8 "
1746	1,602	9 " ¾ "
1747	1,663	9 " 6¼ "
Total	10,491 (Strange, J. B., 1749: 263-266)	

*12 pence = 1 shilling = about 25 cents, American.

About the middle of the 19th century the demand for wolf fur had greatly increased and had stimulated the killing of the animals with strychnine (see p. 327). Though the price of the pelts remained low, the great numbers of wolves that occurred and the apparent ease with which the animals could be poisoned at that time, made wolf hunting a profitable business for nearly 25 years. During the years 1861 and 1862, wolf pelts from the western plains were bringing about $1.25 each. In 1865 they were quoted in New York at prices ranging from $3 to $3.50 each.

Because coyote pelts were often included with those of wolves in the early sale we can not now correctly ascertain the yearly disposals of genuine wolf pelts. The Hudson's Bay Company, during the years 1853-1877 inclusive, recorded the sale of 171,770 wolf pelts, but MacFarlane believes that half or more of them were coyote skins. He states: "The three best sales were in 1855 with 15,419, 12,659 in 1859, and 12,616 in 1866; the three lowest 2,802 in 1872, 2,083 in 1876, and 1,865 in 1877. In 1902 they sold 1,340 and in 1903 1,790 skins" (MacFarlane, R. R., 1905: 694).

For many years the price of wolf pelts fluctuated between $1.50 and $3.50 each. With the turn of the present century, however, these pelts have greatly increased in value. Most of the wolf skins now reaching the market come from the northern parts of Alaska and Canada. Two sales of 964 Canadian wolf skins held in 1926 and 1927 brought a total of $13,861, or an average of more than $14 per pelt (Anonymous, 1927: 3). Similarly, the Alaskan wolf skins have brought a good price. For the period 1925-34, a total of 4,191 skins shipped from that territory were valued at $100,949.69, or an average of more than $24 each (Dufresne, F., 1935: 1).

The revenue derived from wolf skins over a 15-year period from 1923 to 1937 in Alaska totaled $154,710.10, or an average yearly return of $10,313.41. (Alaska Game Commission, 1938: 9, 14-15.) According to the summary of fur shipped from Alaska during the calendar year 1937, 730 wolf skins brought, on the average, $23.75 per skin. This value was exceeded by that of the skins of only the silver-black fox, $40, the lynx $31.60, the marten $27.35, and the polar bear at $24.50 per skin. The average value of 405 wolf skins from Alaska in 1939 was $17 and of 444 in 1941, $18.

A good many Alaskan skins are prepared as trophies, in which condition they bring about $20 each. While interviewing private trappers in the interior of Alaska in the summer of 1938, I found that some of the wolf pelts were being held for future sale, and that a price of $65 per skin was demanded. These were exceptionally large—averaging more than 8 feet in length and the hair was very silky in texture.

THE WOLF AS HUMAN FOOD

Dog flesh is regularly eaten in certain parts of the world so it is not surprising that the wolf also has been laid under contribution in this respect. Early American explorers and trappers occasionally had to eat dog meat. As will be further recalled, various western Indian tribes regularly depended upon it, being often considered by the red men a very choice delicacy, particularly when ceremonial feasts were deemed in order.

To the writer, the thought of eating dog or wolf flesh formerly caused a gastronomic revulsion; but having tried the cooked lean meat of both the dog and the wolf, he now realizes that the reason for the revulsion was purely psychological. Anyway, if circumstances decreed that one eat wolf meat or starve, there is little doubt that the former alternative would be accepted. The meat of the wolf is rather tough, but in taste is not unlike that of an old buck deer. Jerked wolf meat tastes more like jerked venison, though it is somewhat tougher. In texture it resembles dried goat meat, and though somewhat stringy, can be pounded into a flour-like powder. It is difficult to distinguish the taste of the flesh of the dog from that of wolf meat. Wolf meat, unless cooked far beyond the usual time allotted for most domestic meats, is tough and rubbery. Sometimes too it will have a strong odor, similar to the meat of an old bear that has been living on carrion, larvae, and insects for a long period prior to being utilized for food.

Speaking of the buffalo wolf, Cowie, the Hudson's Bay Companys' employee formerly mentioned, writes: "They were generally fat, and yielded a large proportion of the grease eaten by the Indians and made into the finer kind of pemmican by them" (Cowie, I., 1913: 250). He further relates that when buffaloes were scarce, wolves were often resorted to for human sustenance. He stated that man "found his chief resource for food in absence of the buffalo, in the wolves he poisoned with baits of strychnine. The only part not eaten in such cases, was the stomach containing the bait, and our own men often were compelled to live on poisoned wolves, and glad to get them" (Ibid., p. 252). Cowie alludes to this again, mentioning two men who wintered at Eagle Quills in 1870, and "feasted upon any wolf which they had the good luck to poison" (Ibid., p. 425).

In recording the foregoing, Cowie is dealing with the period when wolf poisoning was being carried on over a vast area, including the Canadian prairies.

After the Lewis and Clark Expedition had obtained their first gallon of salt made from ocean water at present day city of Seaside, Clatsop County, Oreg., during the winter of 1806, Meriwether Lewis wrote in his journal "this was a great treat to myself and most of the party, having not had any [salt] since the 20th Ult. [Dec. 20]; I say most of the party, for my friend Cap' Clark declares it to be a mear matter of indifference with him whether he uses it or not; for myself I must confess I felt a considerable inconvenience from the want of it; the want of bread I consider a trivial provided I get fat meat, for as to the species of meat I am not very particular, the flesh of the dog, the horse and the wolf having from habit become equally familiar with any other, and I have learned to think that if the chord be sufficiently strong, which binds the soul and boddy together, it dose not much matter about the materials which compose it" (Lewis, M., and Clark, W., 1905: 313).

The importance of wolf meat in saving human lives is recorded by Ross, based on information obtained from Ramsay Crooks. Crooks, a companion of John Day, had been left by a party of Astoria trappers to spend the winter among the Snake Indians in northeastern Oregon and western Idaho. Ross encountered Crooks and Day accidentally as he was journeying to the interior in the spring of 1812 from the John Jacob Astor fort at the mouth of the Columbia River. This accidental meeting took place near the point where the Umatilla River flows into the Columbia. Ross, in later recording the incident, says:

"The following is, therefore, Mr. Crook's account of their adventures and their sufferings. 'After being left by Mr. Hunt, we remained for some time with the Snakes, who were very kind to us. When they had anything to eat, we ate also; but they soon departed and being without provisions of course they left us without any. . . . Following the example of the Indians, I dug up roots for our sustenance; but not knowing how to cook them, we were nearly poisoned. In this plight, we unfortunately let the fire go out, and for a day and night we both lay in a torpid state, unable to strike fire or collect dry fuel . . . death appeared inevitable. But Providence is ever kind. Two straggling Indians happening to come our way relieved us. They made us a fire, got us some water, and gave us something to eat; . . . These poor fellows staid with us the greater part of two days, and gave us at their departure about two pounds of venison. We were sorry to lose them.

" 'On the same day, after the Indians had left us, a very large wolf came prowling about our hut, when John Day, with great exertions and good luck, shot the ferocious animal dead; and to this fortunate hit I think we owed our lives. The flesh of the wolf we cut up and dried, and laid it by for some future emergency, and in the mean time feasted on the skin; nor did we throw away the bones, but pounded them between stones, and with some roots made a kind of broth, which, in our present circumstances, we found very good. After we had recovered our strength a little, and were able to walk, we betook ourselves to the mountains in search of game; and when unsuccessful in the chase, we had recourse to our dried wolf. For two months we wandered about barely sustaining life with our utmost exertions' " (Ross, A., 1904: 189).

A similar occurrence, in which wolf flesh aided in keeping men alive, is recorded with respect to Col. Fremont's ill-fated fourth expedition in 1849. While on the headwaters of the Rio Grande in early January of that year, and when the struggling survivors were attempting to get out of the snowclad eastern slope of the San Juan Mountains of Colorado it is related that "at last on January 2 a portion of the party reached the Rio Grande, . . . the sufferings of the party under the leadership of Vincent Haler almost beggar description. Their supplies were entirely gone and there was no game. They did succeed in getting one small buck, but it apparently was not evenly divided. A couple of prairie chickens were killed. The remains of a dead wolf were found. This seems to have constituted all of the meat the party was able to get" (McGehee, J. S., 1910: 166).

Further aid in keeping body and soul together during the retreat of Fremont's men, when succor was about to reach them, is noted in McGehee's record wherein it is stated that some of the men partook of wolf meat and drank broth made from the animal's bones (McGehee, M., 1891: 778).

Similarly, Ferris records living in part on wolves during a sojourn in Cache Valley with a party of trappers in the early 1830's while in dire straits because of lack of normal food (Ferris, W. A., 1940: 73). He further notes that while following a small stream "into the mountains that separate the Valley of the Salmon River from the Big Hole, . . . a grey wolf" was killed, "which was fat, and made us a tolerable supper; . . ." (Ibid., p. 162).

Fat taken from a wolf in the fall and rendered was found to make a grease excellent for softening leather.

DOMESTICATION OF THE WOLF

At all periods of its availability in North America efforts have been made to tame wolves and to train them to serve man. Despite the extreme wildness of the animal, these attempts have had a considerable measure of success.

Several hunters of the Fish and Wildlife Service have raised wolf whelps as pets. The best results have been attained with those taken shortly after their eyes were beginning to open. Those caught at 3 to 4 weeks of age proved unmanageable in youth or untrustworthy on maturity.

Generally speaking, on the basis of their experience, tame wolves are strictly "one-man dogs." They may be confiding and playful with the man who raised them, or even with his whole family, if fed and cared for by them, but are suspicious and timid in the presence of strangers. They invariably retain certain reactions of wolf nature, as for instance, an incorrigible desire to kill chickens or other small livestock whenever opportunity occurs.

Dr. E. H. McCleery, of Kane, Pa., reports from experience with many captive wolves that after taking whelps 3½ weeks old and having one man handle them 8 hours a day for one month, then 1 hour a day for the remainder of a year, they have succeeded in taming on the average only one wolf out of eleven.

From the historical record of the taming and training of wolves, we have gleaned the following:

Ash states:

"Writing of the savages in 'The Last Discovery of the North Part of Virginia' (1605), one, James Rosier, 'a gentleman employed in the voyage,' tells us that Griffon on his return reported two or three savages, every one with 'bowe and arrowes, with their dogges, and wolves which they keep tame at command'; and in his 'briefe note of what profits we saw the countrey yeald in the small time of our stay there' he gives a list of 'Beasts,' in which wolves occur and Dogges: some like wolves, some like Spaniels'" (Ash, E. C., 1927:31).

Lawson (1714) wrote:

"The Wolf of Carolina, is the Dog of the Woods. The Indians had no other Curs, before the Christians came amongst them. They are made domestic" (Lawson, J., 1714: 122).

Commenting on the wolf in Virginia, Col. William Byrd states (October 8, 1728): "This beast is not so untamable as the panther, but the Indians know how to gentle their whelps and use them about their cabans instead of dogs" (Byrd, W., 1901: 130).

Catesby (1743) observed:

"Wolves were domestic with the Indians, who had no other dogs before those of Europe were introduced, since which the breed of wolves and European dogs are mixed and become prolific. It is remarkable that the European dogs, that have no mixture of Wolfish blood, have an antipathy to those that have, and worry them whenever they meet; the Wolf-Breed act only defensively, and with his tail between his legs, endeavors to evade the others' fury" (Catesby, M., 1743, vol. 2, p. 26).

Kalm (1750) recorded of the wolves in early colonial Pennsylvania: "There are instances of these wolves being made as tame as dogs" (Kalm, P., 1937, vol. 1, p. 150).

John McLean, who entered the service of the Hudson's Bay Company in the winter of 1820-1821 and continued in its service for the following 25 years, states:

"The Esquimaux breed of dogs are wolves in a domesticated state, the same in every characteristic, save such differences as may be expected to result from their relative conditions; the dog howls, never barks" (McLean, J., 1932: 276).

Washington Irving says of the Indian dog: "Not a family but has two or three dozen belonging to it, of all sizes and colors; some, of a superior breed, are used for hunting; others, to draw the sledge, while others, of a mongrel breed, and idle vagabond nature, are fattened for food. They are supposed to be descended from the wolf, and retain something of his savage but cowardly temper, howling rather than barking; showing their teeth and snarling on the slightest provocation, but sneaking away on the least attack" (Irving, W., 1855: 209).

Chittenden says:

"Scarcely less in importance to the Indian than the horse was the dog, a long slender, wolfish animal, whose general appearance clearly denoted its consanguinity with the cowardly denizens of the plains" (Chittenden, H. M., 1935, vol. 2, p. 822).

Audubon records: "Once, when we were travelling on foot not far from the southern boundary of Kentucky, we fell in with a Black Wolf, following a man with a rifle on his shoulders. On speaking with him about this animal, he assured us that it was as tame and as gentle as any dog, and that he had never met with a dog that could trail a deer better. We were so much struck with this account and the noble appearance of the wolf, that we offered him one hundred dollars for it; but the owner would not part with it for any price" (Audubon, J. J., and Bachman, J., 1851-54, vol. 2, p. 130).

Of the use of wolves for drawing conveyances, Alexander Henry the younger, writing in his journal on April 9, 1801, while in the vicinity of Fort Dauphin, situated on the south side of present Lake Dauphin in west central Manitoba, states: "Another of my men brought in six young wolves he had found in one hole; they were very tame, and we proposed to keep them for the *trains*, as they are of the large species" (Coues, E., 1897: 175).

H. M. Brackenridge, while on a journey up the Missouri River in 1811, wrote about the dogs at the Arikara Indian Village, as follows: "The dogs of which each family has 30 or 40, pretend to make a show of fierceness, but on the least threat, ran off. They are of different sizes and colors. A number are fattened on purpose to eat, others are used for drawing their baggage. It is nothing more than the domesticated wolf" (Brackenridge, H. M., 1904: 21).

While in the vicinity of old Fort Edmonton, northern Canada, in the late 1820's, Alexander Ross observed that the dogs "are in general of the wolf-breed, and are said to be vigorous and long winded: a hundred miles a day is a common journey for them. They are not generally reared about the establishments, but purchased from the natives for a mere trifle when young: when trained, they sell among the whites as high as five pounds sterling—double the price of a horse—and sometimes higher, according to fancy" (Ross, A., 1855; vol. 2, p. 212).

Dr. E. W. Nelson, speaking of the Eskimo dog, says: "The Eskimos sometimes secure the cubs (wolf), and some years ago an old Eskimo near St. Michaels secured several, which he kept until winter and broke them to haul his sledge. They worked well, but became so vicious that they were killed. The natives also claim to have had crosses between wolves raised in this manner and dogs. This is not surprising when the close resemblance between some of the dogs and a wolf is noted, and one can easily believe that such crosses are fertile" (Nelson, E. W., 1888: 238).

Joe LaFlame, of Gogama in northern Ontario, began using a pure wolf team as sled animals in 1923, and since that time has intermittently exhibited them and later sled wolves at various cities and conservation shows and meetings. An account of them during their display in New York, as voiced by LaFlame, says, "When I mushed them down Broadway, thousands of people stood in the streets cheering" (Editor, 1938: 6).

W. R. Gordon trained a young Alaskan female wolf that he had captured with a snare so that it would work in harness with two dogs in drawing a sled. He reported this wolf, which he named Lady, as a willing worker, but that she seemed to tire more easily than the two dogs (Gordon, W. R., 1942: 11).

WOLVES AND DOGS

Wolves manifest a high degree of intelligence comparable to that of man's most thoroughly domesticated animal, the dog. They have many of the same mannerisms. Wolves differ from most dogs with respect to carriage of the tail, however, for normally it is held slightly below the level of the back. But when at play, as with the dog, the tail may be held straight up or in other positions. In fright, the tail as in dogs is tucked between the hind legs. The wolf also wags the tail to express pleasure. As with dogs, the lips of the wolf when angered are curled into a snarl.

The habit of trampling grass, weeds, or other litter by circling before they bed down is probably one inherited by dogs from their wild forebears; in this respect they differ from wolves as the latter do not have this trait.

To the untrained eye there is great similarity between the tracks made by a large dog and those of a wolf. It is with extreme difficulty at times that even the expert is able to distinguish them. A distinguishing feature of the track is that the two front toe marks of the wolf are closer together than those in the track of a dog. Also, the prints of the two front foot toenails of the wolf when made in dry, soft earth are more prominent than those made by a dog. Upon close observation it is evident that the wolf's track is also more

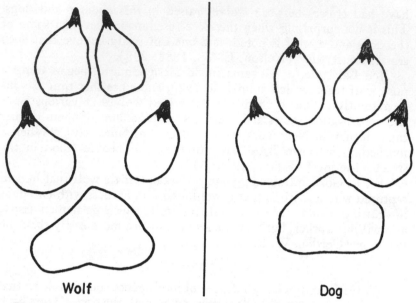

Wolf   **Dog**

Figure 7. Diagram of front foot track of wolf and dog (one-half natural size)

elongated and narrow. The wolf's track roughly fits the form of a trapezoid, while that of a dog is more nearly circular in form.

Measurements of the tracks of 50 wolves made in widely separated areas of the Rocky Mountain region show an average front foot length of 90 mm.; width, 70 mm.; and the width of the footpad, 47.5 mm. The average length of the hind foot track was found to be 82 mm.; width, 64 mm.; and the footpad, 43 mm.

Similar measurements made of ten different wolf tracks on the islands of southeastern Alaska showed an average length for the front foot of 115 mm.; width, 82 mm.; and for the hind foot, length, 95 mm.; width, 80 mm.

The right front foot track of a wolf (*Canis niger gregoryi*) made in the fall of 1934 in Madison Parish, La., approximately 15 miles southwest of Tallulah, measured 96 mm. in length and 78 mm. in width, with a footpad width of 53 mm. The ground was exceedingly soft when this track was made following a downpour of rain the night before.

The right front foot track of a Pleistocene wolf left in sandstone now being quarried 20 feet underground within the confines of the Nevada State Penitentiary grounds located at Carson City, Nev., measures 128 mm. in length and 90 mm. in width.

The longevity of wolves is similar to that of the larger domestic dogs. Evidence gleaned from western wolf trappers and stockmen as to the life span (10-18 years) agrees fairly well with longevity records of wolves in captivity. Flower states that:

"Thirty wolves had an average life of 9 years, 10 mo. and 12 days. A female from New Mexico lived in the London Zoological Garden from Oct. 16, 1901, to Apr. 17, 1915, 13 years, 6 months, 1 day. A wolf in the Copenhagen Zoological Gardens (Report for 1911, p. 28) 14 years" (Flower, S. S., 1931: 172).

Hollister reports that: "A male grey wolf, *Canis lupus nubilus*, in the National Zoological Park, Washington, D. C., 16 years, 3 months, 5 days" (Hollister, N., 1923: 93).

Walker records male and female wolves from Pueblo, Colo., that were received at the National Zoological Park, Washington, D. C., on April 25, 1895. The male died on June 1, 1911, and the female on November 17 of the same year, each having lived in this Zoo more than 16 years.[22]

The wolf has grace and strength harmoniously blended. Its motions are so rhythmic and so well coordinated that the animal appears, when in motion, to move without visible effort. The anatomy of the wolf varies considerably from that of the dog. Its breast has a shallow, keel-like configuration, and the shoulders are narrow and firmly set, with the elbows turned well inwards. This causes the fore feet to swing in the plane of the hind feet on the same side, producing a gait differing from that of the dog in which the fore feet are either more or less separated than the hind feet. Here, apparently, we find a reason for the smooth trotting ability of the wolf. Besides trotting easily and gracefully, wolves also at times assume a pacing gait very similar to that of the horse (Pl. 50).

The medial axis of the shoulder blade lies in a plane of 45 degrees from the perpendicular, and while at rest the shoulder blade is articulated with the humerus at a 90-degree angle. The same rela-

---

[22]Personal letter from Ernest P. Walker, Asst. Director of National Zoological Park, Washington, D. C., to Stanley P. Young, May 4, 1939.

tion prevails in the hip-joint where the ilium, in a matured wolf, articulates with the femur at 90 degrees, and the femur at rest has its medial axis at 45 degrees from the perpendicular. Hence, in the forward stride of the wolf, the elements of the foreleg lie in a straight line, which is a prolongation of the medial axis of the shoulder blade, and the length of the stride is at its maximum, it is generally equal to the height of the wolf at the shoulder, varying from 25 to 27 inches (635-686 mm.). Its structure indicates that the wolf is probably the most completely developed type of the trotting dog.

Wolves are so closely related to dogs that hybridization readily occurs. There is testimony to the effect that both wolves and dogs at times give up their normal affiliations to breed outside of the clan.

An early record is that recorded by Topsell. He relates that some of the last wolves in England were held in captivity in the Tower of London, "to be seen by the Prince and people brought out of other countries, when there fell out a rare accident, namely, a mastive dog was hind to a she wolfe, and she thereby conceived and brought forth sixe or seven young whelpes, which was in the year of our Lord 1605, or thereabouts" (Topsell, E., 1607: 735).

There is much testimony as to the cross-mating of dogs and wolves in North America but a good deal of it seems to rest upon probabilities rather than upon observed instances. However, a number of statements in this class are cited for their general interest.

In 1803, Barton compared the so-called Indian wolf-dog with the domestic dog (*Canis familiaris*), likening it to the wolf (probably *Canis lupus lycaon*) and supplementing his own observations with information obtained from William Bartram. This wolf hybrid existent among the various eastern Indian tribes apparently differed little from the hybrid that existed on the Great Plains of the West. Barton said that "It is not, however, always black, but of different colours, commonly a bay color, and about one-third lefs and has the fame wild and fly look that the wolf has. . . .

"The Indian dog (I mean that which is moft allied to the wolf) is frequently called, by the traders and others, the half-wolf breed. His general afpect is much more that of the wolf than of the common domefticated dogs. He is remarkably fmall behind. His ears do not hang like thofe of our dogs, but ftand erect, and are large and fharp-pointed. He has a long fmall fnout, and very fharp nofe.

His barking is more like the howling of the wolf. When attacked, and when fighting, he does not fhake his antagonift, like our dogs. His teeth are very fharp, and his bite fure. When he fnarls, which he is wont to do upon the flightest occafion, he draws the fkin from his mouth back, prefenting all his teeth to view. Our dogs, when once attacked by thefe Indian dogs, always fear and fhun them. It is a very curious circumftance, that the Indian dog will never attack or purfue the wolf, which the common dogs fo readily do. This fact feems to point very ftrongly to the origin of the American animal. For the purpofes of hunting, the Indian dogs are very ufeful; but, in other refpects, they are by no means fo docile as the common dogs. They have lefs fidelity; for, though never fo well fed, they will fteal from their mafters. In fhort, everything fhows that the Indian dog is a much more favage or imperfectly reclaimed animal than the common dog.

".... this fpecies or breed is ftill preferved in the greateft purity among the Six Nations, from whom the Delawares acknowledge that they received it. The Delawares call this dog *lenchum,* or *lenni-chum,* which fignifies 'the original beaft.' The Nanticokes call him *ibn-wallum;* the Mohicans, *anun-neen-dee-a-oo,* or 'the original dog,' to diftinguifh him from our common dogs, which they call fimply *dee-a-oo,* or *de-a-oo*" (Barton, B. S., 1803: 6).

Of the black wolf-dogs found in early Florida, Ash adds:

".... the black wolf-dogs of the Florida Indians were higher at the shoulder than a Newfoundland dog. . . . They were shorter in the body and very like a wolf, except that the eyes were nearer the muzzle" (Ash, E. C., 1927: 32).

Richardson, the famous early zoological explorer, further stated: "Indeed the wolves and the domestic dogs of the fur countries are so like each other, that it is not easy to distinguish them at a small distance; the want of strength and courage of the former being the principal difference. The offspring of the wolf and Indian dog are prolific, and are prized by the voyagers as beasts of draught, being stronger than the ordinary dog" (Richardson, J., 1836: 492).

Garrard, while among the Cheyenne Indians in the late 1840's, observed this tribe in their moving operations south of Bent's Fort in Colorado. He noted: "Many of the largest dogs were packed with a small quantity of meat, or something not easily injured. They looked queerly, trotting industriously under their burdens; and

Figure 8. Indian-dog travois. Hybrid wolves were valued as beasts of draught among the early day Plains Indians

judging from a small stock of canine physiological information, not a little of the wolf was in their composition. These dogs are extremely muscular, and are compactly built" (Garrard, L. H., 1850: 56).

General John Charles Fremont, on his first expedition to the Far West, while being accosted by a tribe of Arapahoe Indians in northwest Nebraska on July 8, 1842, mentions that "scores of wild-looking dogs followed (the Indians, particularly the Arapahoe women riding up in the rear of the men) looking like troops of wolves, and having, in fact, but very little of the dog in their composition. Some of them remained with us, and I checked one of the men [of the expedition], whom I found aiming at one, which he was about to kill for a wolf" (Fremont, J. C., 1887: 98).

Audubon, at Fort Union in 1843, notes the employment of hybrid wolf-dogs as draught animals by stating that he "saw hybrids, the offspring of the wolf and the cur dog, and also their mixed bloods: some of which resemble the wolf, and other the dog. Many of the Assiniboin Indians who visited Ft. Union during our stay there, had both wolves and their crosses with the common dog in their trains, and their dog carts (if they be so called) were drawn alike by both" (Audubon, J. J., and Bachman, J., 1851-54, vol. 2, p. 160).

Joseph H. Batty, who was associated with the Hayden Surveys, in writing of the western plains Indians, says: "A great number of dogs are seen in every Indian village, though we saw more with the Crows than with any other tribe. There are no pure blooded dogs, nearly all being crossed with the wolf. . . . This dog fights savagely, much to the delight of the young bucks, who never separate them, but let them fight it out. The Indians make an article of food of their dogs, and tan their skins for mats. They also use them to haul sledges and carry light packs" (Batty, J. H., 1882: 61).

George Bird Grinnell, while with the Ludlow Expedition in 1875, found that "Almost all the dogs seen among the Assinaboinis, Crows, and Gros Ventres of the Prairie, appeared to have more or less wolf-blood in their veins, and many of them would have been taken for true wolves had they been seen away from the Indian camps" (Ludlow, W., 1876: 64).

Baird, quoting Clark, makes the following comment on the wolves in northern Mexico: "Wolves have the bitterest of enemies in dogs; the sharp teeth and rapid snap of the former, however, require but a short time to rid them of the most furious attacks. On one occasion while at the copper mines, three dogs attacked a single wolf, and, after an encounter of but a few minutes, one returned so lacerated as to cause its death within a week. Notwithstanding this enmity, traces of the wolf are unmistakable, and frequently seen among many of the dogs of North Chihuahua and Sonora" (Baird, S. F., 1859: 15).

Pierce stated: "Hybrid wolves have always been very common along our Western frontiers. I have seen several of them sired both by dogs and wolves, and all I have seen have resembled wolves rather than dogs" (Pierce, M. P., 1885: 426).

Kurz says: "Indian dogs differ very slightly from wolves, howl like them, do not bark, and not infrequently mate with them" (Kurz, R. F., 1937: 239). He refers to the Indian dog as a wolfhound and adds: "Indians make use of their dogs as beasts of burden and as guards, never for hunting, because their baying and howling would betray the huntsman to lurking foes. Moreover, these wolfhounds are too wild to be good rangers and therefore useful on the chase; they hunt out every living thing that they might be able to catch with their teeth. . . . Dogs are by far the best animals to draw sleds over the snow. . . . It is estimated that a dog, traveling at the rate of from 30 to 40 English miles a day, can haul a load weighing 70 pounds, and can carry a load of 50 pounds" (Ibid., pp. 239, 293).

Further quotation may be made from a number of observers who apparently had more direct evidence of the crossing of dogs and wolves. The name "Demi Wolf" was sometimes applied to the offspring produced by the interbreeding of dogs with wolves.

Alexander Henry, while in the vicinity of the Red River, N. Dak., in early January 1801, makes an interesting observation on the interbreeding of Indian dogs and wild wolves. He states: "We had a bitch in heat; she was very troublesome, and the dogs made a terrible noise on her account day and night. I drove them all to the plains; a band of wolves got scent of the bitch, and a furious battle ensued, in which one of our dogs was torn to pieces. This often happens at this season, when the wolves are copulating and our dogs get among them. The female wolves prefer our dogs to their own species, and daily come near the fort to entice the dogs. They often succeed, and if the dogs ever return, they are in a miserable condition, lean and covered with sores. Some of my men have amused themselves by watching their motions in the act of copulating; rushing upon them with an ax or club, when the dog, apprehending no danger, would remain quiet, and the wolf, unable to run off, could be dispatched" (Henry, A., 1897: 166).

Ross Cox, while among the Flathead Indians of the Northwest during the winter of 1812-1813, noted "that the wolves of this district are very large and daring; and were in great numbers in the immediate vicinity of the fort, to which they often approached closely, for the purpose of carrying away the offals. We had a fine dog of mixed breed, whose sire was a native of Newfoundland, and whose dam was a wolf, which had been caught young, and domesticated by Mr. La Rocque, at Lac la Rouge, on the English River. He had many encounters with his maternal tribe, in which he was generally worsted. On observing a wolf near the fort, he darted at it with great courage; if it was a male, he fought hard; but if a female, he either allowed it to retreat harmless, or commenced fondling it. He sometimes was absent for a week or ten days; and on his return, his body and neck appeared gashed with wounds inflicted by the tusks of his male rivals in their amorous encounters in the woods. He was a noble animal, but always appeared more ready to attack a wolf than a lynx" (Cox, R., 1831: 226).

Maximilian, Prince of Wied, noted that "The dogs, whose flesh is eaten by the Sioux, are equally valuable to the Indians. In shape they differ very little from the wolf, and are equally large and strong. Some of them are real wolf colour; others black, white, or spotted with black and white, and differing only by the tail being rather more turned up. Their voice is not a proper barking, but a howl like that of the wolf, and they partly descend from wolves, which approach the Indian huts even in the day time, and mix with the dogs" (Maximilian, Prince of Wied, 1906, vol. 23, p. 310).

R. R. MacFarlane, Chief Factor of the Hudson's Bay Company, in the Mackenzie River district during the middle of the 19th century, states that "Indians have known of instances where both kinds of wolves [one kind being the coyote] and some of their dogs have mated, and they have always found that the resulting offspring were not only prolific, but also better and stronger as beasts of burden" (MacFarlane, R. R., 1905: 694).

Ross says: "A cross between a male wolf and a domestic bitch makes an excellent breed. The offspring are hardy, docile and strong, easily fed, and capable of enduring great fatigue. . . . When there are not too many dogs to drive him off, a male wolf will sometimes have connection with a bitch belonging to the fort" (Ross, B. R., 1861: 10).

In the course of his trip with the Howgate Polar Expedition of 1877-1878 to the Arctic, Kumlien says: "It often happens that the Eskimo dogs and wolves interbreed; the female dog is especially liable to cohabit with a wolf, and the progeny are considered much superior beasts, but are very hard to manage. I have seen Eskimo dogs that corresponded hair for hair with the Arctic wolf" (Kumlien, L., 1879: 52).

Approximately 18 years after General Greely had visited and explored the Arctic, according to MacMillan, "black and white wolves were reported in Grant Land at 82° N. This mixture, never before reported, was undoubtedly due to the fact that when Greely abandoned his home at 81° 40' N. in 1883, he left there quite a number of black dogs. We know that the Eskimo dog does breed with wolves. In fact, I had a half wolf half Eskimo dog in one of my teams."[23]

Theodore Roosevelt offers the following testimony on this subject:

"On another neighboring ranch there is a most ill-favored hybrid, whose mother was a Newfoundland and whose father was a large wolf. It is stoutly built, with erect ears, pointed muzzle, rather short head, short bushy tail, and of brindled color; funnily enough it looks more like a hyena than like either of its parents. It is familiar with people and a good cattle dog, but rather treacherous; it both barks and howls. The parent wolf carried on a long courtship with the Newfoundland. He came round the ranch, regularly and boldly, every night, and she would at once go out to him. In the daylight he would lie hid in the bushes at some little distance. Once or twice his hiding place was discovered and then the men would amuse themselves by setting the Newfoundland on him. She would make at him with great apparent ferocity; but when they were a good way from the men he would turn round and wait for her and they would go romping off together, not to be seen again for several hours" (Roosevelt, T., 1900: 47).

Of later-day interest in wolf-dog hybrids by the Cheyenne Indians, Grinnell, while camped on the Tongue River in Montana, records the buying by the Cheyenne Indians of six hybrid puppies from Chief White Bull in September 1907. These hybrids were the result of a cross between a small hound-like bitch and a wolf (Grinnell, G. B., 1907: 772).

Rowell states that ". . . in the north and west, wolves . . . readily associate and cross with all sorts of dogs. So far as I have observed, all cross breeds between dogs and wolves are dark colored, some of them being as black as any dog, some exactly on the order of silver foxes, some on the order of cross foxes and some merely darker than ordinary wolves, but marked the same as full-blooded wolves. I have seen these cross-bred wolves bred and reared in captivity, and have killed wild ones that were exactly the same as those that were raised from a captive bitch wolf and a mongrel dog" (Rowell, A. C., 1918: 92).

---

[23]Letter from Donald B. MacMillan to E. A. Goldman, dated April 11, 1941. In files of Fish and Wildlife Service.

Plate 43. Second animal from front is full-blooded wolf used in Alaska dog team

Plate 44. Joe LaFlame, of Canada, with a full-blooded wolf broken to sled harness

187

Plate 45. Wolf and coyote used by LaFlame as draught animals for hauling supplies to aeroplane, shown below

Plate 46. As with dogs, wolves also curl their tail between the hind legs. This specimen of red wolf taken in Oklahoma shows the well developed canine teeth of this species

Plate 47. As with dogs, the lips of the wolf can be curled into a snarl in anger

Plate 48. A. Wolf tracks, south shore of Brooks Lake, Katmai National Monument, September 9, 1940. (Photo courtesy Victor H. Cahalane, National Park Service)

B. Wolf tracks, south shore of Brooks Lake, Katmai National Monument, September 9, 1940. Knife in center is 3-5/16 inches long. (Photo courtesy Victor H. Cahalane, National Park Service)

Plate 49. Wolf tracks on river bar, a mixture of mud and sand, Porcupine River, Alaska. 1926

191

Plate 50. Red wolf in black phase, showing pacing gait assumed at times by all wolves

Plate 51. Hybrid from German Shepherd dog and a female wolf. (Photo courtesy of John Gans and Fachschaft für Deutsche Schäferhunde after von Sephantz)

Plate 52. A. Full-blooded wolf type of Eskimo dog, Greenland. (Photo courtesy of Donald B. MacMillan)

B. A wolf killed by Eskimo in employ of Commander Donald B. MacMillan March 29, 1914, near Schei Island, Greenland, 80° 30′ N., 85° W. (Photo courtesy of Donald B. MacMillan)

Plate 53. "Old Three Toes," wolf which mated with collie dog near Thatcher, Colorado

Plate 54. A. Female offspring of wolf-collie dog cross, one year old

Plate 54 (Continued)
B. Male offspring of wolf-collie dog cross, one year old

C. Mounted specimen of male hybrid wolf-collie dog

Plate 55. The cabin of Frank Glaser at Healey, Alaska. Dogs shown are half and quarter breed wolves, the result of crossing a male wolf to a female malamute in the fall of 1923. They were used as a sled team in snow travel

198

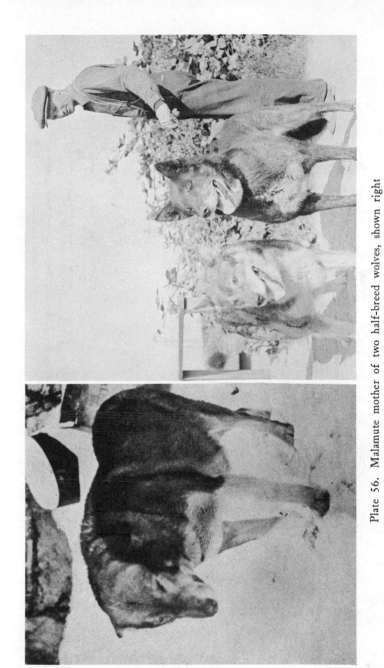

Plate 56. Malamute mother of two half-breed wolves, shown right

199

Plate 57. Front and side views of black wolf hybrid, a female born in March 1927 from a cross between a black male wolf and a quarter-breed female wolf. From the age of six months until her death at twelve years, in the winter of 1939, she led all of the dog teams used by her owner, Frank Glaser, of Fairbanks, Alaska, who stated that she was the most intelligent animal he ever owned. She weighed 125 pounds, and was often used by Glaser in hunting wild wolves, which she would call within rifle range

Plate 58. Quarter-breed wolves owned by Frank Glaser, Fairbanks, Alaska. 1939

Plate 59. Hybrid wolf, one of two half-brother quarter-breed wolves owned and driven in a dog team by Olaus J. Murie. Alaska, 1923

In a recent article on "Eskimo Dogs of the Canadian Arctic," Soper observed that: "In Baffin Island the 'typical' whitish animal may be regarded almost a rarity. Very few are encountered in relation to total population. In one case which came to the writer's attention in Foxe Peninsula, the whitish animal was said by the Eskimos to have had a white Arctic wolf as a sire. Promiscuous mating with wolves, according to native assertions, appears to be a more or less regular, though not a frequent occurrence" (Soper, J. D., 1940: 101).

A case of hybridization not so well known in connection with Biological Survey work in Colorado may well be recounted in fuller detail.

For a number of years wolves had been troublesome in the country north of Thatcher, 40 miles east of Trinidad, in what is locally known as the Butler Pasture, a large, fenced stock-grazing area that extends nearly to Pueblo. Owing to persistent trapping operations, as a result of stock depredations, 32 wolves were taken from this and adjacent ranges, and so far as could be ascertained in 1923, but one wolf remained. This particular wolf was a female, dubbed by the stockmen as "Old Three Toes," because of her being minus two toes on her left front foot, her track thus being easily recognizable.

It was believed that this wolf was the lifelong mate of an old male white wolf (Old Whitey of Bear Springs Mesa) that had been killed a short time previously. After that Three Toes returned to the Apishapa country and behaved as a "lone wolf" in the parlance of the western stockmen. She carried on with much depredating of livestock, particularly on young cattle owned by Monroe Bros. and Henerson, stockmen whose headquarters ranch was located on the Apishapa River, 11 miles northwest of Thatcher.

These ranchmen owned a graded male collie dog that was kept as an all-around ranch dog and pet. During the early evenings in December 1922, Three Toes began to visit the ranch headquarters, and particularly a little knoll that rose to the rear of the main ranch buildings. From this eminence she would utter howl after howl, which were answered by barks of the collie. One night the dog disappeared, but returned in the morning; from then on, however, it made night-time trips away from the ranch. It would sometimes be gone for several days at a time. The stockmen began to suspect that

their collie was being enticed away by this lone female wolf.   Therefore, to keep the dog at home at night, they confined it to a chicken
runway that had a one-by-twelve board all around just above the
ground above which was secured a 6-foot tier of poultry wire.
Locked in this run at night, the collie remained at home for several
consecutive days.   During the time of the dog's confinement in the
runway, however, Three Toes hardly missed a night in appearing on
the knoll at the rear of the ranch buildings, where she continued to
emit howls.   The stockmen attempted to kill her with a rifle, but did
not succeed.   One night the wolf visited the chicken runway confin-
ing the collie and evidence visible the next morning showed that
while the wolf dug a hole under the board holding the wire from the
outside, the collie likewise dug from the inside.   Between them they
eventually made a hole large enough to permit the collie's escape.

The dog never returned to the ranch home, as it had before it was
penned up.   As every known means was being employed to kill this
wolf, poisoning was tried.   Some weeks after the dog had left, it was
found dead near one of the poison stations, having eaten several
poisoned baits.   It had been dead but a few days, and had been gone
from its ranch home about three weeks.   Tracks showed that Three
Toes had been with the dog, but had avoided eating any of the poisoned baits.   Nothing was learned of Three Toes again until the
night of June 8, 1923, when she returned to the Monroe Bros. and
Henerson's ranch with five whelps, and killed six of their young
calves.   She was trapped on June 11 of that year, and the latter
part of that month two of the whelps were roped from a saddle horse
by Roy Spangler, a Fish and Wildlife Service predatory animal
hunter.   These pups, a male and a female, were about 2½ months
old.   By August of that year, Spangler roped another and trapped
two more of the whelps, and so far as could be ascertained, they
completed the litter.

From the size of these young it was evident that mating of their
mother and the collie had taken place at the time she had helped to
dig an escapeway for him.

The male whelp that Spangler first roped was killed in November of that year.   It was predominantly black in color, and showed
the wolf strain particularly.   The female whelp was very reddish
in color, and definitely showed the collie strain, but the typical collie
reddish coloration of its pelt had a somewhat grayish aspect, as much

of the guard hair was tipped with gray. Her muzzle and ears were very wolf-like.

Following the final taking of Three Toes and her whelps, Monroe Bros. and Henerson addressed a letter to the Fish and Wildlife Service on June 30, 1923, from Thatcher, Colo., as follows:

"Enclosed please find pictures of the old gray wolf trapped by Roy Spangler, one of your men. Old Three Toes, as this particular wolf was called, was caught June 11th, in one of the Government traps especially constructed for wolves. Spangler later caught two of her pups.

"Thousands of dollars' worth of calves and sheep have been killed by Old Three Toes and her pack. With her capture this ends the pack of which she was leader. Just a few days prior to her capture Old Three Toes killed six calves for us here on our own ranch on the Apishapa eleven miles west of Thatcher. We hold a private grudge against this old gray wolf as she mated with our pet collie dog, even going so far as to dig him out of a pen. He heard the 'Call of the Wild' and answered it, going off for days at a time, sometimes coming home for a few days. At last he went away for weeks. He was finally poisoned by one of your men, which was a good thing, as a collie hearing the 'Call of the Wild' kills for his young too."

The female wolf-collie whelp was kept alive for some time. At the request of Dr. E. J. Foreman, veterinarian of Trinidad, Colo., I turned this animal over to him for experiments in breeding. Dr. Foreman kept this animal for about two years, during which time it was bred twice with dogs. On February 14, 1927, from Trinidad, Colo., he wrote to the Fish and Wildlife Service as follows:

"Of course you knew that the half breed [wolf] died of rabies on the day she would have whelped her second litter. As she breathed her last I removed from her through the abdomen, six puppies that I hand fed and endeavored to raise. They all died, however, within four days. It was while doing this that I injured my hand and was compelled to take the Pasteur treatment. Her puppy, then a year old that I had kept from her first litter sired by an airedale, I gave the rabies treatment, as it had been running with her up to her death. I kept it until it was a two year old. It was a large powerful built animal with standing ears and a rough gray coat. It was of a kind disposition, but always suspicious and not easy to approach. Roy

Spangler took it out with him to use on the trap line but it never became so that he could make any use of it as it would not fight coyotes. It got away from him finally and he could not catch it. A rancher ran on to it in the night on the road and recognized it by the light of his auto headlights and roped it from the running board. It was returned to me and I kept it for some time. A tourist who saw him in my dog yard took a great fancy to him and wrote me from Cleveland, Ohio, wanting to buy him. I sold to him and shipped to that point after having mated him to a pure bred German Shepard or Police dog here. This litter came in due time. I think there were six pups, all of which were beautiful animals and were all of exceptionally kind and affectionate dispositions. I have one of these animals, a female. It has a very wolfish head, very sharp standing ears with a coarse wolfish coat and wolfish feet and legs. She has the wolf trot and prefers to lie out in the open corral cold days and nights rather than to go inside the shed that is always open to her. She has a very keen nose and is inclined to be a hunter. . . ."

Thus this experiment in hybrid wolf breeding was carried to the third generation from "Old Three Toes," as outlined in the accompanying graph (Fig. 9).

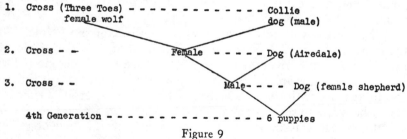

Figure 9
Dr. Foreman's breeding of Three Toes and Monroe Bros. & Henerson's collie dog hybrid

Intentional crossing of wolves with dogs has long been carried on, early instances being cited in the works of Aristotle in the 4th century B. C., and of Pliny (A. D. 23-79) who speak of the Gauls' tying their female dogs to trees for the purpose of breeding them to wolves.

American instances are recorded in the following quotations:

Ash, commenting on the Esquimaux dog, said:

"Valuable information as to the relationship between wolves and these Esquimaux dogs is given by Captain Sir E. Parry, R. N., and Sir J. Franklin. Captain Parry states that the Esquimaux bitches would stray from the ship and return to the ship pregnant to wolves; and Sir J. Franklin informs us that the Indians attached to one of his expeditions, upon destroying a female wolf, carried away three of her whelps to improve their breed of dogs; and that in March the female grey wolves frequently entice the domesticated dogs from the huts" (Ash, E. C., 1927: 139).

Richardson, in his *Fauna Boreali-Americana*, states: "In Captain Parry's and Captain Franklin's narratives, instances are recorded of the female wolves associating with the domestic dog, and were informed that the Indians endeavor to improve their sledge dogs by crossing the breed with wolves. The resemblance between the northern wolves and the domestic dog of the Indians is so great that the size and strength of the wolf seems to be the only difference. I have more than once mistaken a band of wolves for the dogs of a party of Indians, and the howl of the animals of both species is prolonged so exactly in the same key that even the practiced ear of an Indian fails at times to discriminate them" (Richardson, J., 1829: 64).

In his discourse on mental powers with respect to reasoning among lower animals, Darwin refers to the Arctic wolves as "the parent stock of the Esquimau dog"—an opinion shared by many of the latter-day naturalists who have studied the two animals in their polar habitat (Darwin, C., 1874: 85).

Freuchen records with respect to the Eskimo dog and wolf interbreeding, ". . . . it is no uncommon occurrence for a bitch in heat to be tied up where wolves have their run and frequently they are offspring of such mating. These become good sledge dogs as a rule, fierce but faithful" (Freuchen, P., 1935b: 122).

The apparent willingness of an Arctic dog to associate with and countenance the presence of a wild female wolf, even to sharing a portion of its kennel, is attested to by a remarkable case in kind, reported by Gregg, which took place during December of 1942. In this instance a dog which, through its nightly howling, at Fort Selkirk, Canada, had attracted a female wolf on the loose with a trap on one foot. In approaching the dog's kennel it is apparent that the wolf had made friends with the dog in spite of its impediment;

shared one-half the kennel, and only when accidentally discovered by the owner of the dog was it by force driven out of the kennel, away from its new found friend, and eventually shot. While the first attempt was made to drive this wolf out of the kennel, the dog "stood in front of the other entrance, as though to protect his friend. . . ." (Gregg, John, 1943: 31.)

While in Alaska during the summer of 1938, we were informed that because of its endurance, enabling it to overtake almost any animal, the Eskimos will at times cross their dogs with the wolf to give them strength.

R. E. Bateman, District Agent of the Fish and Wildlife Service, experimenting in crossing wolves and dogs, mated a purebred greyhound with a female wolf. The whelps developed into strong animals, but were more vicious and more difficult for a stranger to make friends with than a purebred wolf. A female, from this crossing, was then mated with a purebred foxhound, the resulting cross producing a litter of five that were more docile and had the drooping ears of the hound and were of divers colors.

This female wolf was crossed once more with a purebred police dog. This mating produced a litter of whelps that would pass for pure-bred police dogs, but were of bad dispositions. A male of this litter was then bred to a purebred female police dog: the quarter-breed whelps were more docile, more easily handled, and of a friendly disposition. As in the female wolf-police dog male cross, the color of the pups was more uniform than in the progeny of the female wolf-male greyhound crosses.

Frank Glaser, one of the Fish and Wildlife Service predatory animal hunters in Alaska, had a valuable team of four wolf-dog crossbreeds, which he obtained by crossing a male wolf with a female Eskimo dog. These crossbreeds were large, strong, powerfully built, and very wolf-like in appearance.

In summary, it is evident that the plains Indians of North America had many dogs of varying degrees of wolf blood. Undoubtedly this mixing of Indian dogs and wolves had prevailed for many years prior to the advent of the white man. That it continued afterward is also obvious from the early records. Those wolves taken while young and brought to the Indian camps, which did not prove docile were no doubt dispatched. Experiments with wolves held in captivity have shown that in each litter there are two or three whelps that show tameness early; the remainder are absolutely intractable and often die if one attempts to train them.

Experimentation has likewise tended to show that the offspring of unions between male dogs and female wolves appear to inherit all the wild characteristics of the female mother and seem to be more savage and difficult to control in captivity than are pureblood wolves. There are exceptions to this rule, however, which make likely the possibility that in time a number of sufficiently docile and tractable cross-breeds, that could be tolerated in any Indian camp, might be obtained by elimination. Furthermore, as the plains Indians were versed in the technique of castration, which operation they learned from the Spaniards and are known to have often performed it on some of their dogs, it is likely that docility desired of a hybrid dog for eventual use as a draught animal may have been partially attained in this manner for several centuries after learning the technique from the Spaniards. The early records make it apparent that generally speaking the so-called Indian dog of the 18th and 19th centuries was far from being a gentle creature like the average, modern-day house dog.

Continued experiments in breeding dogs and wolves tend to show that the quarter-breed is the best animal descending from the wolf-dog cross. The crossing of a female tame wolf with a male collie, and the mating in turn of the resultant male half-breeds with a female shepherd dog, have produced in some instances not only exceptionally amenable, but super-intelligent animals as well.

The ease with which the Indian dog-wolf mating took place had apparently so controlled the physical characteristics as to change completely the Indian dog as descended from possible Asiatic ancestors. Hence, by the time Coronado (Whipple, A. W., 1856: 112), David Thompson, and Alexander Henry, and other explorers, observed these dogs, we find that the creature that was in earlier times a true dog, as evidenced by remains found in Indian middens and caves, had practically ceased to exist. Crossing, especially by nomadic Indians, is believed to have been purposely done to obtain a large dog for use as a draught or pack animal. Now this wolf-like animal has completely disappeared with the removal of the Indians to reservations and the change in their mode of living. There has occurred a large diminution in the once overabundant Indian dog population, and the wolves that might have been used for crossing have been eliminated. To see the wolf dogs now we must visit Alaska or other northern countries where sledge dogs are much used and wolves still exist.

FOOD OF THE WOLF

Throughout the centuries that the wolf has been known to man, a diversity of accounts of its presumed food habits have been given. Many of these, as might be expected, are far from being based upon facts. Bewick related that "once the wolves have tasted human blood, they always give it the preference." Also, he stated that "Wolves are capable of bearing want of food for a long time. To allay their hunger, they will sometimes fill their stomachs with mud" (Bewick, T., 1804: 314).

These allegations and others, as that wolves subsisted on their own dung when normal foods were scarce; that they became fattest with the full of the moon, and grew thinner with the waning of that satellite; that they could sustain life by sucking their right front paws; and that they drank only the blood of their prey, were among earlier beliefs, some of which persist to the present day.

Most of the reliable information on the food of the wolf has been derived from field observations. The accounts of these are so voluminous as to require much classification and considerable space.

It is thought best, therefore, to present at once the comparatively small amount of recorded information that rests upon the examination of stomach contents.

RESULTS OF STOMACH ANALYSES

Laboratory

In 72 stomachs of the red wolf, 70 of which came from Texas and 2 from Oklahoma, food habit analyses by the Fish and Wildlife Service show that the chief food items were rabbits, domestic stock, rodents, and carrion, importance being in the order named. The domestic stock included sheep, horses, cows, goats, calves, and hogs; although in the case of the last-named item there may be included wild razor-back hogs. The rodents devoured included the cotton rat, pocket mouse, pocket gopher, deer mouse, wood rat, and kangaroo rat. One stomach contained the remains of a skunk. Birds are found to occur infrequently in the diet of the red wolf; they included a quail, duck, and pigeon. A female red wolf killed near Cisco, Tex., in July 1932 had a stomach content containing 12 percent eggs of the scaled quail about ready to hatch. The rest of the food was rabbit (*Sylvilagus*), 75 percent; carrion, horse or cow, 5 percent; grasshoppers, 5 percent; and long ceram-horned beetle, 3 percent. The invertebrates consumed included crayfishes and a variety of insects, as grasshoppers, beetles, ants, and dragonflies. The red wolf occasionally makes a meal on vegetable food, as mesquite beans, cactus fruits, and persimmons.

In another collection of 31 red wolf stomachs, of which 18 were taken in Texas, 9 in Oklahoma, 3 in Louisiana, and 1 in Arkansas, cottontails (*Sylvilagus* spp.) and jack rabbits (*Lepus* sp.) were the most important food items, being found in 19 stomachs and amounting to 56 percent of the total food, while carrion, consisting mostly of old cow and deer hide, was present in 8 stomachs and comprised 18 percent. Deer remains occurred in 4 stomachs and formed about 1/10th of the food. Grasshoppers (*Acrididae*) composed about 7 percent. Turkey (*Meleagris* sp.), moles (*Scalopus* sp.), a cotton rat (*Sigmodon* sp.), a sparrow (*Passerherbulus* sp.), and persimmons (*Diospyros* sp.) were found in lesser amounts. Traces of a pine mouse (*Pitymys* sp.), a pinacate bug (*Eleodes* sp.), a ground beetle (*Carabidae*), and a spider (*Araneida*) also were present.

Three stomachs taken in Louisiana all contained carrion; in two of these it was bait taken at the trap and formed the entire stomach contents. The third stomach, in addition to carrion (old dried cow hide) amounted to 60 percent, contained 40 percent rabbit (*Sylvilagus* sp.) and a trace of pine mouse (*Pitymys* sp.).

The specimen collected in Arkansas contained 100 per cent rabbit fur, as well as woody trap debris.

In 8 gray wolf stomachs, 6 of which came from Michigan and 2 from Minnesota, the percentages of food by bulk were: Carrion, 38 percent; remains of deer, 25; rabbit, 13; red-backed mouse, 3; great horned owl, 5; red-winged blackbird, 3; and grasshoppers, 13 percent.

Ten wolves captured in Minnesota during the years 1936 and 1939 showed the following in laboratory analysis:

Condition of stomach	Percentage animal matter	Condition
Very full	100	Deer bones, flesh and hair, 100 percent. Size and nature of bones indicated a fawn deer.
¼ full	100	Deer hair and little flesh, 100 percent.
½ full	100	Deer hair and old flesh (carrion), 100 percent.
Full	100	Deer hair and leg bones (old) carrion, 100 percent.
Full	100	Deer hair of belly, legs, leg bone joint and hoof (carrion), 100 percent.
Very full		Deer, 100 percent.
¼ full	100	Old flesh (carrion) unidentifiable, 100 percent.
Full	100	A few deer hairs and mass of tallow-like carrion fat, 100 percent
Less ¼ full	100	1 red-backed mouse (Clethrionomys gapperi), 100 percent.
¼ full	100	Deer hair and fat, 100 percent.

In 10 stomachs of wolves from extreme southwestern New Mexico and adjacent Arizona, remains of domestic livestock made up 50 percent, consisting of cow, 20 percent; calf, 20; swine, 10; in addition to carrion, 20; deer, 20; and rabbit, 10 percent.

FIELD

During the five fiscal years, 1918-22, field examinations of 3,346 wolf stomachs were made. These wolves were captured mainly in steel traps in the majority of cases by the use of scents, and chiefly represent the wolves then occurring west of the 100th meridian, but including some also from eastern Texas, Oklahoma, Arkansas, and Michigan (see Table 2).

The personnel making the field analysis were exceptionally versed in wolf-lore, well acquainted with the animal life about them, and good local naturalists who kept reliable field notes. As Harper says of the native hunters of the Okefenokee Swamp of southeastern Georgia whose "long field experience and rare powers of observation have made the contributions [to natural history] . . . of extraordinary value" (Harper, F., 1927: 260), so may a similar statement be made of the government wolf hunters of the western range states.

Table 3 gives a summary of the field analyses. The figures are arranged by months in order to bring out seasonal variations in feeding habits. They record the occurrence of individual kinds of food; for instance, in January beef was reported as present 27 times and pork 8 times. A given stomach might have contained two or more different kinds of food, i.e., the stomach might have contained both beef and pork, in which case it was tabulated once in the beef column

TABLE 2.—*Wolves taken by the Fish and Wildlife Service and its Cooperators during the fiscal years 1918 to 1922*

State	1918	1919	1920	1921	1922	Total
Arizona	31	39	64	37	51	222
Arkansas	---	---	17	57	82	156
California	---	---	---	1	---	1
Colorado	11	9	22	17	26	85
Idaho	17	16	20	25	19	97
Michigan	---	---	---	---	61	61
Montana	69	48	48	52	42	259
Nevada	---	---	---	---	---	---
New Mexico	92	74	67	56	28	317
North Dakota	---	---	---	1	---	1
Oklahoma	---	34	39	18	29	120
Oregon	2	2	1	5	1	11
South Dakota	1	15	3	10	---	29
Texas	516	242	198	283	240	1,479
Utah	55	17	18	28	1	119
Washington	---	---	---	---	---	---
Wyoming	55	88	26	104	116	389
Total	849	584	523	694	696	3,346

TABLE 3.—*Stomach contents of wolves according to field analyses*

Food	Jan.	Feb.	Mar.	Apr.	May	June	July	Aug.	Sept.	Oct.	Nov.	Dec.	Total
Beef	27	15	14	27	26	20	35	37	20	46	22	14	303
Horse	1	4	2	4	1	3	12	5	1		1	1	35
Sheep or goat	9		3	1	2	3	9	5	6	10	12	6	66
Pork	8	7	1	4	3		1	1	3	3	7	14	52
Poultry							1						1
Grouse											1		1
Waterfowl													
Other birds													
Deer	1	1			1	1	4	1	1			1	11
Elk								1	1				2
Antelope								3	1				4
Rabbit	1			1						4	2	5	13
Ground squirrel													
Prairie dog													
Chipmunk													
Ground hog (Marmot)													
Mouse or rat				1									1
Bait			2	1	1		1		2	3	3	2	15
Carrion	1	1	10	5			10	2	1	2	1		33
Insects or worms							2	1					3
Fish, frogs, or reptiles						1							1
Grass, sticks, or berries					2		2	1		3			8
Total	48	28	22	49	41	28	77	56	36	72	48	44	549

and once under pork. This makes it clear that the totals do not represent the exact number of stomachs examined, but rather the number of times that each of the food items was found in the stomachs. This likewise applies to the column showing the grand totals where, for instance, beef is recorded 303 times and pork 52 times.

GENERAL OBSERVATIONS

VEGETABLE MATTER

Like the coyote, the wolf is not strictly carnivorous.

On the Red River near the Rocky Mountains, members of Long's expedition noted on August 16, 1820:

"The grapes and plums, so abundant in this portion of the country, are eaten by turkies and black bears, and the plums by wolves, as we conclude from observing plumstones in the excrement of these animals" (Long, S. H., and James, E., 1823, vol. 2, p. 127).

The gray wolf is reported as eating watermelons and as doing much damage by picking out only the ripe fruits. Years ago it was recorded that the wolf, during the berry season in British Columbia, feeds almost wholly on berries (Anonymous, 1887: 403).

OFFAL AND CARRION

As true of most of the larger North American carnivores, wolves take a wide range of foods. In this they closely parallel the coyote. However, the trait of carrion-eating characteristic of the coyote is not manifested to the same degree by the wolf. It seems that the wolf does not relish either putrid or dried animal remains to the extent that the coyote does. During the prime years of its life, at least, the wolf lives on its own kills in preference to carrion.

Furthermore, the wolf seldom returns to its kill to feed after the first meal. In fact, when several wolves attack and kill prey of moderate size as calves, yearlings, and wild game of similar age, they leave very little of the victim that is edible. A family of five wolves that attacked a two-year old heifer west of La Junta, Colo., in the fall of 1922, left nothing but some hair and bones, and there was fighting over some of the bones.

After devouring part of a large animal, wolves sometimes drag the bony remains to a concealed spot and bury it, but seldom do they return to the place.

Exceptions to the rule is the wolves' utilization of their own kill in preference to carrion occur; when the animals experience extreme hunger; in the case of old wolves with badly worn teeth and thus handicapped in making kills; and during the denning season, when wolves feeding whelps return to feed from a dead carcass, which, generally, however, is of their own killing.

An early Virginia writer, Colonel William Byrd, recorded being followed by wolves in North Carolina, stating that "These beasts of prey kept pretty much upon our tracks, being tempted by the garbage of the creatures we killed every day; for which we were serenaded with their shrill pipes almost every night" (Byrd, W., 1901: 130).

As to the eating of carrion by a Florida wolf, Townshend records:

"We came across no four-footed game, except a solitary grey wolf, which in company with some hundreds of the disgusting but useful turkey-buzzards, was gorging himself on the rotting carcass of a cow" (Townshend, F. T., 1875: 53).

In the earlier days on the western plains, wolves were observed to clean up the offal and other unused portions of the fresh carcasses of the buffalo, antelope, and other game killed and abandoned by hunters. In country heavily infested with wolves this occurred almost immediately upon the departure of the hunters, when the meat was fresh, and often still warm.

During the peak of wolf abundance, a hunter could rarely leave his killed game unprotected, for wolves would quickly clean up the carcass. Consequently, portions of the hunter's clothing, the blown-up bladder of a buffalo arranged so that it would flap in the wind, etc., were left with the carcass as a scaring device to keep wolves away.

Ferris records a concentration of wolves on a single buffalo bull which hunters of his party had wounded but failed to kill because of ensuing nightfall. He narrates: ". . . . early in the morning we departed, hungry as bears, in the direction of the bull we wounded and left last evening. As we approached, the presence of thirty or forty wolves, proved to us, that some of our balls had been well directed; yet we could not find meat enough for breakfast, that was not torn or mangled by them. However, our appetites were so well sharpened, that we were not long in cooking some half picked bones, which were quickly fastened to our saddle cords, preparatory to going in quest of firewood. In the meantime the wolves, and the multitude of ravens, remained a few yards off, politely waiting for us to serve ourselves; hinting however, by an occasional growl, or scream, for us to be as expeditious as possible. As soon as we departed, they simultaneously sprang or flew to the carcase, with such intimacy, that ravens were seen picking at a bone, in the mouth of a wolf" (Ferris, W. A., 1940: 165).

Similar actions were recorded for Alberta by the missionary John McDougall, who in 1865 stated:

"I have never seen grey wolves so numerous as now. When we are skinning and cutting up the buffalo they form a circle around us and wait impatiently until we load the meat into the Red River carts. Then as we move away, they rush in to fight over the offal. Many wild fights are witnessed but ammunition is scarce and we refrain from shooting" (McGowan, D., 1936: 28).

Charles Sheldon, while hunting in Alaska, also experienced this trait in wolves, when on returning to a caribou bull killed by him and left over night, the wolves had completely eaten the animal, even to "stripping the velvet of the horn" (Sheldon, C., 1930: 165).

Rarely wolves have been known to despoil human graves a short time after burial, but the despoliation appeared to be accomplished during a single visit to the grave, the animals seldom returning.

Certain early European writings alleged that the wolf was particularly fond of human flesh. Instances were reported of wolves following armies and gathering in numbers upon the field of battle; after the battle they devoured such dead bodies as were left exposed or but negligently interred.

During the earlier days of western settlement, the eating of dead humans by wolves seems to have occurred whenever bodies were available. During the outbreak of cholera among the traveling emigrants in 1849-50-51, accounts of the epidemic state that "more than 500 fresh graves on the south side of Platte between the Missouri and Fort Laramie" were visible along the trail. Brigham Young admonished the migrating Mormons to avoid this part of the road while traveling west for fear of the epidemic. Narrators of the Mormon trek at the time state: "Scarcely a grave that had not been robbed of its contents by wolves, and the bones of its occupant lay bleaching on the prairie." At the same time those who perished on the trail while trekking to try their fortunes at gold digging in California were reported "disinterred by wolves."

And as was the case with smallpox among the Indians reported by Edward Umfreville, so "The cholera had been very fatal among the Indians. Mr. Babbitt reported passing, in one place, ten deserted lodges with many dead Indians lying about and the bodies torn and half eaten by wolves" (Little, J. A., 1890: 203, 211, 212, 223, 231, 243).

On visiting the scene of the massacre by the Cayuse Indians of Dr. Marcus Whitman and the inmates of his mission in the Walla Walla Valley during the early spring of 1848, Col. Gilliam, with two companies of his command, found a scene of desolation, "for strewn over the ground were the mutilated remains of the massacre which had been disinterred by wolves" (Bancroft, H. H., 1882-90, vol. 29, p. 716).

While at Bent's Fort in southern Colorado in September 1846, Lt. J. W. Abert commented on the ghoulishness of wolves on human graves. He states in his entry for September 4, 1846, as follows: "In the evening another volunteer died, and was buried. They were obliged to cover the graves with prickly pears, or rocks, to prevent the wolves from tearing the bodies out of the ground. At some places along the Arkansas, the Indians place their corpses in trees, out of reach of the wolf, and the whites would do well to adopt the same plan" (Abert, J. W., 1848: 426).

Again, on his return journey east from Santa Fe to Fort Leavenworth, Lt. Abert, in commenting on his passing the newly-made grave of one C. P. Gibson, states: "The ravenous wolves had already been at work on the grave, but the frozen ground had proved too much for them" (Ibid., p. 529).

Theodore Talbot, who was a member of Col. Fremont's expedition of 1843, states in his journal:

"Mon. 31st [July 1843] . . . passed a small vault built of sticks and mud, in which a Sioux had been buried; the wolves, however, had succeeded in undermining the structure and the head and other portions of the disinterred corpse lay scattered around" (Talbot, T., 1939: 30). This note was made while near old Fort Laramie, Wyo., a good many hundred miles north of the territory where Lt. Abert noticed similar action by wolves.

Kurz relates that

"Indians on the prairie do not put their dead underground; in the first place they have no implements suitable for digging graves and, second, the bodies would have to be buried very deep to be secure from wolves" (Kurz, R. F., 1937: 76).

Lt. George F. Emmons, a member of Commander Charles Wilkes' exploring party and who, in the summer of 1841, led an overland expedition southward from Fort Vancouver into California, observed while en route through the Willamette Valley that here "The graves [of the Indians] are covered with boards in order to prevent the wolves from disinterring the bodies" (Wilkes, C., 1845: vol. 5, p. 234).

While driving a band of sheep overland from Keokuk, Iowa, to San Diego, Calif., during the summer of 1853, Dr. Thomas Flint in his diary for Sunday, June 19th, when he was on the trail west of Council Bluffs, notes:

"Camped for the Sabbath and a good rest. The ground had been dug up about there and I picked up the bones of a human foot and other parts of a skeleton which wolves had cleaned of the flesh" (Flint, T., 1924: 79).

LIVING PREY

Wildlife

The buffalo, antelope, elk, deer, caribou, and moose, in the order named, appear to have been the preferred foods of the wolf. These game animals were the largest of its prey until the time that they were materially reduced in numbers and were replaced by domestic livestock, such as cattle, sheep, and horses, a more complete discussion of which will be found in another chapter.

Bartlett's discussion of the wolf problem in Canada put more emphasis on the killing of game in the national parks than upon the depredations upon cattle (Bartlett, G. W., 1909: 240).

With respect to the Arctic wolf, Criddle reports:

"The Arctic wolf is of importance in reducing northern game animals upon which the natives of those regions largely depend and it should, therefore, be reduced in numbers as much as possible" (Criddle, N., 1925: 8).

Of all the big game animals on the Great Plains that were contemporary with the North American wolves in their greatest abundance, the buffalo was probably their most important prey. To what extent wolves were a numerical check on the buffalo at the time the

Plate 60. A cross between a dog and a red wolf, taken near Ellington, southwest Reynolds County, Missouri

Plate 61. Female gray wolf nursing a litter of whelps, the result of a cross with a hound dog. Hall County, Texas, 1912

Plate 62. Dall sheep on Dean Creek, east of Mt. McKinley Park—these animals are favorite food of wolves

Plate 63. Salmon pulled out of stream and partially eaten by wolves, September 1941, near Anchor Pass, southeastern Alaska. (Photo courtesy *Alaska Sportsman*, Ketchikan, Alaska)

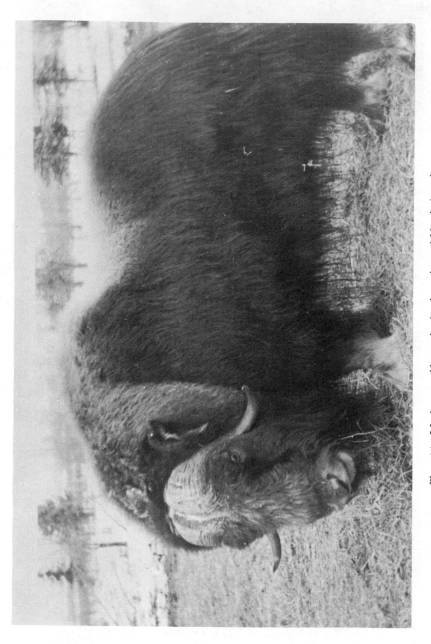

Plate 64. Musk-ox, wolf prey in Arctic regions of North America

Plate 65. Manner of attack of buffalo wolves on their regular prey. (*Canis lupus nubilus*)

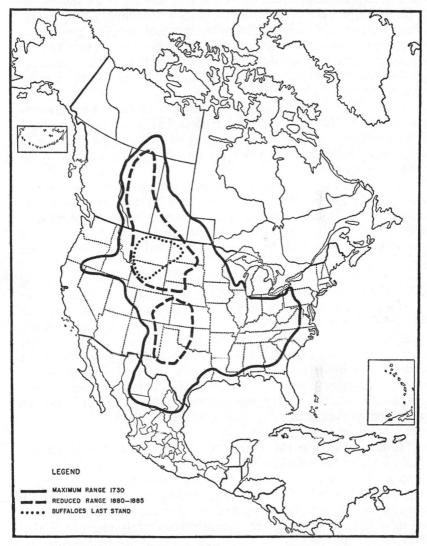

LEGEND

— MAXIMUM RANGE 1730
- - - REDUCED RANGE 1880–1885
• • • • BUFFALOES LAST STAND

Figure 10. Maximum buffalo range in North America according to the literature. The wolf ranged over all the buffalo's habitat

white man first encountered them will probably never be known, but J. A. Allen, writing of them in 1876, said: "Formerly they everywhere harassed the buffalo, destroying many of the young, and even worrying and finally killing, and devouring the aged, feeble and the wounded. Thirty years since wolves, next to the Indians, were the greatest scourge of the buffaloes, and had no small degree of influence in effecting their decrease" (Allen, J. A., 1876e: 67).

It was Vernon Bailey's opinion, while on a study of the mammals of the Yellowstone National Park in 1915, that the lack of appreciable increase of the mountain herd of buffalo [the wild herd] which were native to the mountains was due to the wolf depredations. He states:

". . . . I found big wolves common, feeding their young on elk, and probably also on buffaloes, as they were right in the midst of the buffalo range. This probably accounted for the slow rate of increase of the herd, for after the wolves were trapped out of this section the following winter by Donald Stevenson the herd began to make more rapid increase" (Bailey, V., 1939: 17).

Garretson, in his outstanding volume on *The American Bison,* brands the plains wolf as an outstanding enemy of the buffalo, saying:

"One of the worst, most persistent and ever-present enemies the buffalo had to contend with was the wolves which followed the herds in great packs, destroying many calves and the aged and feeble members that were usually relegated to the rear and outskirts of the herd. Early hunters and explorers often spoke of finding an old solitary bull surrounded by a pack of hungry wolves that fought and tormented him until, finally, through weakness and loss of blood, he succumbed to their attacks" (Garretson, M. S., 1938: 72).

He goes on to quote:

"Catlin [who], in his 'North American Indians,' gives an account of one of these attacks he had witnessed in the upper Missouri country. He says, '. . . . I have several times come across such a gang of these animals [wolves] surrounding an old wounded bull where, it would seem, from appearances, that they had been for several days in attendance, and at intervals desperately engaged in the effort to take his life. But a short time since, as one of my hunting companions and myself were returning to our encampment with our horses loaded with meat, we discovered at a distance a huge bull, encircled with a gang of white wolves; we rode up as near as we

could without driving them away, and being within pistol shot, we
had a remarkably good view, where I sat for a few moments and
made a sketch in my note-book (plate CXIV); after which we rode
up and gave the signal for them to disperse, which they all instantly
did, withdrawing themselves to a distance of fifty or sixty rods, when
we found to our great surprise that the animal had made great resistance, his eyes being entirely eaten out of his head, the gristle of
his nose mostly gone, his tongue half eaten off, and the skin and
flesh of his legs torn almost literally into strings. In this tattered
condition, the poor old veteran stood bracing up in the midst of his
devourers, who had ceased hostilities for a few minutes to enjoy a
sort of parley, recovering strength and preparing to resume the
attack in a few moments again. In this group, some were reclining
to gain breath, whilst others were sneaking about licking their chops
in anxiety for renewal of the attacks; and others less lucky had been
crushed to death by the feet or the horns of the bull.' " (Ibid.)

Describing the moving of a herd of buffaloes from one feeding
range to another, referred to by some writers as "buffalo migrations,"
the late Charles Aubrey, an old buffalo hunter, gives an interesting
account of wolf tactics in the presence of a large buffalo herd. He
recalls that "The bulls were on the flanks and made up the rear
guard of the column. The old cows were in the van and within the
flank next to the bulls, while the young stock were distributed generally through the centers. With the herd marched also the beasts
of prey that fed on the buffalo. Of these the chief gathering were
the great buffalo wolves, each the very incarnation of destruction.
With his powerful jaws of shark-teeth, his wonderful muscular
strength, the tireless endurance of a compact body, the speed of a
grey hound, and the cunning of man . . . . The gray wolf must eat,
and that of the best in the land, for he is no scavenger of the plains.

"The Indian was not the wolf's superior as an expert hunter,
and in concert of action in the attack upon prey, the buffalo, much as
the cowboy cuts out from the herd the animal he has chosen, so the
wolves selected their victim. With deceptive sleepy gait, they closed
in on the flanks of the marching host; when the leader had picked out
his victim—preferably a young cow—he at once changed his gait to
a quick pace, and his followers alert to imitate his movements, at
once closed in. When he saw that they were well in hand, he gave
the signal for attack, a deep hoarse roar, and a bounding rush fol-

lowed. The terrified cow was cut out of the herd, and once out, the powerful leader made a quick sidelong spring and hamstrung the prey, and the others as powerful fastened on her flanks. She was thrown down by the sheer force of the impact, and at once the band was upon her, tearing her to pieces, and scattering her flesh about while she was yet in the throes of death. Or perhaps some bull alert to meet an attack would charge the onrushing wolves, with a lunge and toss, the leader was thrown high in the air, his carcass taking one direction, the entrails another. The band repulsed, shrunk back, to renew the attack elsewhere" (Aubrey, C., 1908: 216).

The number of wolves that sometimes engaged in running down a single buffalo is told by General Fremont when on his first expedition. On July 4, 1842, shortly after starting up the south fork of the Platte River, he observed: "While we were at breakfast, a buffalo calf broke through the camp, followed by a couple of wolves. In its fright, it had probably mistaken us for a band of buffalo. The wolves were obliged to make a circuit around the camp,—so that the calf got a little the start, and strained every nerve to reach a large herd [of buffalo] at the foot of the hills, about two miles distant; but the first one, and then another, and another wolf joined in the chase, until its pursuers amounted to twenty or thirty, and they ran him down before he could reach his friends. There were a few bulls near the place, and one of them attacked the wolves and tried to rescue him; but was driven off immediately, and the little animal fell an easy prey, half devoured before he was dead" (Fremont, J. C., 1887: 91).

Horace Greeley, in noting the wolf and its habits, said: "He delights to lurk around the outskirts of a herd of buffalo, keeping out of sight and unsuspected in the ravines and creek timber, so far as possible; and wo to the unlucky calf that strays (which he seldom does) outside of the exterior line of defense formed by the bulls. If very large and hungry, the gray wolf will sometimes manage to cut a cow off from the herd, and interposing between her and her companions, detain or drive her further away, until she is beyond the hope of rescue, when her doom is sealed" (Greeley, H., 1860: 93).

Mead, in recounting his plains experiences, believed that "Each wolf killed a dozen buffalo a year, many of them calves; but they, with equal facility, could kill the strongest bull, and did, whenever appetite and circumstances made it most convenient" (Mead, J. R., 1899: 280).

From the common practice of wolves loitering on the flanks of large herds of buffalo, the name "buffalo wolf" was colloquially applied to the plains wolf. Hardly a pioneer who journeyed westward and who left any written account of his observations, failed to mention this animal in connection with the vast herds of buffalo. A number of these men have left vivid accounts of how wolves attacked the buffalo, and of how the bisons behaved in warding off wolf attacks. Gregg says:

"Many curious tales are told of the wiles and expedients practiced by these animals [wolves] to secure their prey. Some assert that they collect in companies and chase a buffalo by turns, till he is fatigued, when they join and soon despatch him; others, that, as the buffalo runs with the tongue out, they snap at it in the chase till it is torn off, which preventing him from eating, he is reduced by starvation, and soon overpowered; others, that, while running they gnaw and lacerate legs and hamstrings till they disable him, and then he is killed by the gang. . . . I myself have seen them with muscles of the thighs cruelly mangled . . . . a consequence no doubt of some of these attacks. . . ." (Gregg, Josiah, 1905: 327).

Webb, writing of the Santa Fe Trail and its wolves, relates:

"On one occasion [while] coming down the river [probably the Arkansas] on making a turn around a knoll, we came suddenly upon a buffalo apparently dead, as there were some half a dozen wolves feasting upon him. And as we approached one wolf backed out from the carcass full half his length and ran off. On examination [we found that] the carcass was still warm, and life not extinct as was proved by an occasional kick" (Webb, J. J., 1931: 163).

This is in keeping with the statements of various western explorers, trappers, and hunters, as well as of stockmen, to the effect that "The gray wolf literally eats its prey alive."

During the year 1859, while in company with some surveyors who were encamped on the Saline River near the site of present-day Salina, Kans., Laurens Hawn observed wolves attacking a buffalo. His description vividly portrays the teamwork practiced by the wolves in obtaining their prey. There were "about a dozen brown and white wolves arrayed in a circle around one of the largest buffalos I had ever seen. The attack, cool and deliberate, displayed wonderful sagacity. They did not rush upon the buffalo in a mass, but calmly waiting until his heels were towards them, several of them sprang like darts from the circle and fastened to his flanks or hams and as the buffalo turned to confront these others would seize upon the vulnerable parts. . . .

"The principal appoint of attack seemed to be the hamstrings of the buffalo, which they knew if they could cut, their victim would be helpless. Nor did they seem the least hurried about it. Some tired by their violent efforts withdrew a short distance, and sat down on their haunches with their tongues lolling out to watch and rest.

"In a few moments they returned to the attack and others dropped out to rest. Thus by this system of relief, they kept up the contest with a certainty of overcoming their foe however strong" (Hawn, L., 1878: 190). Hawn watched this attack until the buffalo finally was killed.

Hornaday, among the observers during the heyday of the buffalo, stated that "Buffalo emasculated by wolves are often found on the prairies, where they grow to an immense size; the skin of the buffalo ox is recognized by the shortness of the wool and by its large dimensions" (Hornaday, W. T., 1886-87, 1889: 408, 426, 433).

Colonel Inman records an observation of wolf attack on a buffalo bull in the year 1866:

". . . . we saw standing below us in the valley an old buffalo bull, the very picture of despair. Surrounding him were seven gray wolves in the act of challenging him to mortal combat. The poor beast, undoubtedly realizing the hopelessness of his situation, had determined to die game. His great shaggy head, filled with burrs, was lowered to the ground as he confronted his would-be executioners; his tongue, black and parched, lolled out of his mouth, and he gave utterance at intervals to a suppressed roar.

"The wolves were sitting on their haunches in a semicircle immediately in front of the tortured beast, and every time that the fear-stricken buffalo gave vent to his hoarsely modulated groan, the wolves howled in concert in most mournful cadence.

"After contemplating his antagonists for a few moments, the bull made a dash at the nearest wolf, tumbling him howling over the silent prairie; but while this diversion was going on in front, the remainder of the pack started for his hind legs to hamstring him. Upon this the poor beast turned to the point of attack, only to receive a repetition of it in the same vulnerable place by the wolves, who had as quickly turned also and fastened themselves on his heels again. His hind quarters now streamed with blood, and he began to show signs of great physical weakness. He did not dare to lie down; that would have been instantly fatal. By this time he had killed three of the wolves, or so maimed them that they were entirely out of the fight.

"At this juncture the suffering animal was mercifully shot, and the wolves allowed to batten on his thin and tough carcass" (Inman, H., 1917: 189).

From these accounts it is evident that the buffaloes defended themselves courageously as individuals. They also had cooperative defenses, one of which left a mark on the landscape. On this point Inman states:

"There was, however, a stranger and more wonderful spectacle to be seen every recurring spring during the reign of the buffalo, soon after the grass had started. There were circles trodden bare on the Plains, thousands—yes, millions—of them, which the early travelers, who did not divine their cause, called 'fairy rings.' From the first of April until the middle of May was the wet season; you could depend upon its recurrence almost as certainly as on the sun and moon rising at the proper time. This was also the calving period of the buffalo, as they, unlike our domestic animals, only rutted during a single month; consequently the cows all calved during a certain time; this was the wet month, and as there were a great many gray wolves that roamed singly or in immense packs over the whole prairie region, the bulls, in their regular beats, kept guard over the cows while in the act of parturition, and drove the wolves away, walking in a ring around the females at a short distance, and thus forming the circles" (Ibid., p. 187).

Talbot, who was with Fremont in 1843, gives a similar description of these rings by recording as follows:

"We frequently noticed circles or rather rings varying from 10 to 50 feet in diameter, the grass of which is ranker than the surrounding sward; sometimes the belt is composed of the plant called Lamb's quarters intermixed with large mushrooms; many conjectures have been framed with regard to this curious vegetation. Happening in a buffalo country, it has been connected with them, and I have heard the following solution. The herds of buffalo are always followed by immense packs of hungry wolves ever on the alert to seize some veteran straggler or young calf unable to offer resistance to their fierce attacks. It is a fact well known to hunters, that at night the cows form a compact circle with their heads outward in the inside of which they place all their calves, thus offering an effectual barrier against the wolves, who did they not take this precaution, would succeed under cover of night in carrying off all the young ones. The cows in rolling during the day gather great quantities of seeds, etc., in their heavy fleeces; now it is supposed that in tramping continually in one spot all night they shake off these seeds, and thus spring up the 'Magical Circles of the Prairie'" Talbot, T., 1931: 14).

Elizabeth B. Custer, wife of General Custer, first became acquainted with the "circles" shortly after accompanying her husband to the Far West. She records: "The circles, perhaps fifteen feet in circumference, that I saw for the first time, were one of the mysteries of that strange land. When officers [of the cavalry] told me that the rut was made by the buffalo mother's walking round and round to protect her newly born and sleeping calf from the wolves at night, I listened only to smile incredulously, with the look peculiar to an innocent who desires to convince the narrator of fables that he has met one person of superior intuition who cannot be gulled. . . . In time, however, I found that it was true, and I never came across these without a sentiment of deepest sympathy for the anxious mother whose vigilance kept up the ceaseless tramping during the long night" (Custer, E. B., 1890: 182).

Certain fungi as a result of their own growth habits form "fairy rings," so probably not all of those observed by early plains crossers were connected with the buffaloes (Shantz, H. L., and Piemeisel, R. L., 1917: 191).

However, the circle formation was readily adopted as a mode of defense by numbers of buffaloes large enough to form the figure.

Hawn says of the circular rings found on the prairies: "I had often noticed on the prairies circular spaces covered with a growth of weed, in or near the center of which were usually buffalo skulls, and pondered much over their probable origin. . . . Each of these spots witnessed the death struggle of a buffalo brought to be [sic] by wolves. . . . Wolves though always seen moving around a herd of buffalo like faithful shepherds, are in reality singling out victims to slaughter" (Hawn, L., 1878: 190).

Allen, quoting Dodge, records a little group of six to eight buffalo bulls that had been observed " 'standing in a close circle with their heads outward, while in a concentric circle at some twelve or fifteen paces distant sat licking their chops in impatient expectancy, at least a dozen large gray wolves, excepting man, the most dangerous enemy of the buffalo. . . . the central controlling figure of this mass was a poor little calf, so newly born as scarcely to be able to walk' " (Allen, J. A., 1876e: 58). It appears that these buffalo bulls would break their knot, but still in a compact mass, and start toward the main herd at a trot. "After going fifty or a hundred yards the calf lay down. The bulls disposed themselves in a circle as before, and the wolves along on each flank of their retreating supper, sat down and licked their chops again. This was repeated again and again." Darkness prevented seeing the "finale, but apparently the bulls safely conveyed the baby buffalo to the main herd." (Ibid.)

Antelopes, another of the plains animals, believed to have numbered between thirty and forty millions at the peak of their abundance, were preyed upon by wolves almost to the same extent as were the buffaloes.

Bryant noted while on the Sweetwater River in Wyoming during July 1846 that "The deer and antelope are compelled to frequently shelter themselves from the attack of these animals [wolves] under the strong protection of buffalos and you sometimes see herds of buffalos and antelopes mingle in grazing together" (Bryant, E., 1885: 132).

Curiosity is one of the antelope's outstanding traits, and the wolves took advantage of it, according to Grinnell:

"We may believe also some of the stories told in the old books to the effect that sometimes the prairies wolves enticed the antelope to come close to them by hiding, and showing parts of the body in such a way that the antelope could not tell what they were.

"This practice may possibly have been useful to the wolves in bringing the antelope near to them so that they might get a good start in those races by which they so frequently ran down the antelope by relays" (Grinnell, G. B., 1911: 600).

Wolf teamwork as a means of obtaining a meal was observed by the writer in company with a hunting companion in an attempted wolf attack on antelopes in the Butler Pasture area southeast of Pueblo, Colo. While we were riding from the extreme south end of this large pasture, a herd of antelopes was sighted. To their right appeared two animals which we at first took to be coyotes. There was a dry arroyo to the left, in which we were able to drop and keep out of sight of both the antelopes and the supposed coyotes. The wind was in our favor and we apparently had not been seen, except by the antelopes. In a short time we realized that the other two animals were wolves, and we watched their movements, still unseen. Soon both wolves sprawled low on their bellies and lay watching the antelopes. Then what appeared to be a female got up and trotted slowly back in the direction from which they had come. In so doing, however, it made a slight change in direction, veering toward the antelopes, which by this time were intently watching this moving wolf. This gave the larger wolf its opportunity so it headed in full speed for the dry arroyo where we were concealed. This was too good a chance to miss so we shot at the wolf coming head-on towards us. However, our anxiety to bring rifles into action only succeeded in changing the course of the wolf, which, having not only seen us but at the same time gotten a taste of the dust raised by our misplaced bullets, wheeled, dashed off in the direction of the other wolf, and vanished over the cap-rock. From the entire performance it was obvious that the wolf which ran toward us was endeavoring to gain the dry arroyo for use as a stalking ground to enable it to get within striking distance above the antelopes by following to the head of the wash. The movements of the female wolf before we shot showed, by the gradual circling movement, that the two anticipated joining each other above the antelopes, with the male nearer to the herd and the female on the outside flank. It seemed evident to us that the female in back-tracking was to draw the antelopes' attention until her mate could get within striking distance of the herd.

While it is known that the large and powerful elk was preyed upon by wolves, quotable references to the fact appear to be few. We quote the veteran Biological Survey employe, E. A. Preble, and from Brallier, an Oregon pioneer. Preble observed that:

"The damage inflicted by them on both horses and cattle is serious, and, as they seem to be able to kill elk at will, they must destroy a large number. They kill stock and game on the hills immediately about the settlements, both summer and winter, frequently two or more attacking the prey. They usually hamstring the elk, and after felling them make a meal from the eyes, the udder, and other choice parts, and seldom return to the carcass, preferring a fresh victim" (Preble, E. A., 1911: 20).

During the early fall of 1887, Frank Ellis Brallier saw a number of wolves depredating on elk near the headwaters of the south fork of the Necanicum River about 16 miles southeast of Seaside, Oreg., in the heart of the coast range.

Teamwork by wolves of the eastern United States in hunting and killing deer was observed and recorded by Meshach Browning, an early woodsman of Maryland, born in 1781, and who spent 40-odd years as a hunter and trapper in northwestern Maryland. Browning notes: "When they are able to chase the deer, they all hunt together until they start up one, when they chase it in company till they become tired. Then one keeps the deer all the time at full speed, while the others watch; and if the deer makes a turn, they strike in before the one that is pushing the deer, and continue the chase, while the others watch the wind for the scent. The deer thus pursued alternately by a fresh wolf, soon becomes tired, and takes to some stream to escape its pursuers. As soon as they find the deer takes to the water, they separate, some going on one side of the stream, and some on the other; and as they can run faster on land than the deer can travel through the water, they soon tire it, and it becomes an easy prey to its ravenous pursuers, which in a few moments tear it in fragments, and devour every morsel of it" (Browning, M., 1928: 372).

Cox describes the driving of deer by wolves in the Northwest:

"The wolves almost rival the Indians in their manner of attacking the deer. When impelled by hunger, they proceed in a band to the plains in quest of food. Having traced the direction which a herd have taken, they form themselves into a horse-shoe line, the extreme points of which they keep open on the grand ravine. After some cautious maneuvering they succeed in turning the progress of the deer in that direction. This object effected, they begin to concentrate their ranks, and ultimately hem in their victims in such a manner as to leave no choice but that of being dashed to pieces down the steep and rocky sides of the ravine or falling a prey to the fangs of their merciless pursuers" (Cox, R., 1831: vol. 2, p. 41).

An account of deer hunting by wolves in Newfoundland is of more than passing interest. An anonymous record tells us that "Their cunning in capturing deer is sometimes surprising." Here, while the deer during the winter season were feeding in the marshes surrounded by belts of deep woods, "The ravenous wolves secrete themselves in the deer paths and lie in wait until one or more wolves get around to windward of the deer and drive them through the paths where some of them fall an easy prey to the secreted wolves" (Anonymous, 1875: 390).

Through the kindness and interest of Leo J. Smits, formerly of the National Wildlife Federation, we are privileged to quote an observation made by J. L. MacGregor, in charge of woods operations at the time for the Charcoal Iron Company in the upper peninsula of Michigan: "It was in 1926 in the month of March, Dan Parker, one of our foremen and I were looking over timber near Pictured Rocks about two miles from camp. We walked on crust, but when we got to where we were going to pick up our line we stopped to put on our snowshoes. I saw tracks—looked like horses had been walking, breaking through the crust. There were 7 or 8 wolves. I stopped and heard the wolves howling, in little short howls. The wind was blowing from the north and I was going west and the wolves were north of me. There was quite a steep hill between me and where I heard the wolves.

"I went up the hill to attempt to see them. The scrub, hardwood and brush is quite thick in that place. Just as I got to the top of the hill I saw wolves driving a doe from north to south and as she came out into a clear place other wolves that had been waiting in a ring rushed out and got her. Wolves came from every side of the deer. It was just like a football game. I hollered and they let go, but they had already cut the deer's throat and ripped out her entrails in less than half a minute. The deer was about a 2 year old and had twin fawns in her. The wolves got out of sight before you could wink your eyes. . . . This was ten o'clock in the morning in broad daylight. Deer were quite thick around camp that winter and this bunch of wolves was heard of a number of times."

In the spring of 1907 Vernon Bailey found that the wolves had become exceedingly numerous and so destructive to the deer occurring in the upper peninsula of Michigan, extreme northern Wisconsin and Minnesota as "to threaten to exterminate the deer." He found that the food for the deer "was abundant and the deer would have wintered in good condition if unmolested, but while the snow was soft they were entirely at the mercy of the wolves." In the survey he conducted throughout the many winter "deer yards" of these sections he found "dead deer . . . . in almost every yard visited, some partly eaten, others torn and mangled. Large bucks, as well as does and fawns, had been killed, many more than could be eaten at the time" (Bailey, V., 1907b: 1).

An instance of marked destruction of deer by wolves was observed by a field investigator of the Biological Survey in southern Marquette County, Mich., during the latter part of March, 1922. Evidence had been found that a number of wolves were working in the deer yards of that section, and in the course of the investigation wolves were heard howling one night. Observations were made the following morning while on snowshoes, and the tracks of a single wolf were soon located. The trail led a short distance to a swamp, where several deer were yarding over a small area. The wolf had been joined here by two others, and the round of destruction began. The remains of four freshly-killed deer were found on an area of about three acres. Subsequent investigations disclosed that in the few weeks preceding this time, probably a hundred deer, in yards scattered over an area of about 3 square miles in that locality, were killed by these wolves. This number does not include many unborn fawns. The wolves also worked through other yarding sections, as they spent only a part of their time in the area described.

According to Shiras, "these animals are the most destructive foe of the white-tail deer in the upper lake region." He recounts that during 1907 the wolves of this region destroyed "nearly all the deer within a ten-mile radius of Whitefish Lake. From the carcasses found it was estimated that over two thousand deer were killed in this limited area. A deer's fear of a wolf is only equalled by a wolf's fear of man" (Shiras, G., 3rd, 1921: 133).

During the late winter and early spring of 1941, a large wolf was reported committing heavy depredations between the north and west sides of the Tamarac Migratory Waterfowl Refuge located in Becker County, Minn., at the headwaters of the Ottertail River. This animal was observed to have a cruising range of approximately 20 miles, and is credited with the late winter and early spring killing of 139 sheep and 18 deer. Included in its deer prey that had been killed were 2 does with unborn fawns and a large buck with horns.

The fondness of the wolf for deer gave to it the name of "deer-wolf," and this was generally applied in the New England area.

A considerable proportion of the big game killed by wolves in the northern parts of their range in North America is caribou. As to this important game species Hewitt reported in 1916 that ". . . . the wolves also are responsible for a large decrease in the number of caribou. That is a matter which should be taken up by the Department of the Interior, with a view to getting the Eskimos to kill the wolves and assist them in the export of wolf skins" (Hewitt, C. G., 1916: 35).

In 1940, Clarke estimated that there were 36,000 wolves in the area of the Canadian barren grounds, home of the caribou (approximately 600,000 square miles) and credits them with killing 400,000 of these animals yearly. He was of the opinion that the caribou furnished the bulk of the wolf's food for seven months of the year. He believed that ". . . . it is unlikely, taking disease into consideration, that the number of wolves stays at a level. It probably has its ups and downs, and the degree of caribou predation likewise would fluctuate" (Clarke, C. H. D., 1940: 109).

Speaking of the wolf in the Mackenzie River district, Ross states: "Its migrations are dependent on the movements of the reindeer, its principal food. This kind of wolf lives in considerable bands, which unite in hunting parties to run down or surround the deer, driving them over cliffs, or into rivers or lakes as is most convenient" (Ross, B. R., 1861: 9).

On the occurrence of the wolf on Southampton Island, Hudson Bay, Sutton and Hamilton wrote that "Its present range is apparently more or less determined by the range of the caribou," and further that "The wolf apparently finds it difficult to subsist on a fare of smaller animals, such as hares, and since there are no muskoxen anywhere about the Island, the caribou are practically the sole item of food" (Sutton, G. M., and Hamilton, W. J., Jr., 1932: 33).

At the present time, it appears that the caribou is to the wolf of the North and particularly of Alaska in the way of food, what the buffalo was in earlier years to the Plains wolf. Wherever caribou congregate in the northern area, wolves gather. The following occurrence supports this statement.

While on an airplane patrol of the Alaska-Yukon boundary areas, Agents Sam White and Clarence Rhode, of the Alaska Game Commission, were afforded a splendid opportunity during the latter part of March 1939 to observe wolves and caribou. While flying over

Plate 66. Wolves of the Arctic stalking their usual prey, the caribou

and along Kandik River, northwest of Dawson, Yukon Territory, they reported that the "whole area was alive with caribou and wolves. More than 15 wolves were spotted within a few minutes' travel, and we made several attempts to fly low and pick some of them off from the air (with a rifle), but without results. . . . These wolves were in excellent condition, traveling along within less than 100 yards of bands of caribou. Several kills were noted from the air, and we were impressed by the absolute lack of fear evidenced by the caribou, even when the wolves were in plain sight of them. We noted that the wolves followed the caribou trails and made easy going where the caribou had broken trail. A large proportion of black wolves were noted" (White, S. O., and Rhode, C. J., 1939: 5).

Apparently there was no evidence here that these wolves were picking off the weak and immature caribou whenever hunger forced them to obtain a new food supply. In this instance, some of the choicest caribou had already fallen prey to these wolves that were migrating with the large herd.

In his quest for musk ox in the vicinity of Fort Reliance, Canada, during 1898, Charles Jessie Jones, best known as "Buffalo Jones," speaking of the Arctic wolf noticed in these parts, says "While, of course, wolves cannot catch a caribou in a fair race, yet when they have exhausted all other means of obtaining food, when actual starvation compels them, and not before, they start after a caribou, chasing it day and night without ceasing, until, completely worn out, the poor creature succumbs to its ravenous enemy. It does not make the slightest difference how many herds of its fellows the chased caribou runs through, the wolves keep on its track, paying no attention to anything but the capture of their prey, which event they know is just ahead" (Inman, H., 1899a: 375).

Mrs. Dixon and Mrs. Edmunds witnessed a wolf-caribou chase which is described as follows:

"On July 11 (1932) near Little Stony Creek, Mrs. Dixon and Mrs. Edmunds watched a timber wolf chase a young caribou. At 5 o'clock in the afternoon a yearling caribou came running and panting down the little valley. It was hard pressed by a large black timber wolf. When first seen the wolf was about 60 yards behind the caribou and gaining rapidly on it. Each time that my wife and Mrs. Edmunds shouted, the wolf would stop for a moment, but the caribou kept steadily on down the winding valley. The wolf continued to gain by 'cutting across lots,' so to speak, while the caribou followed the winding stream. When last seen the caribou was spent and staggering and the wolf was closing the gap." (Dixon, J. S., 1938: 166.)

In the winter of 1933-34, Frank Glaser reported an observation of a wolf killing a large cow caribou on Savage Creek, Alaska. With the weather at 58° below zero, this wolf had run the caribou to the point where she tired and had turned to fight. The wolf grabbed her by the nose, threw her, and then ripped her throat open. Approximately a half-hour later Glaser was able to shoot and kill this wolf (Glaser, F., 1934).

The Alaska Game Commission reported for the year July 1, 1937, to June 30, 1938:

"On the whole it is believed that the caribou herds have decreased during the past ten years. The difference is not marked and can be laid presumably to (1) increase in numbers of timber wolves, (2) development of highways, and (3) increased shooting" (Alaska Game Commission: 1938: 14).

David Thompson, writing of the wolves of northern Canada, states:

"Two of these Wolves are a full match of either the moose or Rein Deer [caribou], the only two species found in this region. When they start one of these Deer, they are left far behind, but the Deer must stop to feed, they then come up to, and again start the Deer, and thus continue until the animal, harassed for want of food and rest, becomes weak and turns to bay, in this state ready to defend itself with its powerful feet. The wolves cautiously approach, one going close in front to threaten attack, yet keeping out of reach of its fore feet. The other wolf goes behind, keeping a little on one side to be out of the direct stroke of the hind feet; and watching, gives a sharp bite to cut the back sinew of one of the hind legs; this brings on a smart stroke of the hind legs of the Deer, but the wolf is on one side, and repeats his bites until the back sinew of the other hind leg is soon cut, the Deer falls down and becomes the easy prey of the Wolves; the tongue and the bowels are the first to be devoured. From the teeth of the old Wolves being sharp pointed, it does not appear they gnaw the bones, but only clean them of the flesh, and in this state we find the bones" (Thompson, D., 1916: 75).

One of the early Arctic explorers, Captain George Back, ob-

Plate 67. Circle of defense formed by the musk-oxen in warding off attack from an enemy. Some authorities believe this defense formation was evolved through contact with wolves

239

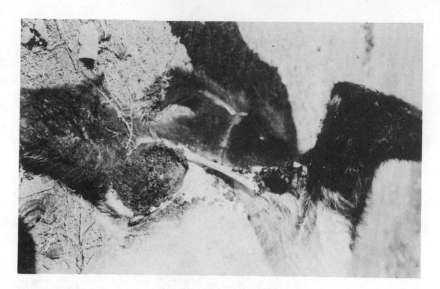

Plate 68. A. A young steer, showing under portions mutilated and tail snapped off. New Mexico

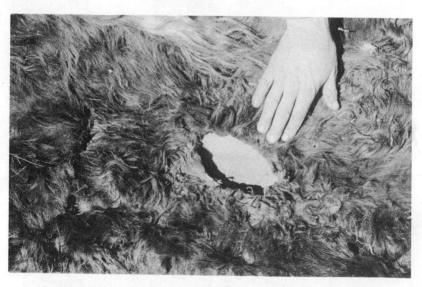

B. Side view of cow showing deep slash in side from wolf bitings

Plate 69. A two-year-old steer bobtailed by wolves in South Dakota, T. H. Richardson Ranch, October 1920

Plate 70. Three registered Hereford cows killed by wolves on the Frank Krentz Ranch, 35 miles east of Douglas, Arizona, May 1, 1934

241

Plate 71. The remains of a two-year-old steer after attack by a family of five wolves, near Thatcher, Colorado, October 1922

Plate 72. The skin of the "Sycan" wolf of southern Oregon. It is estimated that this wolf caused losses of probably $15,000 worth of livestock

served teamwork between two wolves chasing a caribou along a stream containing large rapids near Artillery Lake in northern Canada. The wolves were on opposite banks of the stream, where one lay in wait in the hope that the other wolf, engaged in strenuous pursuit of the caribou on the opposite stream bank, would put it across a ford below one of the main rapids. Back's presence near the scene of action caused the wolves to slink slowly away, or else the animal would undoubtedly have been driven to the wolf awaiting in ambush (Back, G., 1836: 128).

According to Freuchen:

"The Eskimos relate that the wolf's method of hunting caribou often follows certain tactics which the Eskimos themselves have copied. A wolf or two begin to howl, with the result that the caribou herd becomes scared and runs away. Immediately afterwards other wolves give tongue from the opposite side, and from other directions in turn, all in accordance with a pre-determined plan to drive the caribou along a certain route. When there are not wolves enough for this they make up for lack of numbers by running round the herd howling and thus guiding it as they want it" (Freuchen, P., 1935b: 122).

Clarence Birdseye, while doing field work in Labrador during the fall of 1912, records an interesting observation that came to his attention, while at Ticorlack on the north shore of Hamilton Inlet, about 60 miles outside of Rigolet, with respect to three wolves attacking a large male caribou. As observed, the caribou came at full speed and topped a small hill, where it lay down. "Shortly afterwards, a large wolf came in sight and circled around back of the deer, which got to its feet. Another wolf came up and circled to the opposite side. Then a third and smaller one came along, and, while the stag's attention was engaged by the first two wolves, slipped in between its legs from behind and secured a hold high up on its throat. The stag immediately rose to its hind feet, lifting the wolf clear of the ground, and then tried to loosen the wolf's hold by banging it against the ground. At this point one of the men [who had observed this melee] fired and killed the deer, and the three wolves escaped. Jerry said that if they had not shot the deer, the wolf's throat hold would surely have proved fatal."[24]

---

[24]Letter dated April 15, 1941 from Clarence Birdseye, Gloucester, Mass., to E. A. Goldman. In files of the Fish and Wildlife Service.

According to the late famous surgeon Grenfell of Labrador, "The wolf will track a deer day after day till he captures it. Again and again our trappers have seen evidence of the indefatigable zeal and indomitable resolution of a single wolf in following a caribou herd; and observers all agree that each time the track spells the shadow of death. A settler told me the story of a doe caribou which, in the early summer of 1906, he saw brought to bay on the middle of a pond by a single wolf. The ice had thrawed out, and it was necessary for the wolf to swim off to get at the deer. The wolf, after long hesitation in taking to the water, which it apparently hates, swam off, fought the caribou, and though repeatedly knocked down by her fore hoofs, at last pulled her down. . . ." (Grenfell, W. T., and others: 1913: 279).

The wolf's ability to attack and kill the moose is attested by Mac-Farlane in an observation made between Forts Liard and Nelson in the Mackenzie River district. Holding the opinion that the wolves of the Far North "kill not a few moose in this region," he states that we ". . . . came across a big patch of hard-packed snow on the Liard River where a large buck moose had evidently been surrounded and no doubt overpowered, after a most gallant fight for life, by perhaps a score of ferocious and cowardly wolves. A few well-picked bones and the skull were the only relics left. At a short distance, however, we perceived a full-grown gray wolf, which was at once shot. It had one of its hind legs shattered by a kick from the moose, which so disabled it that it could scarcely crawl. Had its companions not been fully gorged they would doubtless have fallen upon and eaten it too" (MacFarlane, R. R., 1905: 692).

The stomach of a black wolf collected in Alaska contained only moose remains, including leg hair and foot bones.

Not much is to be found relative to wolf depredations on mountain sheep, or to indicate that the wolf was a definite factor in their elimination from certain western areas. However, as the bighorn was formerly an inhabitant of the high dry plains on the western edge of the prairies, and thus in one of the main habitats of the wolf, it no doubt was at times preyed upon by the wolf.

Rowell, while trapping in the high country between Green River and Wind River, Wyo. [date not given], observed many wolves. Of their forays, he noted that:

"These wolves passed some hundreds of mountain sheep on every trip across the range they made that winter, and while they tried to surprise them and catch them on the flats the sheep always discovered the wolves in time to beat them to the rocks. So far as I could learn they did not get a sheep that winter. . . . One winter, when there came a wet snow with an east wind, all of the timberline flats were covered with frozen snow . . ; the mountain sheep were starved, weak and forced to leave the high country. . . . I found where wolves had denned in a canyon and killed many mountain sheep, with so little trouble that there were piles of sheep bones— and sheep bones only—at the den. Along the hillside above the den I found the heads of five rams and that without making any search other than merely looking up and down the hill as I passed along" (Rowell, A. C., 1918: 92).

In Alaska, however, mountain sheep have been reported in the normal wolf diet. Regarding the stomach contents of a 140-pound young male wolf killed in Mount McKinley Park in October 1938, near Teklanika River flat, Joseph S. Dixon, well-known mammalogist, states:

"The animal was fat and in good condition. The stomach was about half full of the hair, skin and leg bones of a Dall sheep. These bones had been bitten into small sections about one inch in length by the strong carnassial, or chopping teeth, of the wolf. As near as I could determine, the remains of a Dall sheep constituted approximately 99 percent of the stomach contents of this animal. From the disposition of the fresh blood and from the condition of the blood vessels, it was evident that the sheep represented a fresh kill. A very slight trace of caribou hairs was found in the intestines, but this clearly represented the remains of a former meal."

Charles Sheldon, in his study of sheep in the Alaskan range, holds the opinion that mountain sheep "while feeding in exposed places are much wilder than sheep in similar positions on the inside ranges"—probably because wolves are present on the outside range, while they rarely penetrate far inside (Sheldon, C., 1930: 130).

He further reports: "A wolf frightens sheep more than any other animal, principally for the reason that he continually chases them. Other enemies capture them by stealth!" [Sheldon records supporting observations near Polychrome Mountain, Alaska, during March of 1908.] This method of pursuit by the wolf is "by dashing down on the sheep from above." Sheldon observed nine records, plainly written on the snow, of two wolves having thus tried to catch sheep. (Ibid., p. 315.)

The extent to which northern wolves prey on mountain sheep in Alaska is not definitely known at this time. Some of the resident Alaskans familiar with outdoor conditions feel that it is of serious proportions. Others hold the opposite view. A wolf-sheep survey now in progress by the National Park Service will undoubtedly throw more light on this matter, particularly as far as Mount McKinley National Park is concerned. Very few authentic observations have been made to date. Dixon, one of the few who have studied the mountain sheep-wolf relationship, reported that

"At times during the winter when food is scarce the adult rams wander out on the rolling hills in search of food and fall prey to the wolves. In hunting Dall sheep the wolf usually gets above the band of sheep and waits until some of them wander away from the safety of cliffs or other rugged broken ground. Then the wolf creeps forward and makes a quick dash down the slope, endeavoring to catch one of the sheep before it can reach the safety of nearby crags. Sheldon (1930, p. 315) records nine instances where wolves hunted sheep in this manner and he says 'I saw no signs of any other methods of hunting.' The wolves, Sheldon observed, apparently had not been very successful, for he goes on to say, 'There was no evidence that a wolf had caught a sheep. . . .'

"On June 1, 1932, I examined and photographed a large Dall ram which, judging from tooth marks made in both flesh and bones, indicated that the ram had been caught unawares while in the open and had been captured and killed by a timber wolf. The carcass was well preserved. The teeth of this ram showed that he was in full prime and vigor and the annual growth rings on his horns indicated that he was about 8 years old.

"It has been our experience at Mount McKinley that wolves normally capture Dall sheep by hidden approach and surprise rather than by means of a long chase. Ranger Lee Swisher, in a letter of Nov. 21, 1932, states: 'From my observations of mountain sheep and caribou killed by wolves during the winter I have yet to find a case where the wolves chased their victims more than 200 yards. Last winter I compared the distance of leaps made by an old ram and of the wolf that caught him. For a short distance their leaps were approximately the same (16 feet). When the old ram struck a patch of smooth ice he lost out in a few jumps.'" (Dixon, J. S., 1938: 166).

The musk ox is another northern animal that is attacked by wolves; it forms circles in defense just as the buffaloes were recorded as doing. As a result of his Arctic studies Clarke concluded that "The musk-ox circle formation was plainly evolved through contact with wolves, and is an admirable defense against them" (Clarke, C. H. D., 1940: 82).

Continuing with predominantly vegetarian prey it is evident from Freuchen's statement that the snowshoe hare is so important a food for the wolf as to serve at times as a buffer (or predation-absorbing) species for the caribou. Freuchen mentions meeting "a missionary . . . [at] Chesterfield Inlet, . . . who was very interested in the question [of rabbits, following an abundant year of lemmings] [and who] thought that the rabbit was of direct importance to the stock of caribou in the high arctic lands, as a superabundance of rabbits would keep the wolves down in the woodlands; should a rabbit year follow upon a lemming year, the caribou can count upon peace for a considerable period, and this means that their numbers increase proportionately. He believed he had definitely observed this once or twice" (Freuchen, P., 1935b: 93).

The same writer has commented on a similar buffer action occurring as a result of wolves turning to lemmings as a principal diet in the years of their great abundance.

Writing of the Hudson Bay region, he states:

"In years when lemmings are plentiful the wolves live on them exclusively and seem to prefer them to anything else. Remains of lemmings may almost always be found in the stomachs and excrement of wolves, but in 'lemming years,' they are practically stuffed with them. As a consequence, they do not howl when they have had enough to eat, the caribou therefore are not disturbed and become less shy and nervous, which again means that they become fatter and it is easier for the Eskimos to get within shooting distance" (Ibid., p. 123).

While in the interior of Alaska during 1938, the writer learned that in so-called "lemming years" wolves make a substantial part of their diet of these animals.

In Labrador, according to Cabot, a meadow mouse (*Microtus enixus*) served as the main food supply of wolves during the peak mouse year of 1905. In fact, all predators, including birds, mammals, and even fishes, as trout, joined in living almost exclusively on mice. The effect so far as the wolves were concerned seemed to be a very noticeable diminution in depredation on the caribou during the period 1904-05, when the mouse peak was developing (Cabot, W. B., 1920: 292).

At about the same time Denny noted a similar occurrence which affected the deer and moose because of a shrinkage in the rabbit population. In this observation made while canoeing down the Finlay River, headed for the main Peace River below Fort Grahame, in British Columbia, he found "The wolves were very bold in the mountains . . . . and they were hungry. . . . This year [1905] the rabbits had disappeared, so they had to kill moose and deer, both of which were hard to catch. I got up often during the night to put wood on the fire to scare them off." (Denny, C., 1943: 11.)

The beaver, another vegetarian, does not escape the wolf, despite its aquatic habits.

Snyder reports that "Mr. Campbell (William H., a buyer of furs and a resident of Lowbush on the Canadian National Railroad in Ontario since 1906) . . . . believes the wolves to be very destructive to beaver, preying upon them when they are active at night" (Snyder, L. L., 1928: 10).

N. E. Lane, of Ketchikan, Alaska, reporting on the examination of 15 wolf stomachs taken during trapping operations on the islands of southeastern Alaska, states: "I examined the stomachs of all animals caught and found that *over half* of them contained the fur and bones of beaver.

"I am now convinced that the wolves are responsible for the shortage of beaver in this vicinity."[25]

Warren also lists the wolf among the enemies of the beaver, and states that carnivores that are enemies of this fur-bearer "Kill beavers by surprising them when on land, or perhaps occasionally when in very shallow water" (Warren, E. R., 1927: 146).

---

[25]Letter dated May 1, 1937, Ketchikan, Alaska, by N. E. Lane to Alaska Game Commission, Juneau, Alaska. In files of Fish and Wildlife Service, Washington, D. C.

Passing to the consideration of carnivores (flesh-eaters) in the prey of the wolf, we take up first the bear, which is a sort of transitional form depending upon vegetable as well as animal foods. One Alaskan record shows that even so powerful an animal as the bear does not escape the wolf.

Ligon, during his reconnaissance made of the deer-wolf problem on the islands of southeastern Alaska, found that the

". . . . Time required in pulling down an animal seems to be of little concern to normal wolves when their killing urge and savage energy goad them to attack an animal many times their own size. One of the island trappers, while on his rounds, found mute evidence of a fatal conflict between three wolves and a black bear. On the snow one could read the story. The wolves encountered the bear in an open muskeg and were shrewd enough to avoid letting their captive reach the timber where escape wouild have been possible. The tracks of the wolves and bear, blood-stained snow and scattered hair disclosed the fierceness of the ensuing battle. The remains of the unfortunate bruin, scattered about on the edge of the muskeg, proclaimed the victors in the conflict. A few days before, wolves, and probably the same band, had completely eaten the carcass of a small bear which this same trapper had killed" . . . (Ligon, J. S., 1926: 395).

As regards the Arctic fox, Freuchen states: ". . . undoubtedly its one real enemy is the wolf, which can easily overtake a fox on the run; as a consequence the fox makes for its hole the moment it hears a wolf howl" (Freuchen, P., 1935b: 136).

Colonel Roosevelt, as a stockman and rancher in the Middle West, was afforded many opportunities to observe the food of the wolf. He later wrote with regard to foxes: "They are easily able to overtake them in a fair chase, and kill numbers. If the fox can get into the underbrush, however, he can dodge around much faster than the wolf, and so escape pursuit. Sometimes one wolf will try to put a fox out of a cover while another waits outside to snap him up (Roosevelt, T., 1893: 395).

When the wolf turns to the coyote as prey, it is attacking near kin, but according to Roosevelt, it does that very thing.

"Where there are no domestic animals, wolves feed on almost anything from a mouse to an elk. They are redoubted enemies of foxes. . . . Moreover, the wolf kills even closer kinsfolk than the fox.

When pressed by hunger it will undoubtedly sometimes seize a coyote, tear it in pieces and devour it" . . . (Roosevelt, T., 1893: 395.

The summary of my field observations together with those of twelve old time "western wolfers" show no affection between wolves and coyotes. The latter often followed maurauding wolves, subsisting from abandoned wolf prey. Further, coyotes always held to a safe distance from wolves on the same range.

Numerous observations have been recorded to the effect that wolves under certain conditions will attack and devour their own kind. Early immigrants saw instances of such cannibalism when, following the wounding of a wolf by a rifle ball, companions pounced upon the injured one and soon killed it. Then, apparently, a free-for-all scramble ensued in the eating of the victim.

Wolves will breed in captivity but it is not an uncommon practice for them, when confined, to kill their young (Sclater, P. L., 1868: 623).

In view of the strong affection shown by wolves for their young in the wild, this cannibalism in captivity may be due to a deficiency in diet.

Game birds also are readily eaten by wolves. Whiting records the capture of prairie chickens under unusual conditions. While scouting the country northwest of Fort Riley, Kans., three days after the blizzard of December 3, 1856, he found that "high winds had swept the snow from the burned prairie and piled it in immense drifts in the ravines and sheltered spots. . . . Along the leeward crest of a ridge, where the grass was unburned, a great flock of prairie chickens had taken refuge from the storm and had been covered by the snow. For fifty rods the wolves had burrowed after them, and the blood and feathers bore evidence of the great slaughter and the feast they had enjoyed" (Whiting, A. B., 1912: 119).

In the summer of 1942, Palmer found evidence of a wolf taking a Canada goose near the head of McDonald Bay in the Stikine River area of southeastern Alaska (Palmer, L. J., 1942: 17).

And Swarth records for the same region: "The trampled grass showed (around a wolf's marsh home) here and there bunches of feathers or a few crushed bones of ducks, and geese; waterfowl were evidently a staple food" (Swarth, H. S., 1922: 161).

The varied nature of the food of wolves is exemplified by a

statement in the early eighties by Dr. C. Hart Merriam who says of the wolves then existing in the Adirondack region of New York: "They have hard work to get a living here and are always gaunt and hungry. They can not catch deer with any certainty except in deep snow, and are, therefore, during the greater part of the year, forced to subsist upon skunks, hares, mice, frogs, carrion, and such other foods as they are able to procure. They have been known to kill sheep, pigs, calves, and young colts" (Merriam, C. M., 1882: 42).

Dr. Merriam does not mention fishes but even these somewhat inaccessible creatures do not entirely escape the wolves.

While in the Hudson Bay region during the summer of 1900, E. A. Preble reports being informed that a pair of wolves were captured in the winter in the vicinity of Fort Churchill that had been living on small fishes obtained where the ice did not form in the river—presumably Steel River (Preble, E. A., 1902: 62).

John Stanwell-Fletcher was afforded many excellent opportunities for close-up observations of the wolves in the Driftwood River area of north central British Columbia. Domiciled in this remote section during 1937-41, he found that during August these animals lived almost exclusively on the kokanee (*Oncorhynchus nerka kennerlyi* (*Suckley*), a dwarf form of the blue back, or sockeye, salmon. These fishes start running through the large lakes up the streams in countless swarms. After spawning, and in a dying condition, many of them were left on gravel bars by the receding waters of the streams. The wolves ran the gravel bars, hunting the fish as did also the bears, fishers, foxes, coyotes, minks, and otters.

During September 1941, W. H. Jackson observed wolves feeding on salmon near Anchor Pass in the Ketchikan area of southeastern Alaska. Here he found "they had taken at least ninety percent of the salmon from the creek, eating only the heads. Many fish were not touched at all." Their tactics in catching a salmon, as described by Jackson, vary little from those employed by the Alaskan bears. He further relates while making his observations: "Once a salmon splashed in the shallow stream and two of them [wolves] raced after it. The first wolf to reach it grabbed the salmon by the back and brought it up onto the bank. There he lay down with the fish between his paws and ate off its head" (Jackson, W. H., 1942: 29).

Here it may be stated that so far the salmon fluke mentioned previously (p. 164) has not been found in the northern British Columbia area or Alaska.

An item that, for convenience, may be included here relates to depredations upon the property of man rather than upon a natural food. The Wilkes exploring expedition mentions the practice of the Indians in Oregon in 1841 along the upper Columbia of "drying [salmon] for food, by hanging them on limbs of trees. This is to preserve them from the wolves. . . ." (Wilkes, C., 1845: vol. 4, p. 391).

Regarding the wolf as a feeder at times on mollusks, Rhoads noted:

"The wolf, coyote, Indian dog, and the red and grey fox eat land snails, mussels, and maritime mollusks with avidity, especially when hunger-pressed" (Rhoads, S. N., 1899: 206).

Finally, Mitchell records red wolves as eating fiddler crabs, at Bay Shores, near Gulf, Tex. (Rathbun, M. J., 1918: 401).

Domestic Animals

Among the domesticated animals, the reindeer as handled in Alaska is most nearly in the status of a wild species. Roaming in large herds on unfenced range and with little guarding, this animal probably is more handicapped than helped in relation to the wolf by its imperfect degree of domestication. Reindeer are close relatives of caribous upon which, as noted in the preceding chapter, wolves regularly prey. The North American reindeer herds are largely in Alaska, and to a lesser extent in northern Canada.

Grenold Collins, while an Alaska Game Agent in 1936-37, gave the following report on the situation:

"During the last two years wolves have become most plentiful on the Arctic slope, and seem to be increasing at a rapid rate all through the reindeer and caribou ranges. As Mr. Gubser thoroughly covered the Kotzebue Sound area this fall, I shall confine my report to the regions north of Kivalina.

"There is a natural boundary between the Kivalina-Noatak ranges, and the Point Lay range on the Arctic slope. It is very likely that when the caribou herds began to drift into the Arctic ranges two or three years ago the wolves followed them there. These wolves, moving with the caribou, also drifted into the native-owned reindeer herds.

"During the last two seasons these wolves have been denning on the Arctic slope and raising large litters of young. This denning evidently takes place along the foothills from the Kukpowruk River to the mid Colville section, the chief denning being along the Awuna River.

"Almost all the wolves killed or seen in the Arctic are young wolves, and I believe that the small packs which are now depleting the reindeer herds are family groups. During the entire trip, wolf sign and damage was reported by all natives who had been herding deer or travelling inland from the coast. Lots of wolf damage is reported from the winter of 1935-1936, and this situation continues during the present season.

"Historical information gathered from the natives indicates that there was a large infestation of wolves in the Arctic some sixty or seventy years ago. They remember that caribou were thick in the country at that time and wolves often came close to the villages along the coast. They report that many were killed at that time by means of 'whalebone' baits.

"About forty wolves were killed east of Point Barrow last year, but very few were taken southwest of Barrow. I investigated one instance where three hundred deer were reported killed by wolves last year in the vicinity of the Barrow corrals. These deer really died from faulty castration methods and rough handling in the corrals. This fall extensive round-up efforts were made in the vicinity of Barrow to count the deer herd. Wolf depredations at night were reported, but upon investigation these were found to be exaggerated. The wolves did not do any extensive damage while the deer were being handled by the natives. No doubt the wolves 'got in their work' when the deer drifted back to their winter feeding areas.

"The Brower herd, of about 3,000 deer, located in the Ikpipuk section, was attended by herders and only sixteen wolf kills were reported from last year. The Cape Halkett and Barter Island herds are also watched and they suffered less damage than the unguarded herds in the Barrow-Wainwright vicinity.

"During my trip inland from Halkett to Wainwright very little wolf sign or damage was seen. The carcasses found were mostly shot by natives or died from handling in the corrals. It was very dark and stormy during this trip, and not at all possible to see or determine much because of the almost total lack of visibility.

"On December 28th, 1936, I made a trip inland from Wainwright to investigate reported wolf damage. Near the head of the Nigaluk River we found a female reindeer which had been killed by wolves within the past twenty-four hours. This deer was hamstrung and its tongue had been torn out from the back by ripping open the throat. A red fox, driven from the kill, had eaten the loin off one side.

"As it was late at night we built a snow house and waited until morning. The next morning I followed the tracks of five or six wolves leading away from the kill for about three miles. The wolves were still following the herd of about two hundred deer. Fresh dung was in evidence and the wolves had probably bedded down on the trail of these deer before closing in for further slaughter. After returning to the camp I back-tracked the wolves over a small hill and located eleven more fresh kills. Six of these were so near to each other that I dragged them together and took pictures. Eight females were hamstrung and bitten about the neck, but none of the meat had been consumed by the wolves. Three fawns that had also been killed here had the tongues and liver eaten, but the rest of their bodies were untouched.

"The wolf tracks were about 3½ inches in diameter. The pack evidently divided when they caught up with the herd and each individual made one or two kills. We followed the back-tracks of the deer and wolves for several miles in an effort to find more evidence, but in early afternoon a severe storm blew up and we were forced to turn down the Avalik and camped in a coal mine on the Kuk River. Sixteen other wolf-killed deer were observed by me on this trip. These, however, were several weeks old, and the carcasses had been wasted in a manner similar to the others found. The next day the storm was intensified so we came on into Wainwright.

"Such evidence of wanton killing by wolves indicates that these small bands of predators may make similar kills every night. After feeding they probably sleep on the trail left by the deer and towards afternoon run them down again. If such destruction of reindeer is taking place all over the range by several bands of wolves, it is certain that the deer will be exterminated in a very short time. The animals not killed will be scattered and the survivors will become intermingled with the caribou herds and will be lost to the natives. Another bad feature is that the wolves pick on the females because they are fatter. They also kill steers.

"If only a reasonable amount of killing were done by the wolves, the relative damage would not be so alarming because the many native trappers along the Arctic coast use the carcasses of deer so killed for fox bait and dog feed. When a dead deer is found, the natives cut off the head to indicate ownership. They trap around it and in the spring haul it in for dog feed. It is very likely that if there were no killing by wolves the Eskimos would kill a goodly portion of these deer themselves. However, they would not take so many females and would not scatter and break up the herds.

"In estimating the accounts of damage by wolves as told by the natives and collected by school teachers one must consider the fact that the reports may be exaggerated for several reasons. One is that several natives will see the same deer at different times. Another is that if a native desires dog feed or fox bait in a certain locality and no wolf kills are located he will shoot deer for his own needs and report them as wolf kills. By so doing he does not need a permit and retains his reindeer shares in the company. I know personally instances of this practice, but do not think it is very general. Some Eskimos are very quick to take unfair advantage of a situation, but the majority of the people are honest.

"But these factors are, of course, offset by the fact that not all of the wolf kills are found by the natives. On the whole the outlook for the Arctic herds is very bad. I believe that unless immediate drastic and effective control measures are not taken, the reindeer herds will be lost" (Collins, G., 1937b: 24).

Ralph Lomen, of The Lomen Reindeer Corporation, and until recently long associated with the reindeer industry in northern Alaska, supplemented the foregoing information of the wolf-reindeer relationship. Writing to his brother, Carl Lomen, an associate in this business, he stated:

"George Folger called today to report that Welter had just come in from the range and reports wolves are taking a toll of about fifteen deer each night. . . . The wolf stories may be exaggerated but there is no doubt that many of them are in the country and they are doing a tremendous damage to herds. The pilots all have stories to tell of wolves which they see or are reported by other travellers."[26]

---

[26]Letter from Ralph Lomen to Carl Lomen from Nome, Alaska, dated April 17, 1939. In files of Fish and Wildlife Service.

Finally, Charles G. Burdick, Special Representative of the Secretary of the Interior, to whom was entrusted the assignment by the Federal Government in the acquisition of the reindeer held under white ownership, gives an illuminating story of the Alaskan wolf-reindeer relationship. Mr. Burdick completed his field assignment in the early summer of 1940, and reports:

"In my opinion, based on factual data as determined during the reindeer census taking in the acquisition program this past winter, wolves in their present uncontrolled numbers are a very serious menace to the reindeer herds of northern and western Alaska and accordingly a very serious menace to the economic life of the Eskimos of that region. Without doubt wolves have destroyed a large percentage of the reindeer, which is the only stable source of food and clothing for the Natives. Whalers greatly reduced the number of whales and walrus, in fact, to a point where it has been very difficult for the past half century for Natives in their oomiaks and with hand tools to secure enough for food although apparently the whale is slowly increasing in numbers. The caribou, which were plentiful in the coastal region when the Natives hunted with spears, clubbed animals from skin boats when they were swimming rivers, and secured them in other primitive ways, have been killed off and driven from the country by rifle hunting. Without doubt wolves were present with the caribou on the coast but probably most of them followed their hosts into the interior country. The reindeer was introduced in the 1890's from Siberia to supplement the diminishing food supply.

"Nature was kind to the new species and the Natives were quite thorough for many years in caring for the reindeer and they multiplied very rapidly. When they became fairly abundant the interest of the Natives waned and predators entered the picture in ever-increasing numbers.

"Predators reduce reindeer stock in several ways. The actual kill, while quite heavy, is not too serious. The harrying of herds throughout the winter, keeping the animals worried and nervous so that they are unable to graze and thus carry their fat through the winter, leaves them thin and weak. Any long storms or severe blizzards in late winter or early spring catch the animals too weak to carry through and many starve to death. Many thousands died in this manner during the spring of 1939.

"A few wolves can drive females from the fawning grounds, causing the death of many fawns by desertion and starvation. Fawn crops as low as ½ percent were tallied this last winter. This is far less than the number required to replace ordinary natural losses to hold the herd at a constant figure.

"Losses in various herds which can be charged in large part to wolf depredations have been most serious. The Kivalina herd decreased from a counted 42,000 in 1932 to 6,000 in 1939. Two herds in that vicinity, the Kotzebue Native (17,000) and the Kotzebue Lomen (12,000), have been totally destroyed. These were not driven from their home ranges as they have not been found elsewhere. The Selawik herd decreased from 2,600 last August to less than 1,000 this spring; the Shaktoolik herd from 12,000 to 491 head and owing 825 deer to others.

"These are not isolated cases. The same conditions have occurred on a number of ranges not listed here.

"Constant herding of reindeer would solve the wolf problem in great part. If this was supplemented by the present bounty system and the Eskimos given expert training in trapping and den hunting, I believe the wolf population could be held sufficiently in check to present no serious menace to the reindeer herds or the economic lives of the Eskimos in Alaska."[27]

In the course of the memorable reindeer drive that began in the Napaktolik Mountains in the Kotzebue Sound region of Alaska in December 1929 and terminated in March 1935 at Killigazuit, on the east bank of the Mackenzie River, Northwest Territories, Canada, often referred to as the "Canadian Drive," there was trouble with wolves during almost the entire trek. This reindeer drive was for the purpose of establishing reindeer among the Mackenzie Eskimos and was the result of action of the Canadian Government which authorized the purchase of 3,000 head of domestic reindeer in Alaska. In all, 3,400 reindeer were selected for this drive, and of that number but one-fifth remained at the termination of the drive. The losses were due to straying, predation by wolves, blizzards, accidents, and starvation. With regard to wolf depredations during this drive, Erling Porsild, the leader, recounts:

---

[27]Letter from Charles G. Burdick to Stanley P. Young, dated August 2, 1940. In files of Fish and Wildlife Service.

".... that in the winter months during the entire drive, bands of wolves continually harassed the herd, at times taking a great toll and compelling the herders to remain on watch day and night" (Porsild, E., 1936: 13, 14, 16).

Cattle, though in general the most valuable domestic animals preyed upon by wolves, were in earlier times over most of their range but little better guarded than the reindeer. There is overwhelming evidence of the depredations of wolves upon them, significant examples of which are here reproduced.

Norton quotes from Josselyn's New England Rarities Discovered (1672: 51) to the effect that the wolves are not "man Kind (that is they would not attack human beings) as in Ireland and other Countries, but do much harm by destroying of our English Cattle" (Norton, A. H., 1930: 42).

Among early accounts for the West is that of Charles Wilkes of the United States Exploring Expedition of 1838-42. He noted that wolf depredations in 1841 on the holdings of the Hudson's Bay Company at Fort Vancouver required the bringing in from the field of "large numbers of cattle . . . . for the night, which is a very necessary precaution in Oregon, in consequence of the numerous wolves that are prowling about; in some places it becomes necessary for the keeper to protect his beasts even in the daytime" (Wilkes, C., 1845, vol. 5, p. 234). This was especially true of the Cowlitz farm which furnished much of the necessities of life for inhabitants of early Oregon Territory, who relied upon Fort Vancouver. The economic importance of endeavoring to keep wolves from preying on stock in this area is evident from this further statement: "The price of cattle may be quoted at ten dollars a head; but those that are broken in for labour, or milch cows, command a higher price; and in some places in the Willamette Valley they have been sold for the enormous price of eighty dollars" (Ibid., vol. 4, pp. 390-391).

Daniel W. Jones, as a member of a party coming east from Salt Lake City to succor a party of Mormons—the so-called "Handcart Company" that was stranded on the emigrant trail while trying to make Salt Lake City—gives an account of troubles with wolves. This group of emigrants were driving cattle in their trek westward, but the hardships and vicissitudes of the trail had raised havoc among them. After finding the party and salvaging what was possible of their belongings, food, and means of transportation, Jones gave his

Plate 73. Hole, about 50 feet deep, which the Custer wolf dug after the hunter who effected his capture started using wolf scent on his shoes, 20 miles southwest of Custer, South Dakota. It was apparent from this that the wolf believed that there was a mate on its runway, and proceeded to dig a den

Plate 74. Photo of "Three Toes" of Harding County, South Dakota. The hunter who captured him was rewarded by an engraved gold watch, presented to him by stockmen and others of that locality

259

Plate 75. Dead-fall trap for wolves. Note stones to give weight to the fall of horizontal timber

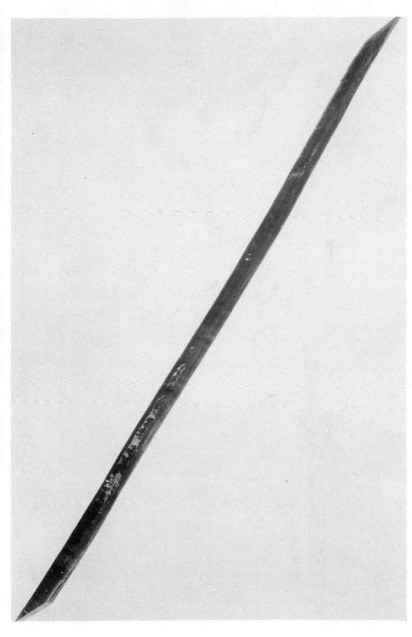

Plate 76. Whale bone used by Eskimos in wolf capture. The bone is heated, twisted into a spiral and tied, immersed in fat which is permitted to congeal, and then laid out on the wolf's runway to be gulped. Body heat and digestion cause the spiral to loosen, when the bone pierces the animal's stomach. The individual Eskimo's mark made on the whale bone determines who killed the wolf

Plate 77. The modern No. 4½ wolf trap developed as a result of wolf depredations in Texas during the early 1890's. Used now mainly for trapping small bears and pumas

attention to saving the cattle. He says:

"On returning to camp, I found that the cattle left were very poor. The weather had moderated and we hoped to get them on good feed and recruit them a little. Over two hundred head of cattle had died in the vicinity of the fort. Along the road each way for a day's travel were carcasses. This led droves of prairie wolves into our camp; it was almost impossible to keep them off from the cattle in the day time. We were obliged to coiral them at night. Once in the day time a small bunch was taken and run off in spite of the efforts of the herders to stop them. In fact it became dangerous to face these wolves—they were at times almost ready to attack men. We soon found it impossible to save the cattle. Already some twenty-five had died or been killed by the wolves within a week. It was decided to kill the rest, some fifty head" (Jones, D. W., 1890: 75).

Joseph Neal, a well-known stockman and conservationist of Meeker, Colo., summarized his long experience with wolves in a statement from which excerpts are here made.

"The history of the Grey wolf in the west is a chronicle of the struggle between the wolf and the livestock industry for supremacy, with the success or failure of the livestock business depending upon its outcome.

"Back as far as 1896 the wolf was making dangerous inroads into the cattle herds and the *Meeker Herald* of November 26, 1898, carried this item: 'It is time concerted action was being taken in this valley regarding the depredations of mountain lions, grey wolves and coyotes. One of our ranchmen saw a bunch of twelve big wolves in one band last week.' By 1904 their depredations had so increased that their toll was practically one fourth of the calf crop, besides their leaving at least 15 percent of the herds marked by severed tails and by great scars from torn flesh between the hind legs. . . .

"Frequently we have counted from three to eight wolves from the door of our home ranch house in the daytime, but they were most numerous and made their largest kills at night. If one has never heard the blood curdling howl of a band of wolves at night he cannot possibly realize the terror that chorus strikes to a cowman's heart as he well realizes the toll his herd will pay before morning. I have had them enter my weaning pen and kill five big weaners in a single night. Many nights I have gotten out of bed, dressed, and taken my rifle and walked down the road and fired several shots in an attempt to drive them away."[28]

Theodore Roosevelt, from experience on his cattle ranch in North Dakota, stated: "the gray wolf, which, wherever it exists in numbers, is a veritable scourge to the stockmen" (Roosevelt, T., 1905: 528). He further wrote: "During the last three years these brutes have killed nearly a score of my cattle, and in return we have poisoned six or eight wolves and couple of dozen of coyotes. . . . The Stockman fears only the large wolves" (Roosevelt, T., 1900: 42).

For Montana, it is recorded that

"During the year 1884, soon after the last buffalo disappeared across the Canadian border, and when the great herds of domestic cattle succeeded to the stamping grounds of the native bison, there was a remarkable increase in the number of gray wolves on the Montana ranges. . . . Not being so particular as to object to beefsteak when buffalo hump was not to be had, they played sad havoc with the cattle herds that year (1884). Cattlemen did not begin to pay much attention to the matter until last year (1883), when it was found that it knocked considerable from their profits to support such immense swarms of these pests. Cattle, and especially young and weak calves, dropped during the winter time, have been the food upon which they subsisted" (Carl _____, 1886: 508).

". . . . A. J. Majoribanks, manager of the Rocking Chair Ranch, in making his report to . . . . headquarters, ... has the following to say . . . : 'On the inventory of cattle we have written off some 3,770 cattle as losses, being five per cent on all, with the exception of ten per cent on yearlings and the year's steer calves already branded. We have written off this ten per cent on account of the depredations of the big loafer wolves, which are getting numerous on the range, and destroying most especially young calves.' " (Sheffy, L. F., 1929: 94.)

In Canada also the ranchers had good reason to combat the wolf. McGowan wrote of that country: "In the year 1885 they [wolves] were still quite common, their raids on stock at the ranches west of Calgary being frequently noted in the newspapers. By this time,

---

[28]Letter of Joe Neal, of Meeker, Colo., sent to Stanley P. Young through Mr. Neal's daughter, Mrs. Blue, and received in Washington, D. C., on February 3, 1939. In files of Fish and Wildlife Service.

however, the creatures were outlawed and a bounty offered for their destruction. A full grown wolf was considered capable of killing horses and cattle to the value of about one thousand dollars annually. A female wolf, with a litter of half-grown pups, was even more of a scourge to the stockman. She dragged down and killed many colts and calves, not for food alone but also to give to her young a lesson in making a kill" (McGowan, D., 1936: 29).

Reports of wolf depredations that deal more with the mode of attack and with the destruction of individual cattle also may well be quoted to illustrate the wolf's relations to livestock.

Theodore Talbot, while in Wyoming, states in his journal of 1843: "Rising an eminence overhanging a little valley, we surprised a pack of large white wolves who had just succeeded in hamstringing a fine Durham Bull (probably lost by some of the Emigrants). The poor fellow fought manfully, but numbers had overpowered him. This sagacious mode by which the wolves disable their prey, has been frequently discredited but here we saw an undoubted proof of its truth" (Talbot, T., 1931: 36).

Theodore Roosevelt gives the following account of wolf teamwork in killing a steer:

"In 1894 and 1896 I saw a number of wolves on the Little Missouri. . . . I frequently came upon the remains of sheep and young stock which they had killed; and once, upon the top of a small plateau, I found the body of a large steer, while the torn and trodden ground showed that he had fought hard for his life before succumbing. There had been two wolves engaged in the work, and the cunning beasts had evidently acted in concert. Apparently, while one attracted the steer's attention in front, the other, according to the invariable wolf habit, attacked him from behind, hamstringing him and tearing out his flanks. His body was still warm when I came up, but the marauders had slunk off, either seeing or smelling me" (Roosevelt, T., 1905: 532).

Of his ranch in North Dakota, he wrote, "the wolves destroy many cattle."

"In early spring, when the cows begin to calve, the wolves sometimes wait upon the herds as they did of old on the buffalo, and snap up any calf that strays away from its mother. When hard pressed by hunger they will kill a steer or a heifer, choosing the bitterest and coldest night to make the attack. The prey is invariably seized by the haunch or flank, and its entrails afterward torn out; while a cougar, on the contrary, grasps the neck or throat. Wolves have very strong teeth and jaws and inflict a most severe bite" (Roosevelt, T., 1885: 21).

It was not uncommon for a single wolf, generally a male, to kill a full-grown cow or steer unassisted. The late Senator Kendrick of Wyoming witnessed evidences of this throughout his many years of cattle-raising in Wyoming. Speaking before the United States Senate Committee on Agriculture and Forestry, he said:

"We had any number of instances where one gray wolf alone would kill a grown cow. And their plan of destruction was by disemboweling the cow through the flank. That was particularly noticeable in the case of cattle that were without horns. Cattle with horns could protect themselves to better advantage. And not infrequently would you find where a gray wolf had eaten his fill of an animal's hind quarter, the animal would survive, and in after years recover entirely, except for the enormous scar in the place where the flesh had been but was no more.

"According to my judgment there is nothing so vicious in its cruelty as the method employed by the gray wolf in destroying his prey. His prey is literally eaten alive, its bowels torn out while it is still on its feet in many cases" (United States Senate, 1930-31: 6, 7, 47).

On many of the western ranges, bobtailing of livestock by wolves was a common occurrence. Typical of such ranges where this often occurred were those in the vicinity of Meeker, Colo. Joseph N. Neal, previously quoted, stated to me on February 13, 1940:

"When the wolves were at their greatest abundance on these ranges at least 25 percent of all cattle had their tails cut-off close into the rump or bob-tailed. This bob-tailing was done when an old female wolf was teaching her half-grown whelps to bring down their victim in the late spring or early summer. The act was accomplished by the wolf and her whelps chasing a cow-brute singled out in age from a 4 year old to a calf. Once an animal was singled out they would work it over, either eventually killing it, abandoning it, or choosing another victim.

"The mechanics of this procedure in bob-tailing are similar or comparable to the technique employed by cowhands in throwing an animal when on the full run. This is accomplished whereby the tail is grabbed and hung on to for a few moments, then given a quick hard side motion jerk, following which the hold is released and causes the animal to lose its balance and inevitably fall forward. The wolf, in grabbing the tail while both it and the victim were in full speed, did so by making a sudden leap at the animal past the animal's rear quarters at an oblique angle. This side-swiping of the tail by the wolf acts as a rudder in changing the course of the running cow-brute, throws it off balance, and causes it to fall. Because of the shearing action of the wolf's teeth on the tail, aided by the full weight of the swinging wolf, invariably cuts the tail off in a clean manner. As the victim fell, the half-grown young wolves that followed either pounced on it or allowed it to pick itself up and go on unmolested many times, following the loss of its tail." On other ranges, bob-tailing was known to have been done by an old single male, and apparently done more with a sportive intent than in an attempt to obtain food.

Referring to the enormous scars caused by wolf-bitings, spoken of by Senator Kendrick, Mr. Neal also stated: "that a wolf bite that just punctured the hide of a cow-brute and did not in any way tear the hide or the flesh seldom failed to cause rapid infection of the wound that would result in the death of the animal in from two to three days. However, if the hide and flesh was torn in the biting, this in time would sluff off, and eventually the animal would get well, but leave enormous scars at those spots where the hide and flesh had been sheared off by the bite of a wolf."

Many range riders of the West held the opinion that the bite of a wolf produced tetanus that would cause death in a few days if the wound failed to receive proper prophylactic treatment.

Bud Dalrymple, of South Dakota, who was very well versed in wolf-lore after close association with the animal in the western ranges for many years, had seen much livestock that had been mutilated by wolves. He wrote on this subject:

"The gray wolf is very fond of colt or horse meat and prefers it to beef, although he is not the least backward about eating beef. They are a good deal like sheep-killing dogs; sometimes they will kill three or four cattle in one night, and likely will only eat a few pounds of meat out of each animal, maybe leaving some of them before they are dead—just eating out a few of the animal's rear parts, leaving it to be finished by the coyotes or else die a lingering death" (Dalrymple, B., 1919: 9). "Sometimes a steer or cow chewed up in this manner will be able to get away from the wolf and will live for two or three weeks or more and then die from the effects of the bite, which seems to be very poisonous, especially if the animal is badly scratched and not torn out entirely. The wound seems to partly heal, then puff up, turn a greenish cast, and the animal soon dies. I have seen where an animal had a chunk of flesh torn clear of its thigh by a wolf and get entirely over it, although the scar always stays with the animal. Several years ago a lone gray wolf went through my pasture one night, and bit a chunk out of two colts, each on the thigh, and both of these animals recovered, except for the scar. Again, where an animal is only scratched by the wolf's teeth, it sometimes dies" (Ibid., p. 10).

Certain wolves at times kill full-grown range cows soon to calf and eat nothing but the unborn calf, leaving the mother's carcass untouched. An observation of this food habit was made during January 1931 on the Frank Krentz cow ranch at the southern tip of the Chiricahua Mountains in Cochise County, Ariz.

W. H. Caywood, formerly with the Fish and Wildlife Service, reports that he has often seen carcasses of deer and livestock killed by wolves from which nothing but the unborn young was taken for food. He states that wolves seem to know just where to rip open the flesh in an animal in such condition to remove the embryo, which seems to be a tidbit for them.

An opinion held by many present-day game conservationists is that one of the outstanding roles which predators play in the complex predator-game relationship is the removal by killing for food, of weakened individuals of the prey species. Predators are assumed, therefore, through a process of selection, to improve the agility and vitality of the herds of deer or other big game. It is assumed that a wolf, for instance, seeks out as its prey the puniest and weakest of the species because of the ease by which it may be attacked and killed. However, the hundreds of observations made and citations left us by other observers, do not in any way bear out the foregoing contentions. In the heyday of the North American wolf it was common knowledge that these animals invariably killed some of the healthiest, choicest, and fattest steers in the herd. These ranged in age from long yearlings up to four-year-olds. Nor is there any evidence that when once wolves entered a herd of cattle they purposely sought out the weakest as their prey.

Horses also, under some conditions, ranged at large over the grasslands, and though large animals, seemed easy prey for wolves. Thus Inman writing of the horses of the Comanche Indians said:

"At times when the herd was very large, the horses scattered over the prairie and were irrevocably lost; and such as did not become wild fell a prey to the wolves. That fate was very frequently the lot of stampeded horses bred in the States, they not having been trained by a prairie life to care for themselves. Instead of stopping and bravely fighting off the bloodthirsty beasts, they would run. Then the whole pack were sure to leave the bolder animals and make for the runaways, which they seldom failed to overtake and dispatch" (Inman, H., 1917: 185).

Cox observed with respect to the Flathead Indians: "As their lands are much infested by wolves, which destroy the foals, they cannot rear horses in such numbers as the Nez Perces, from whom they are obliged to purchase them annually" (Cox, R., 1831: 183).

Presenting some of the early accounts of wolf depredations on horses and mules in chronological order, we begin with that of Jacob Fowler, one of the earliest western explorers. At the time of this notation he was fattening horses to convey his party on a return journey eastward from Taos, N. Mex., a trip which began June 1, 1822. In his journal Fowler states:

"Saturday 25th May 1822, the Wolves maid an atackt on our Horse the(y) Wounded one Hors and two mules We Have maid a strong Pen Close to Camp and Still Shut up all the Horses at night While We Remain at this Place—to protect them from the Wolfes" (Fowler, J., 1898: 141).

Audubon, while at Fort Union, noted that wolves "will pursue and kill mules and colts even near a trading post, always selecting the fattest. The number of tracks or rather paths made by the wolves from among and around the hills to that station are almost beyond credibility, and it is curious to observe their sagacity in choosing the shortest course and the most favorable ground in travelling" (Audubon, J. J., and Bachman, J., 1851-54, vol. 2, p. 160).

On returning eastward from Santa Fe to Fort Leavenworth in January 1847, and again in the vicinity of the Raton Pass, Abert observes: "The wolves had become emboldened by the feeble resistance they had met with from broken down oxen which they find on the road. This morning (January 8, 1847) they attacked our mules, wounding one badly about the nostrils, and gnawing off the 'cabrestos' [halters] of the rest" (Abert, J. W., 1848: 519). Abert again experienced attacks on his mule teams between Bent's Fort and Fort Leavenworth (Ibid., pp. 530-531) and his journal is more or less replete with notations on wolves. One of his last citations on the welfare of the working livestock of his expedition of 1846-47 tells of a mule he was feeding up on corn: "During the past night it had wandered off a few yards and was attacked by wolves, and devoured while endeavoring to regain the wagons; the saddle blanket that I had girted around it was torn to pieces" (Ibid., p. 533).

While trekking to California in the summer of 1849 and when camped "at Sedillo" [near present-day Albuquerque in northern New Mexico], on a branch of the Rio Grande, Charles Edward Pancoast records:

"In this region we were much annoyed by Wolves, which cut the hamstrings of two Burros tied up not far from the Camp, and mangled them so terribly that we were obliged for Mercy's sake to kill them" (Pancoast, C. E., 1930: 222).

Sheffy informs us of "A number of illustrations of serious wolf depredations are listed such as 'John Arnot says that the LX ranch kept one hundred mares for breeding purposes, and from 1890-93 they did not brand a single colt on account of the destruction from the loboes' " (Sheffy, L. F., 1929: 94).

R. M. Allen, General Manager, Standard Cattle Company, Ames, Nebr., stated in a letter of April 3, 1896: "The loss is incalculable. I was told by one man who had 11 colts running in a pasture with 11 mares that he lost all of the 11 colts and one of the mares. The Continental Cattle Co., on the Little Missouri in Montana, who have a yearly brand of colts of some 700 head, lose, as I hear, annually about one third of their colts, and doubtless a great percentage of their calf brand as well. . . ."

Wolves used a variety of stratagem in getting horse meat, three distinct sorts of which are described in the following quotations. Alexander Ross, an early fur trader, wrote:

"Wherever several of the larger wolves associate together for mischief, there is always a numerous train of smaller ones [coyotes] to follow in the rear, and act as auxiliaries in the work of destruction.

Two large ones, such as I have mentioned, are sufficient to destroy the most powerful horse, and seldom more than two ever begin the assault, although there may be a score in the gang. It is no less curious than amusing to witness their ingenious mode of attack. If there is no snow, or but little, on the ground, two wolves approach in the most playful and caressing manner, lying, rolling, and frisking about, until the too credulous and unsuspecting victim is completely put off his guard by curiosity and familiarity. During this time the gang, squatted on their hind quarters, look on at a distance. After some time spent in this way, the two assailants separate, when one approaches the horse's head, the other his tail, with a slyness and cunning peculiar to themselves. At this stage of the attack, their frolicsome approaches become very interesting, ... the former is a mere decoy, the latter is the real assailant, and keeps his eyes fixed on the hamstrings or flank of the horse. The critical moment is then watched, and the attack is simultaneous; both wolves spring at their victim at the same instant, one to the throat, the other to the flank, and if successful, which they generally are, the hind one never lets go his hold till the horse is completely disabled. Instead of springing forward or kicking to disengage himself, the horse turns round and round without attempting a defence. The wolf then springs behind to assist the other. The sinews are cut, and in half the time I have been describing it the horse is on his side; his struggles are fruitless: the victory is won. At this signal the lookers-on close in at a gallop, but the small fry of followers keep at a respectful distance, until the superiors are gorged, then they take their turn unmolested. The wolves, however, do not always kill to eat; like wasteful hunters, they often kill for the pleasure of killing, and leave the carcasses untouched. The helplessness of the horse when attacked by wolves is not more singular than its timidity and want of action when in danger by fire" (Ross, A., 1855, vol. 1, p. 61).

Another style of horse destruction is noted by W. H. Caywood, who as stated was formerly with the Fish and Wildlife Service but now a retired hunter, in reporting an interesting observation of teamwork among wolves. While riding the range in northwestern Colorado, he was attracted by wolf howls. In riding in the direction whence they came, he was confronted by a deep canyon which with a similar gulch not far away bounded a narrow strip of mesa that jutted out in a tongue-shaped formation. The wolves that Caywood

had heard, two in number with their young, were observed by him
at this point, which afforded a splendid observation site.   They were
chasing a range mare, heavy with foal, and had maneuvered so as to
crowd her onto the narrow bit of mesa flanked on each side by a steep
chasm.   The two wolves, followed by the not quite half-grown
whelps, ran the mare to the very tip of the point.   Here the horse
had no alternative but to jump to its death or to face the wolves.   At
this narrow point the wolves closed in and killed her.   That did not
take long, and all that was actually eaten was the unborn foal, the
young wolves taking most of that.   The instance may have been
chiefly a lesson for the young.   Still a third manner of hunting horses
was reported more than a hundred years ago by two observers in
the Northwest.

In the vicinity of the present-day Spokane, Wash., in 1816, Ross
Cox witnessed an attack of between two to three hundred wolves on
Indian horses.   The line of wolves was in "semi-circular form, with
their flanks extended for the evident purpose of surrounding their
prey. . . . The horses, on observing their movements knew from experience its object, and dreading to encounter so numerous a force,
instantly turned round, and galloped off in a contrary direction. Their
flight was a signal for the wolves to advance; and immediately
uttering a simultaneous yell, they charged after the fugitives, still
preserving their crescent form" (Cox, R., 1831: vol. 2, p. 88).

While exploring near Fort Walla Walla during 1841, and when
on a horseback journey to visit the mission established beyond this
point in 1837, by Dr. Marcus Whitman, Drayton of the Wilkes Exploring Expedition "passed over some of the pastures of the horses
belonging to the Company [Hudson's Bay].   An alluvial bank, one
hundred feet in height, was pointed out, over which the wolves had
driven part of a band of the horses of the Company, by surrounding
them just before dark.   This took place some months before, and
the horses were killed and eaten by these voracious animals.   The
wolves are very numerous in this country, and exceedingly troublesome" (Wilkes, C., 1845: vol. 4, p. 420).

Sheep would seem to be more appropriate in size for wolf prey
and they have been taken by wolves ever since their introduction into
this country.

In a letter written May 12, 1688, with reference to observations
in Virginia, John Clayton said: "Their sheep are a midling size,

pretty fine fleeced in general, and most persons of estate begin to keep flocks, which hitherto has not been much regard, because of the wolves that destroy them; so that a piece of mutton is a finer treat than either venison, Wild-goose, Duck, Widgeon or Teal" (Clayton, J., 1844: 35).

It is apparent from Clayton's comment that the wolves in Virginia were among the main factors that had held back the development of the sheep industry in that colony during the half century since colonization. His visit to Virginia occurred during the year 1666, and he was one of the first men to make observations as to the elements, natural history, and beasts of Virginia.

With regard to the livestock industry in North Carolina in 1728, Byrd came to the conclusion "that sheep would thrive much better in the Woods than in Pasture Land, provided a careful Shepherd were employed to keep them from straying, and by the help of Dogs, to protect them from the Wolves" (Byrd, W., 1901: 107).

New York, like the other colonies, experienced severe wolf depredations. By 1790 in that commonwealth, formerly known as New Netherlands, sheep "were kept somewhat extensively, throve well, became fat, and multiplied; but the depredations of wolves, and the loss of wool by brush and tangled thickets were serious drawbacks upon sheep-raising" (United States Commissioner of Agriculture, 1863: 243).

In Pennsylvania, according to Shoemaker:

"Joseph Brooks, a Yorkshireman who died in 1832, made a failure of his woolen-goods manufacturing near Dingman's Ferry because the wolves destroyed the sheep in large numbers . . . ." (Shoemaker, H. W., 1917: 30).

In the far west wolf depredations upon sheep also were serious. Suckley noted that:

"Other domestic animals have been introduced into Oregon and Washington Territories. Among these are sheep, asses, goats, eastern horses, dogs, pigs, cats; all of which thrive very well. The sheep, however, owing to the abundance of wolves, as a general rule, require guarding by shepherds, especially east of the Cascades" (Suckley, G., and Gibbs, G., 1860: 139).

On the Clatsop Plains, 6 miles north of Seaside, Oreg., and about a mile from the Pacific Ocean, Frank Ellis Brallier saw a wolf in 1887 and learned that it had been killing sheep belonging to Josiah

West. It killed seven in 15 minutes while Mr. West went into his house to get a rifle.

Despite close relationship, wolves at times appear to regard domestic dogs as legitimate prey. Several writers testify to this trait, among which we quote:

Richardson, the early Arctic explorer who observed:

"The wolves had now grown so bold as to come along side, and on this night they broke into a snow hut, in which a couple of newly purchased Esquimaux dogs were confined, and carried them off, but not without some difficulty, for in the daylight we found even the ceiling of the hut sprinkled with blood and hair. When the alarm was given, and the wolves were fired at, one of them was observed carrying a dead dog in his mouth clear of the ground, at a canter, notwithstanding the animal was of his own weight" (Richardson, J., 1829: 65).

Back, in the same region, related the following, regarding the capture of a dog: "One of their decoys was as follows: two or three would be down on the ice a few hundred yards in front the house, in order to entice the dogs, which sometimes ventured a little way towards them; and on one occasion when two of them were thus lying in wait, my little terrier, which had been bitten in the neck only two nights before, ran with five dogs to within fifty paces of them, when the larger of the two [wolves] instantly singled it out, and after twice missing, finally seized it by the neck, and carried it deliberately away" (Back, G., 1836: 461).

In Labrador, Grenfell recounts:

"The wolves themselves are larger than the dogs. They may measure in length as much as seven feet eight inches, from nose to tail. They are very bold; on one occasion wolves lurked around a solitary house in Big Bay till they had carried off the four dogs, one by one, and left only after capturing the cat" (Grenfell, W. T., and others: 1913: 279, 280).

In North Dakota, Roosevelt stated: "They will in winter come up to the yards and carry away a sheep, pig, or dog without much difficulty; I have known one which had tried to seize a sheep and been prevented by the sheep dogs to canter off with one of the latter instead" (Roosevelt, T., 1885: 21).

And in New Mexico according to Sheffy:

". . . . Nath Hoard relates the story of how one Mr. Burnett, who owned the T. H. Ranch located near Tucumcari, N. M., brought out to his ranch in 1885 sixteen hounds and fed them up preparatory to a big hunt with some of his eastern friends. An evening or two before the hunt was to take place, he instructed the hands to turn the dogs out and give them some exercise before taking them out on the chase. His instructions were carried out, but not with the results anticipated. The dogs were not out long before they got on a fresh trail, and soon only the distant echoes of their howls were heard . . . . as they sped farther away in search of their prey. These inexperienced hunting dogs finally came upon a pack of fighting loboes, but not at the same time. The wolves had waited until the dogs had become separated in the chase, and then had killed them one by one. Only one dog returned to the ranch, but it was never able to go on another chase after loboes. Mr. Hoard says that it looked as if fifty loboes had been in the fight that night, and they had done their work effectively" (Sheffy, L. F., 1929: 94).

DESTRUCTIVENESS OF RENEGADE WOLVES

In widely separated parts of the western range have occurred a number of individual gray and red wolves that were considered of the renegade type because of individual peculiarities in their depredations on livestock and game. Often written or spoken about, they demonstrated outstanding cunning in avoiding for many years all efforts at capture. Each finally drew such attention that it was singled out for elimination. As Seton puts it, they could show "enormous individual variation, mental and physical; . . ." (Seton, E. T., 1937: 9). The stockmen knew them by sight, by peculiarities of their tracks, or by the characteristic manner of each in attacking, killing, or mutilating its victims (Carhart, A. H. and Young, Stanley P., 1929).

Possessed of marked individualities and identifying scars or defects, they were often popularly christened. Such names as Two Toes, Three Toes, Big Foot, Peg Leg, Old Lefty, the Phantom Wolf, the Custer Wolf, and others, became commonplace in the West.

The deeds that made these master wolves famous, or infamous, in the regions they occupied were of a nature calling for prompt retribution according to the views of their human neighbors. Entire communities sought the renegades by every means, such as the use of dogs, traps, poison baits, or set guns, despite which these wolves often carried on for many years. As these predators were only gaining their subsistence in the manner nature had taught them, they commanded a certain measure of admiration and respect, even from the stockmen who suffered most from their depredations. To that they seemed entitled because of the mental and physical qualities that enabled them to hold their own for so long a period against such overwhelming odds. To terminate their depredations necessitated all of the ability of the most experienced hunters—men thoroughly familiar with more than average wolf psychology and habits. Even they required, at times, many months of hard work to succeed.

There was the so-called "Sycan" wolf of southern Oregon that was finally trapped near Fort Klamath. It was an old male, credited with the killing of many horses and cattle over a period of twelve years in that section. The teeth of this wolf, on examination after capture, proved it to be an old one, as they were greatly worn.

The wolf known as "Lobo—The King of Currumpaw," made famous by the tales about it by Ernest Thompson Seton, was a 150-pound male that was captured in northern New Mexico by Seton. It ranged the so-called Currumpaw region for the period 1889-1894, and was a costly depredator on cattle and sheep. Seton refers to other notorious wolves known as the "Winnipeg Wolf," the "White Wolf of Pine Ridge," the "Roosevelt Wolf," and the "White Wolf of Cheyenne" (Seton, E. T., 1929: 313).

In Montana, one of the renegades was the "Pryor Creek Wolf," which had its runways in the south-central part of the State. This wolf was noted not only for cunningness, especially skill in eluding traps and for its destruction of calves, but also as a depredator upon Shetland ponies.

In Arizona occurred the so-called "Aguila Wolf," a male that ranged the desert country north and west of Wickenburg between the years 1916 and 1924. During these eight years stockmen reported that it had killed a calf about every fourth night. This wolf was known to have killed 65 sheep in one night and 40 at another time. The range of this wolf was unusual as occurring in the low, hot desert section of Arizona at an altitude of not more than 3,000 feet above sea level among paloverdes, mesquites, and cacti. However, this territory was a favorite among the spring ranges utilized by the stock of Arizona sheep and cattle producers and that provided the attraction for the Aguila wolf.

One of the outstanding wolves of the Black Hills region was a male that was often referred to as the "Custer Wolf," because it ranged in the vicinity of Custer, S. Dak., for a period of 6 or 7 years. During that time it is reported to have killed $25,000 worth of livestock, and had escaped all efforts by sportsmen and stockmen to effect its capture, despite the offer of a bounty of $500 for its scalp. The Government hunter who finally killed the "Custer Wolf" did so only after working constantly on that one job from March to October, 1920.

Another noted outlaw male wolf of South Dakota was named "Three Toes of Harding County," because of the loss long before of two toes from one hind foot and one toe from a forefoot in escaping from traps. It was captured about 20 miles northwest of Buffalo, between Gallup and Dry House Creeks in one of 14 trap settings placed out on its runway, with natural wolf scent as the attractant. Fully 150 men had attempted to take this wolf during the 13 years it had been known as a killer in Harding County. It was at last caught by a Biological Survey wolf trapper, whose feat was heralded as one of the best of its kind ever accomplished in that region. Stockmen asserted that losses due to this wolf amounted to more than $50,000 and that it took high rank among the records of great killers of the prairie states. Shortly before it was captured, in the summer of 1925, it had destroyed 66 head of sheep belonging to one ranchman in two nights by forays.

In appreciation of the killing of "Three Toes" and riddance of his depredations citizens of that part of South Dakota presented the hunter with an engraved gold watch.

Colorado had numerous outstanding individual wolves—one known particularly as "Old Lefty" of Burns Hole. This was a male wolf that had been trapped by the left foot in 1913 by a private trapper who was working in Eagle County, but which had succeeded in twisting off the better part of his left foot in making its escape. As a result of this maiming which completely healed in time, the wolf adopted a peculiar gait. It never put the stub of its left leg to the ground, except when endeavoring to get over an obstruction such as a small windfall, or when traveling over rocky ground. In the 8 years it was known on these ranges, "Old Lefty" was credited with killing 384 head of livestock.

In southern Colorado once lived another clever wolf known as

"Old Whitey" of Bear Springs Mesa—a locality about 40 miles east of Trinidad. The farmer stockmen of this area had given the animal this name because of its outstanding white coat. An old male, it was known on these ranges for 15 years. James Shaw, who ranged cattle in this area alone, had known of this wolf frequenting his lands during the years 1909-21, a period of 12 years. The track made by this wolf, in pulverized adobe earth, could barely be covered by the palm of one's hand; he was a big fellow. Between February 1 and March 28, 1921, "Old Whitey" killed 10 head of stock; 9 of these were killed outright, and the tenth was so badly mutilated in the hindquarters that it died while attempting to reach a water hole on a neighboring ranch.

One of the outstanding traits of "Old Whitey" was his addiction to the bobtailing of calves. Many so-called long yearlings were then being held in this portion of Colorado, providing numerous potential victims. The bobtailing was generally done as he came away from another victim that he had killed, and from which he had eaten. A study of several weeks' duration made at the time indicated that "Old Whitey" did this bobtailing for no other reason than sport. As he was exceedingly cunning in avoiding all manner of trap sets, the conclusion was drawn that the only way to eliminate him was to use a set gun. However, he was finally taken in a so-called blind set, before the gun arrangement was tried.

In the vicinity of Cathedral Bluffs, southwest of Meeker, Colo., ranged another old male wolf that was called "Rags the Digger." He was given this name because of the shaggy appearance of his fur and of the fact that he often dug out traps set for his capture, and avoided springing the trap. The track of this wolf was rather peculiar, in that the imprints made by its hind feet were a little longer and heavier than those of its front paws, whereas generally the hind foot of a wolf is smaller than the front foot. These characteristic tracks of "Old Rags" readily served to identify him on the runways that he covered. He was reported to have used runs in the Cathedral Bluffs area for some 14 years. Like "Old Whitey," he was finally taken in a blind set. Stockmen in an area of 15 square miles where "Old Rags" was taken claimed that $10,000 worth of damage had been done by this animal.

An outstanding female renegade was the so-called "Unaweep Wolf," named for Unaweep Canyon near Whitewater, Colo. Some

Plate 78. First step in setting a trap for wolves. The stubble and weeds near the trap are the scent post. Trap and stake in position, and "setting cloth"

279

Plate 79. The trap in position, showing distance from the scent post

Plate 80. Trap pan covered with canvas. Note slot on far edge of canvas which fits about trigger. Canvas cover keeps the small pit clear beneath trap pan. Trap is now ready to be covered

Plate 81. Wolf held in captivity in camp for making wolf scents. Black Range, New Mexico

Plate 82. Wolf whelp used as a decoy near den entrance

Plate 83. Old hand-forged bear-wolf traps from the mountains of North Carolina. These are probably like the wolf trap used by David Thompson in 1785, and by Peale with Long's Expedition near Council Bluffs, Iowa, in 1819. (Photos by Roy Moore, Fish and Wildlife Service)

stockmen in this area also called her the "Queen Wolf," because during her last two years on these ranges she had with her 12 other wolves, which apparently were the survivors of two litters of her whelps. These were eventually found to be 8 of one size and 4 of another size. She was identified from the track she made, by its large size and by the peculiar imprint of her right front paw. On this foot her middle toe was crossed, due to malformation following trap injury some years prior to her final capture. She likewise was finally captured in a blind set in October 1921. After death she was found to weigh 110 pounds; her shoulder height was 39 inches; and her length, 6 feet 4 inches. Between July 1 and October 1, 1921, her known kills were 19 yearlings and one five-point deer; in addition a range cow was mutilated by the tearing off of the udder. This wolf is now in possession of the Colorado Museum of Natural History in Denver.

Probably one of the best known Colorado wolves was that dubbed "Big Foot" (Terror of the Lane Country). It made a track that barely fitted inside a No. 2 horseshoe. This wolf became much sought after on account of its great killings of cattle. It ranged in the oil shale country 16 miles west of DeBeque, Colo. At certain seasons of the year, and particularly in the spring, it moved down to a range on the semi-desert area south of Grand Junction. "Big Foot" was finally trapped on a runway leading to its den. Through E. J. Currier, Jr., of Currier Bros., Grand Junction, Colo., following the capture of this wolf, a communication was sent to the Fish and Wildlife Service with respect to this wolf and its mate. This letter, received May 11, 1922, reads as follows:

"I have heard that 'self-preservation is nature's first law,'—and we were merely obeying that law when we did our best to cooperate. ... We have used the range where that particular family of wolves were working, only two years. The first year something happened to about half of the calves. Last year, we put three hundred cattle out there, with just about an even hundred little calves. Results,— a 40 percent loss among the calves, besides a number yearlings killed.

"I presume that the fact of the she wolf having a hind foot gone, and the he one's teeth being badly worn,—accounts for their taste for calves more particularly than old stuff."

To reduce losses from "Big Foot's" depredations, Currier Bros.

even tried belling their stock on this range, in the hope that the sound
would drive the wolves away, but this brought no relief.

Two other outstanding Colorado wolves were the so-called
"Phantom Wolf" that ranged near Fruita, and the "Greenhorn
Wolf" of the Butler Pasture country near Pueblo. Another was
"Three Toes of the Apishapa," the female wolf whose antics with
the collie dog have been noted previously.

Oklahoma and Arkansas also had their noted red wolves, among
which were those dubbed "The Traveler," "Old Guy Jumbo," "Old
Doctor," and "The Black Devil." Each had its own peculiar traits.
"The Traveler," for instance, would make a kill, eat his fill, and
then travel 40 or 50 miles, never to return to that particular kill.
This was contrary to wolf custom, for as has been noted, these animals generally go but a short distance and then lie down to rest after
they have gorged themselves. "The Traveler" had been subjected
to several long chases by dogs and apparently had learned the de-
sirability of changing territories. Thus he departed from the vicinity of his latest kill and was usually gone from six or eight weeks.
He was well known in Perry County, west-central Arkansas. In the
words of Hunter J. A. Woodward, who finally captured the animal,
we read: "After learning his habits [accomplished by persistent following of this wolf's tracks, and meticulously noting the country it
was prone to travel] I set four traps on a special trap line on the
trail that I concluded he would travel when he came back. Just one
month later he did come back. On his way he was known to have
killed a fine two year old heifer. After eating all the round steak he
could carry he started to travel. He first went to Brush Creek for a
drink. The trail where my traps were placed led west of Brush
Creek.

While plodding along the trail full of good steak . . . . he trotted
by the first trap 10 or 12 feet away. Then he caught the odor of
the scent [wolf urine placed near these traps]. As the trap was in a
sandy place, I was able to learn from the tracks what had happened.
He turned around and went back. Then he placed his foot right on
the pan of the trap. The trap got a good hold. . . ."

One federal-state hunter in Texas captured 350 red wolves during the years 1938 to 1941, in Refugio County and vicinity. Among
them was a male named "Crip" because he had a clubbed forefoot
that was a well-known calf killer in this part of Texas, and a very

wary animal. This wolf's hunger seemed to be for calf meat more than any other food. Under cover of night the animal would sneak into a cattle herd and help himself to veal. On one ranch alone his tell-tale tracks were found around seven partly-eaten calves. Four months' dogged effort was necessary before this wolf was finally captured. Like most of the greatest individual livestock-killing wolves, this animal, although crippled, had no difficulty in obtaining food.

In many parts of the West ranchmen are still to be found who vividly recall the depredations and the costliness of these renegade wolves. It is probable that never did more intelligent wolves exist. Rarely have more dramatic hunts been planned and carried out, nor greater ingenuity employed, than the efforts put forth by the hunters who trailed these wolves and finally killed them. These animals had become wise beyond all other wolves through constant experience with the devices employed for capturing them. At times they seemed to be possessed of uncanny intelligence in avoiding steel traps, and in detecting various poisons, despite the variety of methods used in attempting to give the drugs to them. They likewise seemed to know when a man was armed and when he was weaponless. With every hand turned against them, their wisdom was respected by the stockmen upon whose cattle they depredated, as well as by the wolf trappers who finally eliminated them at the cost of much time, money, and patience.

Regularity of habits is the weak point in the wolf's armor, and it provides most of the opportunities that have been taken advantage of in eliminating these animals.

VI

MEASURES USED IN WOLF CAPTURE
AND CONTROL

TRAPS

MANY means and devices have been used for killing wolves, some of which doubtless antedate recorded history. Among the first of these mentioned in preserved writings are traps made of metal. Topsell says:

".... the Auncients haue inuented manie deuises and gins, and first of al an yron Toyle which they stil fasten in the earth with iron pins, vpon which pins they leaue a ring, being in compasse about the bignes of a wolue's head, and in the midst whereof they lay a peece of flesh, and couer the Toyle, so that nothing is seene but the flesh, where the Wolfe commeth and taketh holde of the flesh, feeling it sticke, pulling hard, he pulleth vp the ring, which bringeth the whole Toyle on his necke and sharpe pins. This is the first manner that Crescentiensis repeateth of taking Wolues, and he saith there are other deuises to ensnare their feet, which the Reader cannot vnderstand except he saw them with his eies.

"The Italians, cal the nets wherein wolues are taken, Tagliola, Harpago, Lo Rampeno, and Lycino, the French Hauspied, and Blaudus affirmeth, that the shepheardes of Italy make a certain ginne with a net, wherein that part of the Wolfe is taken which is first put into it." (Topsell, E., 1607: 741.)

286

Again he records

"The Rhatians vse to raise up to a tree a certain engine like a mouse-trappe but much greater, through which there is a cord where they hange a bate of flesh or pullin, or some such thing which the wolue loveth; when he commeth vnto it, he suddenly snatcheth at it, and so pulleth the trap vpon his own pate." (Ibid.)

Ancients as well as moderns used wolf catchers in variety. Among contrivances here described are: pitfalls, corrals, deadfalls, snares, and other traps. A special chapter is devoted to steel traps and their use. Various methods of hunting wolves that were also used are discussed.

PITS

The pit means of capturing animals is evidently of great antiquity. It was used for overcoming mammals, now extinct, such as the woolly mammoth. Remains of one of these in Moravia indicated that primitive men had driven it into a large pitfall and then dropped huge stones upon its head (Osborn, H. F., 1930: 239).

In the Old Testament, it is recorded that Benaiah "went down also and slew a lion in the midst of a pit in time of snow" (II Samuel, Chapter 23, 20th verse).

During the Roman emperors' rule several centuries before Christ, and again in the early Christian era, pits were used as a means of capturing tigers, lions, and other African beasts of prey that were used in the animal displays in the Roman amphitheaters. They also served as one of the principal methods of capturing wild animals for the zoological gardens of the Egyptian Ptolemies.

This scheme of capture was essentially the same wherever used, though in each region there might be some modification in its structure. Probably the most primitive form was that employed in Africa. A hole was dug in the center of which was left a dirt column. On this was put the bait in the form of a live sheep, lamb, or young dog, so placed as to be in discomfort, which would cause it to make an outcry. The carnivore being attracted, and making a jump for the bait, would fall to the bottom. The pit was generally fenced, making it impossible for the captured animal to jump out.

An improved pit trap of this plan (Figure 12), seen in Mexico by the late Dr. E. W. Nelson, former Chief of the Bureau of Biological Survey, was believed to have been introduced there by

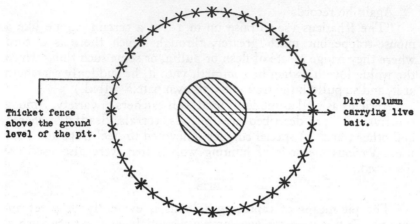

Thicket fence
above the ground
level of the pit.

Dirt column
carrying live
bait.

Figure 11. Plan of Early African Pit

early Spanish shepherds. The place where Dr. Nelson observed this type of pit was an open pine and fir forest on the northern slope of the volcano of Toluca, near the southern end of the Mexican tableland.

This trap was made by digging a ring-shaped trench about 20 feet deep, from 7 to 8 feet across the top, and tapering to a V at the bottom. The diameter of the circular trench across the outer walls was approximately 25 feet and the round, island-like center was 8 or 9 feet across. Both walls of the trench were carefully built from bottom to top with fairly smoothly-faced rock. To operate this trap, a young goat was staked on top of the round island in the middle, and poles loosely covered with branches and other vegetation were so laid across the trench that when a wolf tried to make his way to the bait, he would slip through and become helplessly wedged at the bottom of the pit. Such traps proved very effective in an area of heavy wolf infestation. Nelson was informed that the pits had not been used for more than 10 years previous to the time of his visit to this area in 1893.

Exemplifying other types of pitfalls are the accounts of Topsell, 1607, and Bewick, 1804, two English authors who are quoted as follows:

Bewick, in writing of their use during the eighteenth century in Germany, states: "In a convenient place, at the foot of a declivity,

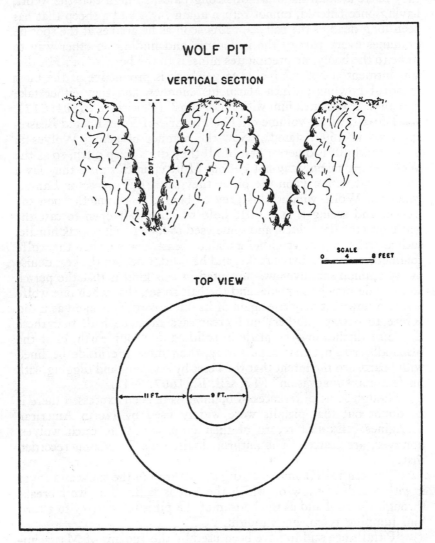

Figure 12

they make a small inclosure of strong pales, so high that the Wolf, having once entered, cannot return again . . . . and a sheep that has been long dead, is the bait; . . . . As soon as he arrives at the spot he examines every part of the inclosure; and finding no other way to come to the booty, he precipitates himself to the bottom. . . . His disappointment at not being able to get back is productive of the most dreadful howlings, which alarm his enemies, and they either take him alive or despatch him with bludgeons" (Bewick, T., 1804: 317).

Topsell, whose volume on The Historie of Four-Footed Beastes appeared in 1607, stated: "Now the manner of taking Wolves in ditches and pits is diuerse, first of all they dig a deep ditch, so as the Wolfe being taken, may not get out of it, vpon this pitte they lay a hurdle and within vpon the pillar they set a liue Goose or Lambe, when the Wolfe windeth his prey or booty, he commeth vpon the trench, and seeing it at a little hole which is left open to cast the wolfe into the deep ditch, and some vsed to lay vpon it a weak hurdle, such as will not bear vp either a man or beast, that so when the wolfe commeth vpon it, it may breake, and he fal downe, but the best deuise in my opinion that ever was invented in this kind is that the pertch and hurdle may be so made, and the bait so set, that when one wolfe is fallen downe it may rise again of its one accord, and stand as it did before to entrap another; and great care must be had, that these Kinde of ditches may be made in solide and strong earth, or if the place affoorde not that opportunity, then must the inside be lined with boards, so the intent that the beast by scraping and digging with his feet make no evasion" (Topsell, E., 1607: 741).

Though some differences of opinion have been expressed there is no doubt but that pitfalls were widely used by North American aborigines. Explicit record of their employment to catch wolves, however, are scarce. The anthropologist Otis T. Mason recorded that:

"The central Eskimo . . . . dig a wolf trap in the snow and cover it with a slab of snow on which the bait is laid. The wolf breaks through the roof and as the bottom of the pit is too narrow to afford him jumping room, he is caught. . . .

"Pitfalls are said to have been used by the Indians of Massachusetts. They are described as oval in shape, 3 rods long and 15 feet deep. . . .

"The Ochomawi, or Pit River Indians, dug deer pitfalls 10 or

12 feet deep by means of sticks, and carried the earth away in baskets" (Mason, O. T., 1902: 467, 473).

Pitt Mountain (Bushnell, D. I., Jr., 1938: 20) (now Mount McLoughlin in Jackson County, Oreg.), although formerly spelled with two t's, and Pit River in northeastern California (Brown, T. P., 1934: 28 p.), as well as a few other local place names are so called from the pitfalls formerly dug there by Indians.

Pits made by the Indians for catching wolves were noted by some of the earlier explorers of the plains regions, particularly in the areas inhabited by the Mandans. Some were recorded in 1806 near the mouth of the Knife River in North Dakota, that were about 10 feet deep by 30 feet wide at the bottom but only 5 feet broad at the top. They were apparently made only where the runway used by the wolf narrowed and the opening corresponded to the width of the travelway. This narrow opening was carefully covered with a matting of grass. In the bottoms of these pits the Indians often drove inverted sticks that were sharpened to acute points, which protruded upwards, so that when a wolf fell through the camouflaged opening at the top of the pit, it was punctured at some point, a wounding which might or might not produce rapid death.

Maximilian, Prince of Wied, while in the Mandan country along the Missouri River in December, 1833, had an opportunity to view such a wolf pit. He writes: "At this spot 1,000 or 1,200 Sioux had attacked the United Mandans and Manitaries thirty years before, but lost 100 of their people. One of those Indians was afraid to proceed on this path, because he suspected that wolf pit, or trap, might be in the way, but the partisan or chief, wishing to shame him, went before, and actually fell into such a pit, with sharpened sticks at the bottom, by which he was killed.

"We had here an opportunity of seeing the wolf pits, in which the Indians fix sharp stakes, and the whole is so covered with brushwood, hay, and dry grass, that it cannot be perceived" (Maximilian, Prince of Wied, 1906, vol. 24, pp. 21, 23).

There is record near the close of the sixteenth century of a deep pit, or animal trap, being dug by Indians of western New Mexico. It was into this trap that Captain Gaspar Perez de Villagran fell with his horse while in search of his leader Oñate, whom he had failed to find at the pueblo of Puaray, on the west bank of the Rio Grande opposite present-day Bernalillo, N. Mex. Villagran had returned to that point from a trek to Chihuahua, Mexico, that he had made in the fall of 1598, and failing to find Oñate, he struck out westward through present-day Valencia County, toward Moqui in search of him, when he rode into the pit mentioned. He was more fortunate than the Indian chief just mentioned for though hurt and stunned he was able to extricate himself. His horse, however, was killed.

As near as this record can be interpreted, the pit was concealed in a way similar to those previously described. Whether these New Mexican Indians had by this time learned of pit entrapment of wild animals from their neighbors to the south, or whether they had invented the device themselves, has not as yet been determined (Lummis, C. F., 1920: 145).

White men colonizing the Atlantic seaboard used pitfalls whenever needed.

Near the town of Northampton, Mass., is a swamp known today as "Wolf Pit Swamp," a name doubtless perpetuating an early attempt at wolf control.

Freeman records for Barnstable County [Mass.], 1643 — "Wolves were making great depredations upon herds and flocks, wolf-traps were ordered by the Colony Court to be made." These may have been pit- or possibly dead-falls (Freeman, F., 1852: 171).

Sewall found amongst the early colonial records of Woburn in Middlesex County, Mass., the following notation: "Among other noted places in Woburn, in former days, was 'the Ould Wolfe penne,' apparently referring to a wolf pit that had been in use, and possibly built by one Izack Brooks" (Sewall, S., 1868: 57).

The use of the wolf-pit on early-day Long Island, N. Y., is recorded in the provision for a bounty promulgated by the settlers of Jamaica. Here on January 16, 1661, the authorities "ordered that a rate be made to pay for a wolf of Abraham's killing, and one that John Townsend's pit catched. . . ." (Dutcher, W., 1887: 105).

Pits for the capture of wolves were used along the seacoast of New Jersey. Samuel N. Rhoads reports some being shown to him in 1891 that had been used in the early days. They were in the vicinity of Tuckerton in the southern part of Ocean County, and similar pits were still to be observed at that time (1891) even farther south.

Use of wolf pits along the shoreline of New Jersey was unquestionably a defense against the depredations of wolves upon the stock, such as swine, sheep, cattle, and horses brought over by the colonists. From Cape May on the south to a point near Barnegat Bay on the north, an airline distance of about 84 miles, are to be found beaches which in colonial days afforded excellent pasturage for livestock. The stock was ear-marked, turned loose on these grounds, and handled much as on the open ranges of the West at the present time. This system gave the wolves a good opportunity and required the wolf pits as a partial means of control.

The utilization of sea beaches for open grazing of stock still prevails on some portions of the Atlantic coast, as on the eastern shore of Maryland and Virginia and on the barrier beaches of North Carolina.

From the Atlantic seaboard, the wolf pit scheme of wolf capture gradually came into use westward, eventually reaching the Pacific coast.

Its use in Pennsylvania was referred to as pitfall hunting. Shoemaker narrates that: "In the Seven Mountains, in Centre and Mifflin Counties, the old settlers used this method of trapping Pennsylvania black wolves. Daniel Karstetter, who was born near the Blue Rock, on the Karoondinha (John Penn's Creek) in 1824, and died in Sugar Valley in 1907, maintained several of these pits near his hunting camp at Greenbriar knob. A haunch of venison or a dead sheep was usually placed in the pits, which were eight feet deep, broadest at the bottom so as to render it impossible for the most active animals to escape from them. The mouth of each pit was covered with a revolving platform of boughs and twigs, and attached to a cross piece of timber, which served as an axle. When the hungry animals scented the bait and sprang on the covering it revolved, hurling the brutes, sometimes two or three at a time, into the pit below. Often Karstetter's cabin was entirely 'weather-boarded' with wolf hides obtained in this way. Susquehanny County, where 'animal drives' were practiced to rid the section of wolves and other more or less troublesome animals, was also the scene of much 'pitfall' hunting. An aged German hunter from the Schwarzwald in the Old Country, was a leader in this pastime" (Shoemaker, H. W., 1919, vol. 2, p. 28).

One of the earliest Americans to comment upon the use of wolf pits was William Byrd, long connected with the development and progress of early Virginia, and the eventual founder of Richmond.

Concerning the wolf pit in colonial Virginia, and its apparent efficiency, Byrd stated in 1728 that:

"The inhabitants hereabouts take the trouble to dig abundance of wolf-pits, so deep and perpendicular, that when a wolf is once tempted into them, he can no more scramble out again than a husband who has taken the leap can scramble out of matrimony" (Byrd, W., 1901: 78).

Wailes recorded the means used for the capture of wolves in Mississippi during earlier days, among them pits:

"They are taken in pens or traps made of poles, and baited with fresh meat, which is previously dragged over the ground for miles through the woods near their haunts, to lure them to the trail. Pits are also constructed with a slight covering of twigs and leaves, into which they fall in attempting to reach the bait suspended over them" (Wailes, B. L. C., 1854: 314).

Audubon noted wolf pits being used in Indiana in 1843 while he was traveling to Vincennes. Of these he wrote:

". . . . we chanced to stop for the night at the house of a farmer, ... After putting up our horses and refreshing ourself, we entered into conversation with our worthy host, and were invited by him to visit the wolf pits which he had constructed about a half a mile from the house. . . . we accompanied him across the fields to the skirts of the adjoining forest where he had three pits within a few hundred yards of each other. They were about eight feet deep, broadest at the bottom, so as to render it impossible for the most active animal to escape from them. The mouth of each pit was covered with a revolving platform of boughs and twigs, interlaced together and attached to a cross piece of timber, which served for an axle. On this light sort of platform, which was balanced by a heavy stick of wood fastened to the under side, a large piece of putrid venison was tied for bait. After examining all of the pits, we returned to the house, our companion remarking that he was in the habit of visiting his pits daily, in order to see that all was right; that the wolves had been very bad that season, had destroyed nearly all his sheep, and had killed one of his colts. 'But,' added he, 'I am now paying them off in full, and if I have any luck, you will see some fun in the morning.' With this expectation we retired to rest, and were up at day-light. 'I think,' said our host, 'that all is right; for I see the dogs are anxious to get away to the pits, and although they are nothing but curs, their noses are pretty keen for wolves.' As he took up his gun and axe and a large knife, the dogs began to howl and bark and whisked around as if full of delight. When we reached the first pit, we found the bait had been disturbed and the platform was somewhat injured, but the animal was not in the pit. On examining the second pit, we discovered three famous fellows safe enough in it, two black and one brindle, all of good size. They were lying flat on the earth, with their ears close down to their heads, their eyes indicating fear more than anger. To our astonishment the farmer proposed descending into the pit to hamstring them, in order to haul them up, and then allow them to be killed by the dogs, which, he said, would sharpen his curs for an encounter with the wolves, should any come near his house in the future. . . . he glided down, on a knobbed pole, taking his axe and knife with him, and leaving his rifle to our care. We were not a little surprised at the cowardice of the wolves. The woodman stretched out their hind legs, in succession, and with a stroke of the knife cut the principal tendon above the joint, exhibiting as little fear as if he had been marking lambs. As soon as he had thus disabled the wolves, he got out, but had to return to the house for a rope, which he had not thought of. He returned quickly, and whilst I secured the platform in a perpendicular position on its axis, he made a slip knot at one end of the rope, and threw it over the head of one of the wolves. We now hauled the terrified animal up; and motionless with fright, half choked, and disabled in its hind legs, the farmer slipped the rope from its neck, and left it to the mercy of the dogs, who set upon it with great fury and worried it to death. The second was dealt with in the same manner; but the third, which was probably the oldest, showed some spirit the moment the dogs were set upon it, and scuffled along on its forelegs at a surprising rate, snapping all the while furiously at the dogs, several of which it bit severely; and so well did the desperate animal defend itself that the farmer, apprehensive of its killing some of his pack, ran up and knocked it on the head with his axe. This wolf was a female, and was blacker than the other dark coloured one" (Audubon, J. J., and Bachman, J., 1851-54, vol. 2, p. 129).

CORRALS

The corral type of wolf trap used by the Blackfoot Indians was made by digging a deep trench in which were set heavy 8 to 10 foot posts tied closely together and slanted inward at an angle of 45 degrees. This trap was generally 12 feet in diameter, and when completed had the appearance of a truncated cone. Bait in the form of meat was placed on the inside of the structure. On the outside of this trap, earth was heaped up at one place so as to afford an easy approach. An animal lured to the top would leap down a distance of 8 feet to the bait, but could not escape because of the funnel-shaped enclosure. These traps were generally constructed in the larger, meadow-like openings of river or creek bottoms, and were efficient in the earlier days when wolves were common on the plains.

George Bird Grinnell, who lived with and was adopted by the Blackfeet, notes the use of these corral traps, and records that Hugh Monroe caught 83 wolves and coyotes in one of them in a single night (Grinnell, G. B., 1892: 241).

DEADFALLS

In the early 1800's the so-called "log trap" or deadfall was more or less widely used in wolf capture. It was made by raising one log above another at one end by means of an upright stick, which rested upon a rounded horizontal trigger on the lower log. This device was very similar to the Figure 4 trap, but used one stick less in the tripping mechanism. The log held in suspension by the perpendicular stick was of heavy dimensions and was raised sufficiently high to permit the wolf to enter under it in full stature. Occasionally two or three upper logs would be lashed together to give added weight, as would the under logs, to form a platform. The suspended logs would sometimes have a fall of more than 6 feet. The horizontal trigger, to which was attached the bait, extended well back under the raised log. This trigger was notched so that the upright stick could be firmly fitted into it, and the weight of the log caused the horizontal trigger to assume a 45-degree angle. This device was intended to crush the wolf by means of the heavy upright log held in place by the upright stick and the horizontal trigger until the latter was sufficiently disturbed by the wolf while trying to remove the bait. When the trap worked according to plan, the wolf was generally caught in the middle of the back and was instantly killed.

Lewis and Clark mention the use of deadfalls "in taking the wolf, the raccoon and fox . . . ." by the several tribes they became conversant with while at Fort Clatsop which they built near the mouth of the Columbia River in the late fall of 1805 (Lewis, M., and Clark, W., 1905: 347).

ICE BOXTRAP

This device used by the Eskimos seeming to be intermediate between a boxtrap and a deadfall may be termed the "ice boxtrap." One of the best descriptions is given by Richardson in his *Fauna Boreali-Americana*. He states: "The wolf trap is made of strong slabs of ice, long and narrow, so that a fox can with difficulty turn himself in it, but a wolf must actually remain in the position in which he is taken. The door is a heavy portcullis of ice, sliding in two well-secured grooves of the same substance, and is kept up by a line which, passing over the top of the trap, is carried through a hole at the further extremity; to the end of the line is fastened a small hoop of whalebone, and to this any kind of flesh bait is attached. From the slab which terminates the trap, a projection of ice, or a peg of wood or bone, points inward near the bottom, and under this the hoop is lightly hooked; the slightest pull at the bait liberates it, the door falls in an instant, and the wolf is speared where he lies" (Richardson, J., 1829: 65).

Many of the ingenious devices employed by Eskimos today have been handed down from one generation to another for centuries. Commenting on the absence of wolves in South Greenland, MacMillan states: "It is evident, however, that at one time they did inhabit this section, since the Norsemen upon their arrival in 986 [A. D.] reported finding wolf traps, such as are built by Eskimos of today."[29]

EDGE TRAP

An ingenious device, the "edge trap," as described by Otis T. Mason, was a mechanism in which "blades are attached to one end of a lever, the other end of which is inclosed in a torsion spring of rawhide. The animal stops to pick the bait, pulls the trigger and releases the unstable hook catch; the knives fly over and the victim is brained" (Mason, O. T., 1902; 467, 473).

PIERCERS

Probably one of the cruelest devices used in killing the wolf is that ingenious scheme employed by the Eskimo, wherein a slender

---

[29]Letter dated April 11, 1941, from Donald B. MacMillan, Provincetown, Mass., to E. A. Goldman; in files of Fish and Wildlife Service, Washington, D. C.

piece of whalebone (that is baleen from the upper jaw of the bow-head whale) is employed. Grenold Collins, formerly of the Alaska Game Commission, gives a good description of this method of wolf killing. He observes:

"The whalebone springs are coiled and folded in an 'S' shape or bent double to make a bundle of the proper size to be swallowed easily by a wolf but too large to be bolted by foxes. The spring is moistened to enable bending without breaking the fibre.

"Seal fat or blubber is then wrapped around the whalebone and the tension held by tying with sinew. The bait is then put out to freeze. After freezing the sinew is cut and the bait ready for use. The owner's mark . . . . is cut into the whalebone spring to identify the kill.

"These baits can then be distributed all through the wolf area. When swallowed by the animal the fat thaws out, releasing the whalebone, which springs out and pierces the wolf's stomach" (Collins, G., 1937a).

Collins further observes that:

"During the spring and summer this method can be used by dipping the spring into warm tallow. When a sufficient covering is made to hold the spring the sinew is removed and the bait is ready for use. Various scents, such as castor, may be added.

"One advantage in the whalebone method is that thousands of baits can be distributed at very small expense. Also, if a band of wolves gets to these baits, the whole pack may swallow some before the alarm is given. If one or two wolves out of a pack is caught in a trap the rest of the wolves escape and become more difficult to catch. By the use of seal oil and other scents the wolves could be led into the vicinity of a large number of baits.

"The old natives claim that a wolf does not travel far after swallowing a piece of whalebone but lies down because of the pain and either dies there or is found by the natives. Other wolves will often turn on and kill one that is stricken with a whalebone spring." (Ibid.)

Freuchen records the use of the whalebone device by the Eskimos in the Hudson Bay region. (Freuchen, P., 1935b: 123.)

A related contrivance for killing wolves was that dubbed the "wolf knife." Mason describes it as follows: "A sharpened blade was enclosed in a frozen mass of fat and stuck up in a block of ice. The wolf, licking the fat, cut its tongue. The taste of blood in-

Plate 84. Low tide-water scene between two southeast islands of Alaska, near Petersburg, showing typical wolf crossing in center of picture

Plate 85. A view of the tide-water set used very effectively in southeast Alaska in trapping wolves

furiated the animal, so that by licking the knife more it caused a larger flow of blood. All the members of the pack were attracted to the same spot, devouring one another for the sake of the blood, till all were destroyed" (Mason, O. T., 1902: 467, 473).

Peter Freuchen describes in very similar terms the use of an embedded knife by the Eskimos and adds:

"Still another method, used by the Netsilik who have no baleen (whalebone) is to bind up a gull wing with sinew thread and leave it for the wolf to swallow: this too is said to be unfailing in its effect. And finally, in recent times it has become a common practice to throw broken glass [probably mixed with baits] to the wolves. The Eskimos assert that they never lose a wolf when hunted by these methods, as they always die quite close, so that it is easy to find them" (Freuchen, P., 1935b: 123).

Probably best included here is a statement by Norton, quoting Josselyn [1672], giving an interesting description of a control device developed in New England. This was made by "binding 4 Maycril Hooks across with a brown thread, and then wrapping some Wool about them, they dip them in melted Tallow till it be as round as an Egg; these (when any Beast hath been Killed by the Wolves) they scatter by the dead CarKase, after they have beaten off the Wolves; about Midnight the Wolves are sure to return again to the place where they left the slaughtered Beast, and the first thing they venture upon will be these balls of fat" (Norton, A. H., 1930: 42).

FISH HOOKS

Speaking of the wolf as noticed by him while on an exploratory journey in the late summer of 1817 in the Columbia River drainage between what he called She-waps and the Rocky Mountains, Ross tells us that:

"During the winter season a good many wolves and foxes are caught by the whites, with hook and line as we catch fish; with this difference, however, that the latter are taken in water, the former on dry land. For this purpose three cod-hooks are generally tied together back to back, baited, and then fixed with a line to the branch of a tree, so that the hooks are suspended in the air at the distance of four or five feet from the ground. To get hold of the bait, the wolf has to leap up, and the moment the hooks catch hold it finds itself either in a standing or suspended position, which deprives the animal of its strength; neither can it in that posture cut the line; it is generally caught sometimes dead, sometimes alive" (Ross, A., 1855: 166).

SNARES

Doubtless these devices known to every trapper were often used to catch wolves, but our material includes only one published mention of them. George Bird Grinnell writing of the Blackfeet Indians says:

"Deadfalls were used to catch wolves, foxes, and other fur animals, and small apertures in the pis'kun walls (a large corral used to capture buffalo) were provided with nooses and snares for the same purpose." (Grinnell, G. B., 1892: 240.)

SET GUNS

The first mention of the so-called "set" or "wolf gun" in the United States that has come to our attention relates to Long Island, N. Y. There, it seems, the general court, sitting at Easthampton March 7, 1650, "Ordered that any man may set guns to kill wolves, provided they be not set within half a mile of the town, and also to take up the guns by sunrise; . . . ." (Dutcher, W., 1887: 105.)

Towards the close of the nineteenth century, the set gun was used on some of the western stock ranges in attempts by stock owners to kill particular wolves that had succeeded in avoiding every other means of capture employed against them. The mechanism used was simple. A 12-gauge shotgun, loaded with buckshot, a 30-30 rifle, or in some instances a .38 revolver, was employed. The gun or revolver was placed at a right angle to the runway of the wolf at some narrow point. Often the gun was securely fastened by straps or wires to a stump or boulder. A bait was placed on the muzzle of the gun, to which was attached a small cord that ran down the barrel towards the breech and through a screw eye attached there. The cord ran from the screw eye and was tied to the trigger of the cocked hammer. When the animal came along its runway, scented the bait, and tugged at it, the pull transmitted through the cord would release the trigger and discharge the gun. The whole action took place within a split second and as the wolf's head or front quarters were in direct line with the muzzle of the gun, its death was inevitable.

This scheme never became widely used in the United States, however, because of the hazard involved to other animals and to man.

The "set gun" as it was used for killing wolves in the Canadian North is described by Ross as follows:

"This is a very sure method though rather dangerous to the hunter, if he do not take great care. The gun is tied upon two saplings or stakes, set on purpose, opposite the trigger is another thinner stick firmly planted on the ground, a piece of wood is laid across this stick, one end pressing the trigger, the other attached to a line to the other extremity of which the bait is affixed. This line is carried under the snow by boring holes in pieces of board and passing it through them; this also prevents the animal from pulling the bait out of the aim of the gun, which he [the wolf] discharges as soon as he hauls upon the line to obtain the meat. Instances have been known of wolves cutting the line close to the trigger of the gun, after which they eat the bait in safety" (Ross, B. R., 1861: 12).

STEEL TRAPS, SCENTS, AND THEIR USE

Modern Use of Steel Wolf Traps and of Scents

Modern wolf trapping technique, comprising the use of steel traps and scents, involves divers schemes on the part of those engaged in the art. Generally speaking, each wolf trapper has some carefully guarded plan that he believes to surpass anything possessed by others. By and large, however, everyone engaged in wolf trapping must basically consider that every wild animal possesses some defense against danger. With wolves this comprises an acute sense of smell, alert hearing, and keen eyesight. To trap these animals successfully, one must work to defeat these highly developed senses when placing traps, and success in so doing will come only with knowledge of the habits of the predator and after repeated experiments with trap sets. The wolf is the most difficult of our larger predators to trap. It is cunning, and as it matures from the yearling to the adult stage its cleverness at times becomes uncanny.

The steel trap in sizes 4, 4½, and 14 (114 in Alaska), is recommended for capturing wolves. American steel wolf traps apparently modeled from the early day beaver trap which in turn was modeled in colonial times from the steel rat trap of England have been used in this country by many generations of trappers, and although deemed by many persons to be inhumane, no better or more practical device is yet available to take their place (Ballantyne, R. M., 1859: 42).

As noted previously, on the open range wolves have what are commonly referred to as "scent posts," or places where they come to urinate. The animals usually establish these posts along their runways on stubble of range grasses, on bushes, or old bleached-out carcasses. Where ground conditions are right for good tracking, these scent posts may be detected from the toenail scratches on the ground made by the animals after they have urinated. This habit of having scent posts and of scratching is similar to that familiar in dogs. As wolves pass over their travel ways, they generally stop at these posts, invariably voiding fresh urine and occasionally excreta also.

Finding these scent posts is of prime importance, for it is there that traps should be set. If a natural scent station can not be found, artificial ones can be readily established along the travelway on clusters of weeds, spears of grass, or stubble of low brush. The trap should then be set at this point. Any number of scent stations can be scattered along the wolf runway.

Time consumed in finding a wolf scent post is well spent, for the success of a trap set depends upon its location. Wolves can not be caught unless traps are set and concealed where the animals will step into them. If traps are placed where the animals are not accustomed to stop on their travelways, the chances are that they will pass them by on the run. Even if a wolf should detect the scent, the fact that it is in an unnatural place may arouse the suspicion of the animal and cause it to make a detour. Often the fresh tracks of shod horses along wolf runways are sufficient to cause the predator to leave the trail for some distance. A lone wolf is much more cautious than a family of wolves running together.

Travelways of wolves are confined to open and more or less broken country. In foraging for food over these runways the animals may use trails of cattle or sheep, canyons, old wood roads, dry washes, low saddles on watershed divides, or even highways in thinly settled areas. Any one of these places, or any combination of them, may as previously mentioned form part of a wolf runway. Wolves as has been noted have been known to cover a circuitous route of more than a hundred miles in an established runway.

Places where carcasses of animals killed by wolves or of animals that have died from natural causes have lain a long time offer excellent spots for setting traps, for wolves often revisit them. It is always best to set the traps a few yards away from the carcasses at weeds, bunches of grass, or low stubble of bushes. Other good situations are at the intersection of two or more trails, around old bedding grounds of sheep, and at water holes on the open range.

Traps used should be clean, with no foreign odor. In making a set, a hole the length and width of the trap with jaws open is dug with a trowel, a sharpened piece of angle iron, or a prospector's pick. While digging, the trapper stands or kneels on a "setting cloth," about 3 feet square, made of canvas or of a piece of sheep or calf hide (Pl. 78). If canvas is used, the human scent may be removed by previously burying it in an old manure pile. The livestock scent acquired in this process is usually strong enough to counteract any man scent later adhering to the setting cloth and likely to arouse suspicion. The dirt removed from the hole dug to bed the trap is placed on the setting cloth. The trap is then placed in the hole and firmly bedded so as to rest perfectly level.

Instead of using digging tools, some hunters bed the trap where the ground is loose, as in sandy loam, by holding it by the base and with a circular motion working it slowly into the ground even with the surface and then removing the dirt from under the pan before placing the trap pad to be described later. An important advantage of this method is that there is less disturbance of the ground around the scent post than when tools are used, for the secret of setting a trap successfully is to leave the ground as natural appearing as it was before the trap was concealed.

The trap may be anchored or left unanchored. Either draghooks may be attached to a chain (preferably 6 feet long) fastened by a swivel to the trap base or to a spring, and all buried underneath, or a steel stake pin (Pl. 78) may be used, attached by a swivel to a 6-foot chain fastened to the base or a spring of the trap. If a stake pin is used, it should be driven full length into the ground near the right-hand spring of the trap, with the trigger and pan directly toward the operator (Pl. 78). Anchoring the trap is the preferred method, because the wolves caught are obtained without loss of time and because other wolves are not scared away by one of their kind dragging about a dangling, clanking trap, as may occur when drag hooks are used.

The next stage (Pl. 79) is the careful burying of the trap and building up of a so-called shoulder around and under the pan. This should be so built that, when it is completed, the shape of the ground within the jaws of the trap represents an inverted cone, in order to give a foundation for the pan cover, commonly called the "trap pad." The trap pad may be made of canvas, of old "slicker cloth," or even of a piece of ordinary wire fly screen cut into the shape shown in Plate 80. The trap pad, to be effective, must bear no foreign odor that might arouse the suspicion of the wolf.

In placing the trap pad over the pan and onto the dirt built up for carrying it, the utmost care must be taken to see that no rock, pebble, or dirt slips under the pan, which would prevent the trap from springing. With the trap pad in place (Pl. 80), the entire trap is carefully covered with the earth remaining on the setting cloth (Pl. 78).

Cover traps at least half an inch deep with dry dust if possible. It is well to have the covered surface over the trap a little lower than the surrounding ground, for a wolf is then less apt to scratch and expose the trap without springing it. Furthermore, the animal will throw more weight on a foot placed in a depression, and thus is more likely to be caught higher on the foot and with a firmer grip. All surplus earth on the setting cloth not needed for covering the trap should be taken a good distance away and scattered evenly on the ground.

A few drops of scent are now applied to the weed, cluster of grass, or stubble used as the scent post or on the ground 6 or 8 inches from the place where the trap is set. The farther from the travel-way the trap is set, the more scent will be needed. A little of the scent should be rubbed on the trapper's gloves and shoe soles to conceal the human odor.

A scent tested and successfully used by the Government hunters is made as follows:

Put into a bottle the urine and the gall of a wolf and also the anal glands, which are situated under the skin on either side of the vent and resemble small pieces of bluish fat. If these glands cannot be readily found, the whole anal parts may be used. To every 3 ounces of the mixture add 1 ounce of glycerine, to give it body and to prevent too rapid evaporation, and 1 grain of corrosive sublimate to keep it from spoiling.

Let the mixture stand several days, then shake well before using.

In the absence of genuine wolf scent or to use as an alternate bait an effective fish scent may be prepared in the following way:

Grind the flesh of sturgeon, eels, suckers, carp, or some other oily variety of so-called rough fish in a sausage mill, place in strong tin or iron cans, and leave in a warm place of even temperature to decompose thoroughly. Provide each can with a small vent to allow the escape of gas (otherwise there is danger of explosion), but screen the aperture with a fold of cloth to prevent flies from depositing eggs, as the scent seems to lose much of its quality if many maggots develop. This scent may be used within 3 days after it is prepared, but it is more lasting and penetrating after a lapse of 30 days. It is also very attractive to livestock, and its use on heavily stocked ranges is not recommended, as cattle are attracted to the scent stations and will spring the traps.

An excellent system for a hunter to follow is to commence with a quantity of ground fish placed in large iron containers similar to a milk can. As the original lot is used on the trap line, it should be replenished by adding more ground fresh fish. The addition from time to time of new material seems to improve the quality of the scent mixture.

When no moisture has fallen, renewing of scent posts need be done only every four or five days. In wet weather doing it every third day is good practice. For dropping the scent it is convenient to use a 2 to 4 ounce shaker-corked bottle.

The actual trapping of a wolf by the method here described occurs when the animal comes over its runway and is attracted to the "post" by the scent that has been dropped. In approaching the spot for a smell the animal puts a foot on the concealed pan; the jaws are thus released and the foot is securely held. The place where a wolf has thus been caught affords an excellent location for a reset, due to the scent left by the animal while in the trap.

It is advisable always to wear gloves while setting traps and to use them for no other purpose than trap setting.

Decoys have sometimes been successfully employed as an aid in trapping wolves. Individuals reared in captivity have been picketed on a runway and traps set around them. It has been observed that a tame wolf staked out away from its home will invariably respond to the howl of a wild one, thus attracting the latter.

Attempts have been made to use a whelp fastened near the entrance of a den as a decoy to trap the parents. In all such instances the whelp has been killed presumably by the female wolf when she found she could not remove it.

THE TIDEWATER SET

The tidewater wolf set herewith illustrated (Pl. 85) has been successfully used by several wolf trappers in southeastern Alaska.

A suitable location is any place where the ebbing tide leaves a shallow pool of water for several hours each day and night. A dead seal makes the best lure. The carcass should be well scored with an ax or knife, then dragged into one of these shallow pools and covered with heavy rocks. In a short time the decaying flesh and fat produces a strong scent, and a thin scum of oil forms on the surface of the pool near the rock pile.

Traps may be set in a ring around the rock pile, where each will be covered with from 6 to 10 inches of water at all times, and may be fastened either to clogs made by wiring the traps to rocks, or to grapples. From 4 to 8 traps may be set at one location. The first high tide should wash away human scent, leaving a set that proves very attractive to the wolves and which requires but little care except in extremely cold weather when ice may form over the pool.

Such a set has taken as many as 3 wolves in a single night, and at the end of five years I found one that was taking wolves regularly near Petersburg, Alaska.

The tidewater wolf set is used by homesteaders, fox ranchers of southeastern Alaska, and others who are located where they can keep it working all the time.

Occasionally where no shallow pool exists near a low tide wolf-crossing from one island to another, a hunter may dig out a saucer-like depression, 6 to 8 feet in diameter and 6 inches to a foot in depth, which will be covered with water at flood tide. Thus, when low tide comes, a desirable pool will be available for placing the dead seal as a lure, as well as the traps around it.

THE MUSKEG SET

In southeastern Alaska some wolf trappers also utilize muskegs where wolves travel, as locations for trap setting. In so doing they place the traps just below the water level, covering the trap pan with moss (lichens) and the trap with bog slime which is kept as wet as possible. Short moss is then pulled and thrown, a small pinch at a time, into the slime, where it will keep on growing and render the trap set as natural in appearance as the surroundings. It has been found that by setting the traps below the water level, they will keep comparatively free from rust and in perfect working order. A muskeg set may be blind, that is, so that a wolf will step into it as it comes over the runway; or scent may be employed on an established scent post at the usual distance employed with traps set in dry ground.

SNOW AND ICE SETS

Setting of wolf traps in localities where snow and ice prevail requires special care. Particular caution must be taken in snow because it is very porous and any foreign odor on the trap will often not be sealed in. Also, rise and fall of temperature make it difficult to operate snow sets. Trappers, by preference therefore, often place trap sets in the ice of glacier streams, where wolf runways occur, and selecting places that are not subject to overflow, for here the temperature of the ice varies less than that of snow.

When a snow set is to be used, the hunter tramps down the snow with snowshoes, making a half-moon-shaped depression near a trail made by sled or snowshoe and in front of a low bush or similar object satisfactory for a scent post. Another deep depression the shape of the set trap is made nearby. There the trap-stake that will hold the trap and chain or drag-hook is driven in the bottom. An inch or so of light screened earth is placed in this depression, upon which the trap is laid. A flat chip is then put under the loose trap jaw, and the trap is made to lay solid in the bed. A half-inch of fine, dry earth is then applied so that all the metal of the trap is encased. This is followed by a covering of snow, and every attempt is made to leave the spot as natural-looking as possible.

In making the ice set, a hole is cut to receive the trap. The trap-stake is then driven into the bottom, on top of which a few drops of water are poured to aid in freezing the trap-stake in the ice. From this point on the procedure is the same as for the snow set.

In all wolf trapping, the climatic factor determines which technique is to be employed by those that have been developed by many outdoorsmen and woodsmen since the beginning of the use of steel traps by trappers in North America.

A variety of means are used by wolf trappers in deodorizing their traps. Some bury them for a period in a manure pile, others cook the traps in a tea made by boiling one bushel of hemlock bark for an hour in 20 gallons of water. Alder bark or leaves are sometimes substituted for hemlock. The modern wolf trapper never uses paraffin, oils, or other rust preventatives on wolf traps because of the odor that remains, which would cause a wolf to become suspicious and avoid the set.

HUNTING

Ring Hunts and Drives

A form of wolf hunting comparable to the much-later-day "jack rabbit drives" of the West was in vogue during certain periods of the settlement of the United States.

They were called "ring-hunts" or "circular hunts." As conducted in the Wabash Valley, Ind., they are described by S. C. Cox (1860):

" 'Black, gray and prairie wolves were quite numerous, and in many localities it was next to impossible to raise sheep or pigs until they had been hunted out. The Legislature enacted laws granting a bounty on wolf scalps, sufficient to stimulate a more active and thorough extermination of these noisy serenaders, who often approach within a few rods of the cabin, and make night hideous with their prolonged howling. Wolf hunts were then common in which the inhabitants of several neighborhoods and sometimes of a whole county, took part. They were usually conducted in the following manner: The territory to be hunted over was circumscribed by four lines, sufficiently distant from each other to enclose the proper area. To each line was assigned a captain, with his subaltern officers, whose duty it was to properly station his men along the line; and at the hour agreed upon to cause them to advance in order towards the center, on horseback, with dogs, guns, and clubs, thus completely investing whatever game was within the lines, and scaring it from the advancing lines toward the center where the excitement of the chase was greatly heightened, and the greatest carnage ensued. Often from two to ten wolves and as many deer were taken in a day at these hunts, and wild cats, foxes and catamounts in abundance. Horses and dogs soon became fond of the sport, and seemed to enter into it with a zest surpassing that of their masters' " (Lyon, M. W., Jr., 1936: 153).

Throughout New England in earlier times, a form of the so-called "circular ring hunts" for wolves and other predators was often put into operation as a means of ridding certain sections of these animals. Beals humorously describes one of these events that transpired in early day New Hampshire "with an account of the famous siege of wolves which took place in 1830. Although the battle took place in Tamworth, nevertheless it was from our mountains that the wolves descended upon that town, and to our mountain fastnesses the surviving wolves retreated after the battle.

"All this region, during the first third of the nineteenth century, abounded in moose, deer, bears, wolves, and perhaps panthers. On the evening of Nov. 14 couriers rode furiously through Tamworth and the surrounding towns, proclaiming that 'Countless numbers' of wolves had come down from the Sandwich Range mountains and had established themselves in the woods on Marston Hill. All able-bodied males, from ten years old to eighty, were therefore summoned to report at Marston Hill by daylight on the following morning.

"Marston Hill was crowned by about twenty acres of woods, entirely surrounded by cleared land. Sentinels were posted around the hill and numerous fires were lighted to prevent the wolves from effecting a return to the mountains. All through the night a continuous and hideous howling was kept up by the besieged wolves and answering howls came from the slopes of the great mountains. The shivering besiegers were regaled with food and hot coffee furnished by the women of the country-side throughout their long lonely watch.

"All night long reinforcements kept arriving. By daylight there were six hundred men and boys on the scene, armed with rifles, shot-guns, pitchforks, and clubs. A council of war was held and a plan of campaign agreed upon. General Quimby, of Sandwich, a war-seasoned veteran, was made commander-in-chief. The general immediately detailed a thin line of sharpshooters to surround the hill, while the main body formed a strong line ten paces in the rear of the skirmishers. The sharpshooters then were commanded to advance towards the center, that is, towards the top of the hill. The firing began. The reports of the rifles and the unearthly howling of wolves made the welkin ring. The beleaguered animals, frenzied by the ring of flame and noise, and perhaps by wounds, made repeated attempts to break through 'the thin red line,' but all in vain. They were driven back into the woods, where they unceasingly continued running, making it difficult for the marksmen to hit them. In about an hour the order was given for the main line to advance, which was done.

"Closing in on the center, the circular battle-line at last massed itself in a solid body on the hilltop, where, for the first time in sixteen hours, the troops raised their voices above a whisper, bursting into wild hurrahs of victory. Joseph Gilman records that few of the besieged wolves escaped. But the historian of Carroll County maintains that the greater part of the frantic animals broke through the line of battle and escaped to the mountains whence they had come. Returning to the great rock on which the commander-in-chief had established headquarters, the victorious warriors laid their trophies at the feet of their leader—four immense wolves—and once more gave thrice three thundering cheers.

"The little army then formed column, with the general, in a barouche, as its head. In the barouche also reposed the bodies of the slain wolves. After a rapid march of 35 minutes, the triumphant volunteers entered the village and formed a hollow square in front of the hotel, the general, mounted on the top of his barouche, being in the center of the square. What a cheering and waving of handkerchiefs by the ladies in windows and on balconies, there was! General Quimby then made a speech befitting the occasion, after which the thirsty soldiers stamped to the bar to assuage the awful thirst engendered by twenty mortal hours of abstinence and warfare" (Beals, C. E., 1916: 269).

Apparently this scheme was employed as a method of wolf control in several of the States bordering the Mississippi on the east, and undoubtedly was the forerunner of the coyote drive, which is still utilized in certain parts of the Far West.

This is perhaps the best place to mention the single drive, the men not necessarily converging in a ring. It was no doubt employed in all periods of the combating of wolves. An early American instance is recorded by Arnold for Rhode Island. "Wolves are often mentioned in the records of Aquedneck, as in Jan. 1658, when Portsmouth asked Newport to aid in driving the island, and again on 10th

Nov., 1663, when 'the island was to be driven the next fair day on account of the destruction of sheep by wolves and other vermin.' On the mainland they existed much longer, and were repeatedly the subjects of legislation by the Assembly, to the close of the century and even later." (Arnold, S. G., 1859: 154.)

HAMSTRINGING AND LASSOING

Among the Indian tribes of the West and the Southwest, horses were trained to carry their riders close to the side of a running buffalo and the Comanche Indians had a contrivance for hamstringing an animal in pursuit. This consisted of a crescent-shaped piece of sharp iron that was passed under the left flank of the animal as it fell away from the horse and rider, which severed the tendons of the right leg, thus bringing the animal speedily to the ground. This practice was sometimes used on a wolf by the Comanches.

Running the animals on the open plain was a sport engaged in later by the cowboy, who, however, used the lasso in place of the sickle-shaped iron to bring down the wolf. After which it was either dragged along the ground and killed, or hog-tied, taken to camp and later dispatched.

USE OF DOGS

The dog as an adjunct of the shepherd has defended flocks against wolves and other marauders from the earliest years of man's pastoral existence. Throughout American history dogs have served in this way. Two comments relating to the Southwest are appended.

Abert in 1846 noticed an attempt by the natives at close herding, with the aid of dogs, horses, sheep, and cattle in northern New Mexico, as protection from various hazards, among which was the wolf (Abert, J. W., 1848: 443).

Nearly a decade earlier Gregg similarly observed that the New Mexican sheep flocks were "well guarded during the night by watchful and sagacious dogs against prowling wolves. . . ." (Thwaites, R. G., 1904-07, vol. 19, p. 322).

In earlier times dogs kept about homes or towns were able to deal with wolves.

Morton recorded that every Virginia colonial housing kept "3 or 4 mongrel dogs to destroy vermin such as wolves. . . ." (Clayton, J., 1844: 35).

In 1648 the Massachusetts General Assembly "ordered that the select men of every towne shall & hereby have power given them to purchase or procure of the townes stock so many hounds as they thinke meete, & to impose the keeping of them on such as they thinke fitest, that so all meanes may be improved for the destruction of wolves, and that no other doge shall be kept in any towne but such as the select men shall see meete: no magistrate is to have any hound imposed upon him, nor any dog taken from him, without his consent" (White, W., 1853: 252).

Later, dogs were very useful about the western ranches. An interesting account of their strivings with the wolves is here quoted from Theodore Roosevelt:

"A spirited dog will always attack a wolf. On the ranch next below mine there was a plucky bull-terrier, weighing about twenty-five pounds, who lost his life owing to his bravery. On one moonlight night three wolves came round the stable, and the terrier sallied out promptly. He made such a quick rush as to take his opponents by surprise, and seized one by the throat; nor did he let go till the other two tore him almost asunder across the loins. Better luck attended a large mongrel called a sheep dog by his master, but whose blood was apparently about equally derived from collie, Newfoundland, and bulldog. He was a sullen but very intelligent and determined brute, powerfully built and with strong jaws, and though neither as tall nor as heavy as a wolf he had yet killed two of these animals single-handed. One of them had come into the farmyard at night, and had taken a young pig, whose squeals roused everybody. The wolf loped off with his booty, the dog running after and overtaking him in the darkness. The struggle was short, for the dog had seized the wolf by the throat and the latter could not shake him off, though he made the most desperate efforts, rising on his hind legs and pressing the dog down with his forepaws. This time the victor escaped scatheless, but in his second fight, when he strangled a still larger wolf, he was severely punished. The wolf had seized a sheep, when the dog, rushing on him, caused him to leave his quarry. Instead of running he turned to bay at once, taking off one of the assailant's ears with a rapid snap. The dog did not get a good hold, and the wolf scored him across the shoulders and flung him off. They then faced each other for a minute and at the next dash the dog made good his throat hold, and throttled the wolf, though the latter contrived to get his foe's foreleg into his jaws and broke it clear through. When I saw the dog he had completely recovered, although pretty well scarred" (Roosevelt, T., 1885: 21).

The breeding of dogs especially to combat wolves was an age old practice in Europe and we have borrowed these breeds without improving upon them. One of the largest of these animals was the Irish wolfhound, about which some interesting details may be presented here.

Ireland had its share of wolf infestation and depredations, and its earlier people developed the breed of dogs known as Irish wolfhound. It was apparently this breed of dog, according to an interpretation we give to Jennison's account, that was shipped to ancient Rome during the third and fourth centuries for use in the animal shows the early Romans held in the Coliseum. It is recorded that these dogs "aroused great interest" (Jennison, G., 1937: 97). Their employment, coupled with bounty payments, dealt many staggering blows to the wolves of Ireland. These Irish wolfhounds became so useful that by 1652 Oliver Cromwell issued an Order in Council forbidding their removal to the Continent, where they were much in demand. The customs officers were hence required to seize all wolfhounds wherever and whenever attempts were made to take or smuggle them out of the country.

The introduction of wolf dogs, including coursing hounds, to this country was not without its disappointments. One pack was eaten by its intended victims (See Section on Food-Domestic Animals, p. 274). In rough terrain the coursing dogs trained to run in open country were not efficient. R. M. Allen, General Manager of the Standard Cattle Company, Ames, Nebr., stated in a letter of April 3, 1896, that his efforts to use hounds against wolves were of little avail as the dogs "cannot catch them [the wolves] in a rough country as the wolves have much greater endurance. The Allen dogs were approximately 70 in number, and though they caught few wolves, it was hoped they might eventually drive them from the range by continued chasing.

However, in the late seventies, coursing wolves with dogs, such as the greyhound and staghound breeds, was common. This form of hunting, in the main, though, was carried on more for the sport of the chase than an effective means of wolf control. As a general rule, also, there are but few running dogs that can survive a fight with a wolf. There were, however, some excellent hounds bred for running wolves, notably in Texas. However, the coursing was followed mainly with respect to coyotes in level prairie country.

Occasionally, some highly useful packs were developed, one of which is praised by Colonel Roosevelt:

"One of the most famous packs in the West was that of the Sun River Hound Club, in Montana, started by the stockmen of Sun River to get rid of the curse of wolves which infested the neighborhood and worked very serious damage to the herds and flocks" (Roosevelt, T., 1893: 408). He further comments that this pack of dogs was made up of greyhounds and deerhounds and "In the season of '86 the astonishing number of 146 wolves were killed with these dogs" (Ibid., p. 409).

In the early nineties there developed on the cattle ranges of Texas a coterie of professional wolf hunters, encouraged by the stockmen because the wolf was such a large factor in lowering the profits of the livestock business. Thus in Texas such professionals as C. G. Orr, F. B. Fuller, Ed. Paine, Jack Leonard, Bill Elliott, the Hickman brothers, "Babe" Robbins, and Vince Terry, were constantly on the job of wolf control by the use of horses and hounds. An outstanding professional wolfer of this time in northern Oklahoma, west Texas, and eastern New Mexico was Allen Stagg of Vega, Tex. Mr. Stagg followed this vocation for at least 7 years. He used as many as 64 trained dogs and a proportionate number of horses in running wolves. Bounties on wolves paid by the ranchers and the counties made the job of professional wolf hunter a paying one.

STALKING

In the Far West, some of the wolf hunters who were adept on skis used them in stalking wolves. Following every snowfall, in an area where wolves were known to occur, the hunter would don skis and scout the country looking for wolf tracks. When fresh tracks were found the hunter would then put on a white outer garment that covered him from head to foot. Thus blended with the snow-covered landscape, and with rifle in hand, he would follow the tracks and would be able often to get within rifle range of the wolf and shoot it. One of the foremost hunters, practicing this scheme with considerable success, was former U. S. Government Hunter Bill Cozzens of Idaho.

Plate 86. A Government wolf hunter's camp, showing wolf and coyote catch from one range in eastern Wyoming

Plate 87. Nux vomica beans from which is obtained strychnine, the weapon of the "professional wolfer" during the quarter-century 1860-1885

DEN HUNTING

This type of wolf control was very laborious, as ordinarily practiced, involving much digging and removal of soil or rock. It was very effective, however, in cutting down the annual increase in wolves and was altogether one of the most valuable techniques employed. One hunter in Rio Blanco County, Colo., had a unique but most hazardous way of doing it sometimes. He employed his small son who, when the hunter observed that a wolf den was not too deep would crawl into the hole and, when far enough in, grab a young wolf by a hind leg. Calling to his father that he had a wolf, he would speedily crawl out to the den's entrance, crayfish style, until his father could grab one of his feet. Then the boy and young wolf were pulled clear of the den and the animal dispatched. This was repeated until all of the young wolves were removed.

This trapper told me that his son often took hold of a young wolf that was extremely difficult to handle, and that occasionally he got hold of an old adult female, but never suffered any disastrous results. This method often enabled the hunter to remove young wolves that were found to have denned in natural lime- and sand-stone cavities. In such situations, he stated, it would be impossible to use common digging tools advantageously. Later, after the son had grown too large to enter the usual wolf den, the hunter resorted to the use of a forked stick, or a wire so twisted as to catch in the young wolf's fur, as an aid in its removal.

PROFESSIONAL HUNTING

Hunters who were adept at using a variety of the hereinbefore described methods of combating the wolf, besides others more direct as the bow and arrow, the spear, and later the gun, have been employed in all ages. During Roman times Keller, quoting Haller, *Helvetien unter den Romern*, II 44, states:

" 'In Switzerland at the time of the Burgundian and Frankish Kings, each Staathalter's duty was to support two special wolf hunters called "liparu" in order to check this nuisance.' " (Keller, O., 1887: 158.)

It is recorded also that James I of Scotland (1406-1437) employed two wolf hunters.

On this side of the Atlantic, Rhode Island set one of the first examples in 1642 by hiring men by the day to hunt wolves. Pennsylvania followed in 1683 with the following law:

"(Section II) And be it further enacted by the authority aforesaid, That all and every person or persons who are willing to make it their business to kill wolves, and shall enter into recognizance before two or more justice of the peace of the respective counties where he or they dwell, with sufficient security in the sum of five pounds, that he or they shall and will make it his or their sole business, at least three days in every week, to catch wolves, shall have twenty-five shillings for every wolf dog or bitch, that he or they shall so catch and kill within the time mentioned in the said recognizance; to be paid out of the county levies where the wolves are taken as aforesaid" (Pennsylvania, State of: 1896: 238).

The bounty law of 1705 induced many in Pennsylvania to become professional hunters, and these men, many of them picturesque characters, devoted all of their time to wolf hunting, the recompense received thereby furnishing one of their chief sources of personal income. Eventually they destroyed hundreds of wolves during the 70-odd years the law was in existence, and made a good start on elimination of wolves from the State.

The employment of salaried hunters was the principal means used in the Federal campaigns against wolves in the Western States. The personnel hired for this task were men long familiar with range conditions, well versed in wolf lore, and competent and reliable field naturalists. The pick of the range country, these government wolf trappers, in many instances, were the progeny of the picturesque western pioneers. Outstanding field men, versed in a full knowledge of the out-of-doors which had been gained from long years of experience, nevertheless, their knowledge of wolf ways was often put to severe test in the course of wolf control before success crowned their individual efforts. Particularly was this true with respect to certain of the better known wolves (previously mentioned under renegade wolves, p. 275) that depredated more severely than others on the western stock ranges. Much of the natural history concerned with these predators was obtained by the Service from such men— the majority of whom are now incapacitated and have been retired, or have passed on. Of the latter, it is to be regretted that with their death, much intimate knowledge of the life habits of our western mammals has been lost forever.

Individual stock ranchers often hired professional wolfers, either employing them by direct salary as a part of the ranch personnel or contracted with them collectively or individually at a certain price per each wolf they would kill. They devoted their entire time to this vocation. Their exploits in this business formed the basis of many accounts in the pioneer press of the West.

PREVENTIVE MEASURES

Fencing

Since colonial days various experiments from time to time have been tried in North America to develop a practical, cheap, and durable wolf-proof fence. It has always been felt during the pioneer and later development of the livestock industry that if such a fence could be constructed, the industry could be protected from wolves. What seems to be the first recorded attempt proposal of a wolf-proof fence in the colonies was in the year 1717, in the Cape Cod region of Massachusetts. According to Freeman: "This fence would have been a little N. and W. of the projected canal intended to unite 'Barnstable and Manomet Bayes.' The starting of such a project shows how troublesome wolves for a long time were. . . ." (Freeman, F., 1862, vol. 2, p. 355).

This fence as proposed would have been built " 'from picket Cliff to Way Quausett Bay, to keep the wolves from coming into the county,' was agitated, and the plan was thought to be highly important. The town clerk was instructed 'to confer with the several towns of the Cape' to ascertain 'if they will respectively furnish their proportion of 500 £s to make a good board fence of more than 6 feet high'; and the clerk was directed to 'promise in behalf of this town that whatever the fence shall cost more than 500 £s shall be borne by this town alone.' Falm [outh] acceded to the proposition; the rest declined. In this dilemma, the town's representative was 'instructed to apply to the Gen. Ct. for an Act requiring the towns below, in consideration of the great destruction of sheep by wolves, to bear their part of the expense across the isthmus, sufficient to exclude wolves.' It is hardly necessary to say the application was unsuccessful. The scheme was not so visionary as many later enterprises; but local interests were supposed to conflict." (Ibid.) It appears that one of the main drawbacks to the acquiescence in this plan for a wolf fence was that "Some beyond the county limits were opposed to permission being granted by the General Court, as they did 'not wish all the wolves to be shut out of the country upon their own limits.' " (Ibid.)

If this wolf fence plan had become a reality, it would have fenced off the better part of Cape Cod near the boundary between present-day Plymouth and Barnstable counties.

In later times exclusion of wolves by fencing was tried by stockmen and finally by the Federal Government; however none of the plans proved practicable.

For the purpose of devising the best methods of utilizing the grazing lands in the national forests, the Forest Service, between 1907 and 1910, in cooperation with the Bureau of Plant Industry of the Department of Agriculture, initiated experiments with wolf- and coyote-proof fences surrounding certain lambing grounds known as Billy Meadows, located on the Wallowa National Forest of northeastern Oregon; also on the south fork of Carnero Creek, and the west fork of Cochetopa Creek on the Cochetopa National Forest in southern Colorado. The practicability of such a protective measure against the depredations of the larger predators was carefully studied, particularly with respect to the coyote. The results of these findings were published in three circulars and one bulletin by the Forest Service, as follows: U. S. Forest Service Circular No. 156, *Preliminary Report on Grazing Experiments in a Coyote-Proof Pasture*, 1908, 32 pp., illus.; U. S. Forest Service Circular No. 160, *Coyote-Proof Pasture Experiment*, 1909, 40 pp., illus.; U. S. Forest Service Circular No. 178, *The Pasturage System for Handling Range Sheep*, 1910, 40 pp., illus.; and U. S. Forest Service Bulletin No. 97, *Coyote-Proof Inclosures in Connection with Range Lambing Grounds*, 32 pp., illus.

The Forest Service wolf-proof fencing experiments were planned by the Bureau of Plant Industry, and cooperated in by the Biological Survey. Thus three Federal bureaus were giving attention to the necessity of wolf control—a great advance indeed from the local actions of colonial times.

WOODS BURNING

Along timbered courses controlled by some of the cattle and farming interests, and where ground cover was dense and composed in part of heavy thickets, woods-burning was often resorted to as a measure of wolf control. As late as 1928 this practice was still in use in certain portions of western Arkansas, particularly in the national forests. Here, successful fire control in forested areas had permitted the growth of hardwood thickets dense enough to harbor wolves. On the Ouachita National Forest, residents suffered such heavy losses of livestock from wolves that woods-burning was considered as a measure of driving out the predators. Such steps annulled in part the efforts to control forest fires, and in such instances necessitated more direct measures to control wolves so as to make woods-burning unnecessary.

POISONING

Nux vomica, an East Indian tree which has been introduced in other parts of the Tropics produces an orange-like fruit in which are numerous somewhat button-shaped seeds. From these is obtained the highly toxic strychnine, which in the alkaloid or sulphate form is a white, crystalline powder. It is readily soluble in alcohol, but hard to dissolve in water. It has an intensely bitter taste, being exceeded in that respect by no other drug than quinine.

According to Wilbert:

"The nux vomica tree has an imposing appearance, bearing in the autumn clusters of greenish or yellow fruits, according to their maturity. The fruits are the size of an apple and contain a soft pulp, in which are embedded numerous round flattened seeds of a greyish-green color [the nux vomica bean]. The first quality of seed is obtained by collecting the fruits, washing out the seeds and drying them in the sun. The more inferior qualities of the drug usually consist of seeds gathered from under the trees, which have been rejected by the birds and monkeys, who eat freely of the pulp when ripe" (Wilbert, M. I., 1904: 587).

It has been difficult to ascertain when man first began to apply strychnine as a means of killing noxious mammals and birds. One author mentions the use of strychnine in Egypt in the 13th century B.C., but this probably is incorrect. Its toxic efficiency in killing unwanted animals was known in the Old World, however, by 1640, when Parkinson writing on nux vomica, sometimes also referred to as the Quaker, or Batchelor Button, poison nut, dog button, vomit nut, and vomiting bean, said that: "The chiefest use that they are put unto is to kill Dogs and Cats, and other creatures by mixing some of it with meat, as also to give unto Crowes, Ravens, and other suchlike troublesome birds that by their noyse disquiet mans sleepe or studies" (Parkinson, J., 1640: 1602).

To what extent this drug was imported for poisoning mammals in colonial America is not definitely known. If wide use later is any criterion, it was probably extensively employed. Carney gives a little insight into the problem when he states: "In the days when the early pioneers pushed their way into the forests of the eastern States, grey wolves were found in great numbers in most of the States. They are, of all the larger North American animals, among the swiftest runners, the hardest to trap, the hardest to get sight of in the forest country . . . . There is no doubt that poison was the chief means of their destruction so complete at so early a date [meaning the eastern United States]. (Carney, E., 1902: 84.)

The use of strychnine probably gained momentum gradually as its effect on wild animals became known during the more than two centuries between 1640, when Parkinson wrote about it, and its wide and promiscuous use by 1860 in Canada and the United States where it was employed from the Atlantic to the Pacific and from Texas to the Arctic. An impetus to strychnine poisoning doubtless occurred in the year 1834 when Rosengarten and Denis, of Philadelphia, Pa., believed to be the first American firm to do so, began the manufacture of the drug (McIntyre, W., 1904: 304).

In Pennsylvania strychnine was employed as a wolf poison in fairly early times. Shoemaker says: "Many wolves in this region (headwaters of White Deer Creek in north central Pennsylvania, Lycoming County) were poisoned by stuffing the hide of a lamb with lard, in which was hidden nux vomica. These wolves bit into the 'tempting morsel' and soon succumbed, three being found near Shader Spring, in Hope Valley, one morning" (Shoemaker, H. W., 1917-19, vol. 2, p. 31).

However, in the East poisoning of wolves apparently ceased fairly early because many of the animals had been disposed of by other means such as the modification of habitat, reduction in food supply, in addition to the use of the steel trap and other mechanical devices. In 1865 Newhouse stated: "Poison is used very little by woodsmen at the present time" (Newhouse, S., 1865: 13).

Yet we find one final reference by Rhoads as late as 1895:

"In a more recent note Mr. Miles announces the killing of 2 wolves by poison about the 10th of December 1895, within 7 miles of Brownsville, Tennessee by a man who had killed hogs and heard the wolves howling near where he had put out poison with the above results" (Rhoads, S. N., 1896: 200).

Tracing the history of strychnine poisoning in the West and North, mainly in chronological sequence, we note that its use against wolves near Puget Sound in 1841 was recorded by Peale, one of the naturalists accompanying the Charles Wilkes Exploring Expedition. This drug, used at times on the then Hudson's Bay Company's holdings may have been imported from England. (Cassin, J., 1858: 17.)

Sometime during 1847 or 1848, a shipment of strychnine was consigned by Rosengarten and Denis from Philadelphia to a South American port. However, news of the gold discoveries in California reached the vessel and it was turned to California and landed at San Francisco. The strychnine cargo was sold there and was used in the control of harmful animals. This was one of the first lots of strychnine to reach the Far West.[30]

It was about this time, too, or possibly a few years later, that the drug in the crystalline sulphate form made its appearance in quantity on the shelves of the frontier stores for sale to the trappers for killing wolves. Westport, Kans., was a notable trading post of the time of which Bernard states, in the late 1840's or early 1850's: "Westport was the gathering place for hunters, trappers, traders, and Indians. On its streets every type of man of the West was represented. About this time, or a little later, an unusual article of trade was in great demand, namely, strychnine, and it was imported and sold in wholesale quantities to hunters who pursued wolves for their pelts" (Bernard, W., 1906: 558).

At the start it was the value of the pelt in the West, low as it was, that caused the great kill of wolves, rather than any incentive in the way of bounty payments. At that time bounties had either not been established or those that were carried payments so low as hardly to justify wolf hunting for the bounty, considering the outlay that

---

[30]Letter from Dr. James C. Munch, dated June 30, 1939. In files of Fish and Wildlife Service.

was necessary for a field outfit in addition to the cost of the drug—the essential tool for doing the job.

Even that great fur collecting agency the Hudson's Bay Company at one time permitted at least experimental taking of fur animals by poisoning.

In the Mackenzie River district, Ross, who spent 13 years there with the Hudson's Bay Company experimented with aconitine, atropine, and corrosive sublimate, he says: "without success. The two former may not have been pure enough, though I obtained them from the finest chemical works in England and at a very high price. The only poison that I have found strong is strychnine" (Ross, B. R., 1861: 11, 12, 19).

He recommended two grains of the drug as the dose to each meat bait as "required to kill a wolf quickly." (Ibid.)

McGowan, quoting from the journal of Sir James Hector, February 3, 1859, states:

" 'A pack of thickwood wolves having been killing a number of horses belonging to the Hudson's Bay Company during the winter and the hunter having found a fine young mare just freshly killed the other day salted the carcase well with strychnine, and this morning we set off to observe the effect. Crossing the lake we walked about two miles through the woods when we fell on the track of the poor mare and her pursuers. She had been hard pressed by three of them, one on each side cutting off the bends she made while the other followed close behind and had at last seized her haunch and thrown himself down, so that he left a broad track in the snow. On reaching the carcase we found that the poison had done its work, for there lay four enormous wolves. . . . . The large wolves were splendid brutes. The two youngest were nearly black, while the old ones were grizzled grey, like Scotch Stag Hounds. The largest measured 30 inches at the shoulder and was five feet eight inches in length. The hunters say there is yet another of the family and that the survivor is well known by its track, as he has only three feet, for having once been caught in a steel trap he freed himself by gnawing off the foot he was held by' " (McGowan, D., 1936: 27).

By 1860, however, the Company strictly prohibited the use of strychnine over the larger part of the territory under its jurisdiction. It appears that Robert Kennicott, while collecting in the Hudson's Bay country during 1859-60 for the Smithsonian Institution, had contemplated the use of strychnine in obtaining foxes and other mammals. Governor George Simpson, on learning of this, requested of Smithsonian Secretary Spencer F. Baird that he acquaint Mr. Kennicott with the poison restriction of the company, as well as decline to issue any of the drug to him.

It will be recalled that in the early explorations westward, the beaver was the main fur sought by the trappers. However, with diminution in the supply of beaver pelts, an increased demand for wolf robes—in part to make overcoats for soldiers in the Russian Army—gave a great impetus to wolf killing.

With an established demand for wolf pelts, and the availability of a powerful drug that could easily be employed in killing wolves, strychnine eventually was to be found in use over much of our western prairie lands.

Not only was the former trapper of beavers enabled to make a fair living at this new vocation of taking wolf pelts that heretofore in the history of the fur trade in the West had been little valued, but he had many others join him, as homesteaders, discharged soldiers, and ne'er-do-wells, the latter working at wolf poisoning for the thrill of the game, as well as for the financial return. The killing of wolves by strychnine in North America was at its height between the years 1860 and 1885. Apparently, none of the western states or territories forbade the use of strychnine in killing wild animals. Wisconsin, for instance, permitted the use of poisoned bait in the year 1866.

The "professional wolfer" of the 1860's, and onward for nearly a quarter of a century was so called because he made his business that of killing wolves that followed the vast buffalo herds. Other of the smaller mammals, such as the coyote, swift fox, skunk, or the prairie red fox, that also took the poisoned baits so carelessly strewn served to augment the total returns the wolfer received at the end of each poisoning season. No better description of this happy-go-lucky individual who became a part of western history is found than that given by Taylor, who wrote: "With a full knowledge of his game, the wolfer riggs up an outfit similar to that of the hunter or the trapper with the exception of traps and baits. In place of these, he supplies himself liberally with strychnine poison.

"If it was in the autumn, he moved slowly in the wake of a buffalo herd, making open camp, and shooting down a few of the beasts, and after ripping them open, saturating their warm blood and intestines with from one to three bottles of strychnine to each carcass.

"After his line of poisoned buffalo has been put out to his notion, the wolfer makes a camp in a ravine or coulee and prepares for the morrow.

"With the first glimmer of light in the eastern sky, he rises, makes his fire, and cooks his coffee, then hitches up, if he has a team, or saddles up if with packs, and follows his line to the finish. Around each buffalo carcass will probably be from three to a dozen dead wolves, which he packs off some distance from his baits, and skins them.

"The most frequented winter grounds of the professional wolfers on the southern plains were along the Republican and Smoky Hill Rivers of Western Kansas, and the country about the neighborhood of the Staked Plains in northern Texas. The northern wolfer found their best grounds along the Milk, Musselshell and Judith Rivers, and around the Bear Paw Mountains of Montana, and the Peace River country in Manitoba.

"The northern wolfers had the business well systemized, and while many lost their lives by Indian hostility, and the exposure incident to that kind of life, yet many of them made fortunes at times, but an infatuation born of the calling held them as in a serpent's charm until some reverse in his affairs, left him where he began—in rigorous poverty.

"The wolfer's winter life was much the same in his general rounds as his autumn experience. If on the plains near camps of hostile Indians a small party gets together, form a common camp, and erect a "dug-out," a kind of half underground house. These dug-outs can be made warm and comfortable. Being thus partly below the prairie level, they are enabled to resist the bitter cold, blowing blizzards that sweep over the Great Plains with terrible fury at intervals during the winter months.

"These underground habitations are also used by the wolfers to thaw out the frozen carcasses of the wolves . . . . so that they could be skinned.

"The Indians have an especial antipathy to the wolfer. Poisoned wolves and foxes in their dying fits often slobber upon the grass, which becoming sun dried holds its poisonous properties a long time, often causing the death months or even years after of the pony, antelope, buffalo or other animals feeding upon it. The Indians losing their stock in this way feel like making reprisals, and often did" (Taylor, J. H., 1891: 70).

Stuart adds to the record: "The wolfer was the successor of the trapper. About the time that the beaver began to be scarce in the streams, men who had followed the avocation of trapping turned their attention to wolfing. Not until about 1866-'67 were the skins of wolves valuable but from that time on there was a good market for the pelts and wolfing became quite an important industry in Montana. . . . A wolfer's outfit was a pack horse, a saddle horse each, flour, beans, sugar, coffee, and salt; a pair of blankets, a buffalo robe, the best rifle he could procure, a good revolver, plenty of ammunition, a hunting knife and a supply of strychnine. These supplies were purchased in the fall at one of the trading posts and at the first freeze the wolfers took to the plains and did not return until spring. Just after the first freeze the wolfer begins to set his baits:—a buffalo would be killed and the meat poisoned. He would then follow on a short distance and repeat the operation. The baits were usually set in a circle but extended over a wide section of open valley and blizzard swept plains and the poor wolfer suffered severely from cold while attending the baits . . . . A good season was very remunerative, often netting from two to three thousand dollars. . . . The wolfers' lines of bait extended from far up into Canada to Colorado and Nebraska. Their principal trading posts were Fort Peck, Fort Benton, Fort Hawley, Fort Brown, the Crow Agency, Fort Pease, and Bozeman" (Stuart, G., 1925, vol. 2, p. 172).

Batty, the official hunter and taxidermist connected with the Hayden Government surveys, stated that these "wolvers": "are Yankees and half-breeds, and are brave and courageous beyond expression. The buffalo wolf is chiefly sought after, though the coyotes, red, gray and kitt foxes are often taken. The wolfers are exposed to greater hardship than any other class of hunters; they have to live in the most barren country, exposed to the severe weather and winds of the plains, which in their fierce and cutting sweep, seem to imitate tornadoes. Remote from civilization, deeply drifted in with snow, they can scarcely travel, and often wonder how life will be sustained for the winter; but their pluck seems to keep them alive until Spring dawns on them and their half-starved ponies. They often make a good winter's work on the upper Missouri and Milk Rivers; but their hard earned money too frequently goes for Indian whiskey, for which they pay a fabulous price. . . . [Besides its use on wolves apparently strychnine was valued for another purpose at this time. Of Indian whiskey, mentioned by Batty, for which so much of the wolfer's earnings was spent, it is recorded that the recipe for making it on the plains was as follows: To one barrel of Missouri River water was added two gallons of alcohol, two ounces of strychnine, three plugs of tobacco, and five bars of soap to give it a "bead," following which one-half pound of red pepper was stirred into the mixture. This concoction was then further supplemented by the addition of sagebrush, and then boiled until the liquid turned brown, after which the mixture was strained into a stock barrel, and then bottled. Strychnine, it is said, was added for its stimulating properties, while the tobacco was a necessity because of the nausea it produced in the Indians of the time, for no whiskey was of value unless the one who drank it eventually became deathly sick. Of the white man it is said that when he drank the mixture he became so inebriated that he could not close his eyes. Regarding one of the prices paid for this liquor, if it can be called such, one bottle was worth a buffalo robe, but increased in value of robes per bottle as the individual became drunker and desired more of this "fire water." It is further recorded that this concoction was never sold anywhere except from trading posts on the Missouri River.] In spring, the wolfers used to come down the Missouri River in Mackinaw boats loaded with packs of pelts, the skin of the buffalo wolf predominating. When we were once camped with wolfers, traders were giving one dollar per pelt; in St. Paul they were bringing one dollar and a half, and in New York two dollars." (Batty, J. H., 1882: 214.)

A word on the methods of the wolfer may not be amiss. To enable handling of the strychnine sulphate crystals in what was believed to be the most economical and efficient manner, these were often partially dissolved in water to the consistency of loose mush or paste. In this form the drug was more easily used on the windy prairies. It was applied to the carcass of a buffalo or antelope by first stripping back the skin and then pouring the pasty form of the poison over the meat. The skin of the dead animal was then slipped back over that part of the carcass. Plenty of strychnine was used and it was generally applied as soon as the buffalo or antelope was killed, often being mixed into the coagulated blood as well as the intestinal lining of the still-warm animal.

Sometimes small birds, such as the junco or horned lark, were killed and used for bait. The bird was slit down its breast-bone, and into the slit was placed a pinch of strychnine. The cut was squeezed together again, and the bird placed on the ground along a wolf runway, or along trails that led to water.

Some conception of the kills made with strychnine may be obtained from "The Life and Adventures of George W. Brown," where it is recorded that from one poisoned buffalo carcass on the Kansas plains "13 big gray wolves, 15 coyotes, and about forty skunks" were taken in one night (Kansas State Historical Society, 1928: 129).

Speaking of the wolf in the then Washington Territory, Suckley reported that the wolf occurring on Nisqually Plains was "Formerly . . . . quite abundant in that vicinity, much to the detriment of the sheep of the Puget Sound Agricultural Company, but of late years, owing to the persuasive influence of strychnine, they, together with the wolf-like Indian dogs, have become quite scarce" (Suckley, G., and Gibbs, G., 1860: 111).

Webb, in writing of the Santa Fe trade, said:

"To give some idea of the numbers of wolves on the prairie in the buffalo range, I will give an account of two men formerly conductors of the mail from Independence to Sante Fe. I think it was in 1854 or 1855 [that] they went to Walnut creek and built a small mud fort, and in summer they would sell what few knicknacks they could to traders and other passing travelers, and in winter their business was to kill wolves for the skins. They would kill a buffalo and cut the meat in small pieces and scatter it about in all directions a half a mile or so from camp, and so bait the wolves for about two days. Meantime all hands were preparing meat in pieces about two inches square, cutting a slit in the middle and opening it and putting a quantity of strychnine in the center and closing the parts upon it. When a sufficient amount was prepared, and the wolves were well baited, they would put out the poisoned meat. One morning after putting out the poison, they picked up sixty-four wolves, and none of them over a mile and a half from camp. The proceeds from that winter's hunt were over four thousand dollars" (Webb, J. J., 1931: 163).

James R. Mead records that while on a Kansas trip he came upon a vast variety of game near what is now known as Paradise, Kans. While hunting in this area he "shot two bulls, and a little further I shot three cows. On returning I found the bulls surrounded by a mass of big wolves near white, . . . busily engaged in tearing the bulls to pieces. They paid no attention to me. I walked up within seventy-five yards and fired my rifle several times into the mass before they would leave. Four of them lay dead and others were crippled. I went to camp, got the team, and hastened back to the cows, and found them nearly devoured. . . . I put out a quantity of strychnine that night for my friends, the wolves, and next day we gathered in eighty-two. As these pelts were worth $2.50 apiece, we had no fault to find with the wolves" (Mead, J. R., 1906: 16).

During the winter of 1861-62, Robert Morris Peck and two companions who had been mustered out of the United States Army of the frontier shortly before at Fort Wise, located in Colorado, then a Territory, took, with the aid of strychnine, more than 3,000 wolves, coyotes, and swift foxes. They did their poisoning in the valley of Walnut Creek in what is now Rush County, Kans., using as bait the carcasses of buffaloes, and at times of antelopes. Their entire catch for this period brought these ex-soldiers $2,500, a large sum for those days, the value of the wolves being $1.25, of the coyotes 75c, and of the kit foxes 25c, per pelt (Grinnell, G. B., 1914: 286).

Concerning similar operations of wolfers, Webb records:

". . . . the strychnine had been doing its work . . . . effectually . . . . Twenty-three dead wolves were found, and the even two dozen was made up by a large specimen of the gray variety—or timber wolf, as it is called in contradistinction from the Coyote—who was exceedingly sick, and went rolling about in vain efforts to get out of the way.

*   *   *   *

"At Grinnel Station, ... we afterward saw over forty dead wolves, and most of them of the gray variety, stacked up, like cordwood, as the result of one night's poisoning by the soldiers" (Webb, W. E., 1872: 292).

As might be expected, strychnine got into the hands of some of the western Indian tribes, and they were soon using it also for killing wolves. One characteristic incident is recorded about the Comanches while hunting on the Salt Fork of the Red River in southwest Oklahoma in November 1883. Of it, Batty says: "At this camp the wolves were very plenty; they gave us a free concert each night and kept it up all night. I tried to shoot them with a rifle but did not succeed very well. The Chief had two ounces of strychnine along, and we began to poison them, and saved about 150 of their hides, which came in very useful later on" (Batty, J. H., 1884: 163).

As a further aid in comprehending the number of wolves that were killed at the height of the poisoning campaign we may consider what Fouquet saw near Sun City, Kans., at the mouth of Turkey Creek, where there was a little cave village of buffalo and wolf hunters during 1871. He states: "Not far above this cave village was a road going thro the swampy creek valley, about 75 yards wide, and this had been artistically and scientifically paved with gray wolf carcasses and I drove over this bone road several times" (Fouquet, L. C., 1925: 344).

Success in poisoning wolves with strychnine is attained more often with young wolves than with those which are fully matured. In that stage of its life cycle wolves are more prone to eat carrion than when adult. Exceptions to this statement are the old, toothless or so-called "gummer wolves" previously mentioned.

Apparently, a large proportion of the wolves killed by strychnine on the plains were of the younger age. An incident from modern experience pointing in that direction is recalled of a stockman on Bear Springs Mesa in southern Colorado who, in the late fall of 1921, inserted two grains of strychnine into each of a half-dozen crudely made baits of beef suet. Each bait was roughly the size of a hen's egg. These were distributed at random around an old cow carcass that lay on a wolf runway. Two days later he found three dead wolves, each not more than two years old that he had poisoned out of a family of seven. Three days later in the same manner he killed two more of the same age. However, he never succeeded in poisoning the old male or female of this family. On their last visit to the spot, following the killing of the last two of the young, they mouthed some of the baits but rejected them. From all subsequent indications they never stopped at this point again.

Profiting from the success of the wolfers, the cattlemen and the cowboys were not slow to adopt strychnine poisoning as a means of decreasing the numbers of what they considered their greatest enemy.

Granville Stuart, long familiar with the Far Western frontier, recorded that "Predatory animals were quite troublesome especially the large gray timber wolves that surpasses any other animal in sagacity, fleetness of foot, and powers of endurance. Added to these qualities is an insatiable appetite. . . . The cattle herds were an easy prey for these grizzly marauders as the cattle were afraid of them and ran at sight of one. The wolves being much fleeter and possessing more endurance found it easy to surround a range animal and drag it down. The range cows would fight desperately to protect their young calves but were never a match for even one large wolf, and these wolves are very large weighing one hundred twenty-five to one hundred fifty pounds. They are prolific breeders having as many as ten whelps in a litter. It is next to impossible to get within gunshot of one and almost equally as difficult to trap or poison them. With plenty of dead cattle on the range they would not touch a dead carcass preferring to kill their own meat. We carried strychnine with us all the time and by putting it in lard and then spreading it on bacon rinds it was a 'piece de resistence' for them and we poisoned not a few in that way" (Stuart, G., 1925, vol. 2, p. 171).

R. M. Allen, General Manager, Standard Cattle Company, Ames, Nebr., in a letter of April 3, 1896 states:

"I have personally taken all the pains I could since about '90 in the encouragement of bounty legislation and in other means for killing them. I have known of a few instances of success in poisoning or in hunting. Geo. A. Keeline of Council Bluffs, Iowa, tells me that he has had a good deal of success in poisoning, also Patrick Bros. of Omaha. As for ourselves, we have tried every possible means of killing them, but have met with only moderate success. In poisoning probably twice as many wolves are killed as carcasses are found, but in our experience we have only occasionally had any success at all in this way. . . ."

G. E. Lemmon, manager of the Sheidley Cattle Company, Rapid City, S. Dak., on April 3, 1896, wrote that in three years' time, $400.00 had been expended for poison to combat wolves. This company ranged stock in Wagner, Martin, Choteau, and Rinehard counties.

James T. Craig, Supt. of Western Ranches, Ld., of Belle Fourche, S. Dak., reported on March 23, 1896 that the "loss sustained by calves is fully 3 percent, grown stock 1 percent while on young colts fully 5 percent." He further commented, "have found strychnine tablets the most effective means of destroying them, ... using old horses and big jawed cattle" (probably lumpy jaw cattle disease) for bait.

Thus the pioneer stockman of the West used every means at his disposal to get rid of the wolf, beginning approximately in 1885 and onward for about 30 years. He employed strychnine poisoning among other methods used, but this means of killing the wolf did not reach as high a peak as to quantity of poison used, or as to extent of territory over which it was distributed, as was the case during the preceding 25 years. This was mainly due to farming and fencing which left less range available for wolves. That factor coupled with the results of their own poison campaigning and of the previous years of warfare on the wolf by the hide hunters had very greatly decreased the numbers of the animals.

With reference to middle and western Kansas in the early seventies the effects of wolf poisoning were plainly evident. At that time J. A. Allen wrote of the

"*Canis Lupus*, Gray Wolf, Buffalo Wolf. Formerly very abundant, but during last few years their numbers have greatly diminished, thousands having been killed for their skins every winter by means of strychnine. Comparatively few now remain" (Allen, J. A., 1874a: 45).

Destruction by this strychnine poisoning campaign that covered an empire hardly has been exceeded in North America, unless by the slaughter of the passenger pigeon, the buffalo, and the antelope. There was a sort of unwritten law of the range that no cowman would knowingly pass by a carcass of any kind without inserting in it a goodly dose of strychnine sulphate, in the hope of eventually killing one more wolf. The hazard to other forms of wildlife involved by this lavish use of strychnine was not taken into consideration by stock interests at the time. Kit foxes, so prevalent at the time on the plains, were poisoned by the thousands, for they were

Figure 13. Lined section of the United States and Canada shows the approximate area worked during the heyday of the "professional wolf poisoners," 1860-1885. Here strychnine was widely and promiscuously applied to carcasses of buffalo, antelope, deer, elk, and birds as bait. Thousands of wolves, coyotes, and other smaller mammals were killed, among which the kit fox was practically extirpated from the plains region

generally the first to take the poisoned meat. The predominating thought was "to get the wolf by any and all means possible."[31]

Not only the wolves were killed but also innumerable other carnivores, including the kit fox (*Vulpes velox*), just mentioned, the northern plains red fox (*Vulpes regalis*), the northern plains skunk (*Mephitis mephitis hudsonica*), and the Texas skunk (*Mephitis mephitis varians*). In addition, many birds, such as hawks, eagles, magpies, and ravens perished from feeding on poisoned baits.

A minor use of strychnine in the poisoning of wolves was for collecting scientific specimens. What was probably the most northern employment of the drug for this purpose occurred in approximately latitude 82° N. near Fort Conger on Ellesmere Island as described by members of the Greely Expedition of the early 1880's. One of its members, Lt. Kislingbury, "after many futile efforts with arsenic succeeded in poisoning many wolves with strychnine" at this point (Lanman, C., 1885: 100-102, 116, 199).

Lt. Lockwood, who was later assigned by General Greely to the care of the scientific collections the expedition was making, in lieu of Dr. Pavy, lists among the mammals obtained several wolves apparently obtained by the use of strychnine.

THE BOUNTY SYSTEM

It is questionable if any animal other than the wolf has had directed against it, over such a long period of time, so many legal acts putting a price upon its head.

Hogs, sheep, tobacco, grain, wine, rum, lead, powder, and English, Mexican, and American money were among the commodities used at various times as rewards for killing wolves in North America.

In this country wolf bounty legislation developed during a period of more than 300 years, and included an immense volume of laws. In no other country have laws for the riddance of wolves been passed in such numbers or amended so frequently. While it must be admitted that the destruction of wolves by any means affords some relief from their inroads, nevertheless, the extirpation of this predator from many parts of North America was mainly due

---

[31]Letter dated March 21, 1921, from James Shaw, Thatcher, Colo., to Stanley P. Young. In files of Fish and Wildlife Service.

to the modification of habitat through human settlement, and the consequent reduction of its natural food supply. It is a conservative estimate that bounties, including those for the wolf, far exceeding $100,000,000 have been paid in North America. The bounty system in the course of time became honeycombed with fraud.

It cannot be specifically determined when the plan of paying rewards for killing wolves was first put into effect, as the date is buried in antiquity. From what can be gleaned from available records, however, it appears that considering the entire world wolf bounties have been in existence for at least 2,700 years. They were paid by the early Greeks, and it was apparently from them that the plan was adopted and eventually put into operation throughout most, if not all, of Europe.

We find in Plutarch's *Lives* that: ". . . [Solon] appointed that he which brought a he woulfe, should have five drachmes, and him one drachme for reward of a she woulfe. Where of as Demetrius Phalerian writeth:—the one was the price of an ox the other of a mutton" (Plutarch, 1876: 235).

The drachma [or drachme] was a coin of ancient Greece varying widely from time to time in value. The standard value usually given is 4.37 grams of silver.

Topsell, writing of the same period, states:

"Men haue bin forced to inuent and fiindout many deuices for the destroying of wolues, for the necessity hath taught them much learning, and it has become a shameful misery to indure the tyranny of such spoiling beastes without laboring for resistance and reuenge: for this cause they propounded also a reward to such as killed wolues for by the law of Dracho, he that killed a young wolfe received a tallent, and he that killed an old wolfe reecived two talents.

"Solon prescribed that he that brought a Wolfe aliue, shoulde receiue fiue pieces of money, and he that brought one dead, should receiue two" (Topsell, E., 1607: 741).

Search has thus far failed to reveal in the Draconian code any mention of wolf bounty payments. However, Solon, whose life history was apparently prepared by Plutarch near the close of the first century A.D. effected his sweeping reforms of Athenian law approximately one generation after Draco, or most probably by 594 B.C.

It will be of interest to review early practice as to payment of bounties on wolves in the British Isles as being the foundation of the system that later came to prevail in the colonies in America.

In an attempt to rid England of wolves, King Henry III made grants of land to individuals provided they would always work toward wolf destruction; this was during the years 1216-1272 A.D. This land donation from King Henry was in reality a wolf bounty; the amount of land given was called a carucate, that is, as much land as could be cultivated in one year by one plough. The King kept dogs for wolf hunting, and a carucate was donated to an individual who hunted the wolf with the Royal Dogs. During the reign of Henry IV (1422-1461), a bovate (the eighth part of a carucate) of land was given for attending to the blowing of a horn for frightening wolves, as well as for chasing them.

In Scotland in 1427 during the reign of James I a bounty of two shillings was provided to reward any man that slew a wolf in a barony, the amount to be paid by the baron. The baron was also a sort of head wolf hunter, and could summon his tenants to hunt the wolf, at least four times a year or more often if necessary. A tenant could be fined for non-attendance at a wolf-hunt. The bounty act of James II's time (1457) reduced the payment to six pennies. In 1621, however, there was a bounty of 6£. 13s. 4d. for one wolf. In 1661 during the reign of Charles II, two ounces of silver were paid for 20 wolf skins.

In Ireland in 1653 a bounty of 5£ was paid for every male wolf, 6£ for every female, and 10s. for each whelp. A wolf was counted as a fully matured wolf if taken between the last of September and the middle of January. Thus, the 10s. on the whelps was paid during the late spring and summer months. The revenue to pay these bounties was raised by the Commissioners of Revenue of Ireland, who were ordered to assess all equally within their respective precincts.

With bounties of one kind or another in effect for centuries in Europe and the British Isles, it is not surprising that a similar plan should be instituted by colonists in North America. For convenience in discussion, bounty legislation on wolves may be considered by the following periods:

1. 1630 to 1775—The Colonial Period.
2. 1776 to 1865—Territorial and State period to the close of the Civil War.

3. 1865 to 1939—Period of greatest depredations upon livestock when more stringent measures were taken looking toward total wolf elimination, with eventual federal aid.

Together these periods cover a span of more than three centuries,
during which wolf bounties have been available in a majority of the
States of the Union.

The first wolf bounty law in the area now known as the United
States was adopted in the year 1630 by the colonial law-makers of
Massachusetts. It was followed by a similar act in Virginia in 1632.
A history of the Massachusetts, Virginia, and other early wolf bounty
laws is given because such laws of these States were used as models
by other commonwealths and with some modifications from time to
time were the basis of those adopted later throughout North America.

Just a decade following the landing of the Pilgrims at Plymouth
Rock, the first wolf bounty in colonial North America was provided
from Massachusetts. This was promulgated by:

A Court of Assistants, holden att Boston, November 9th, 1630.
Present, The Gounr,   Capt. Endicott,
      Deputy Gounr,   Mr. Coddington,
      Sr Rich: Saltonstall,   Mr. Pinchon,
      Mr. Ludowe,   Mr. Bradstreete.
whereby

It is ordered, that euy Englishe man that killeth a wolfe in any
pte within the lymitts of this pattent shall have allowed him 1d for
euy beast & horse, & ob. for euy weaned swyne & goate in euy plantacon, to be leuied by the constables of the sd plantacons. (1d means
1 penny, ob. ½ penny.) (Massachusetts, 1853-54, vol. 2, p. 81).
This was repealed by "A court holden att Boston, November 7th,
1632," wherein "It is ordered, that neither Englishe nor Indeans
shall have any more rewards for killing woolfes." (Ibid., vol. 1, pp.
101-102.) Then a reenactment took place "Att the Genrall Court,
holden Att Newe Towne, Septr. 2, 1635," and accordingly "It is
ordered, that there shalbe Vs for euy wolfe, Js for every foxe, paid
out of the tresury to him that kills the same." (J was formerly often
used for I and meant *one.*) Ibid., vol. 1, p. 156.)

An increase in the bounty was ordered by "A Generall Court,
held at Newetowne, the 2th Day of the 9th Mo, 1637," and "It
is ordered that there should bee 10 shs a peece alowed for such
wolves as are killed." (Ibid., vol. 1, pp. 205, 218.)

Again the bounty was repealed by "A Generall Courte, houlden at Boston, the 13th of the first Month, 1638," whereby "The laws for money to be given for the killing of wolves and foxes are repealed." (Ibid., vol. 1, pp. 250, 252.) [In the 17th century March was the first month of the year.]

A further reenactment of the bounty took place at "A Genrall Cort, held at Boston, the 7th Day of the 8th Mo, 1640," when it was

"Ordered, that every man that kills a wolfe uith hounds shall have 40s alowed him, & whosoever kils a wolfe with trap, peece, or other engine, shall have 10 s alowed him, to bee paid by that towne where the wolfe is killed, & if hee bee killed out of any towne bounds, it shalbee paid by the Treasurer.

"And it is further ordered, that such as shall keepe any hound, mastife, or grayhound, wch shalbee ayding to the death of any such wolfe, shall not be contributory to the recompence to be given for such woolfe." (Ibid., vol. 1, pp. 301, 304.)

Once more a repeal of the bounty took place at "A generall Court of Elections, held at Boston the 2th 4th Mo, 1641," which body stated that "The order for giving 40 shs a peece for wolues killed with dogs, and 10 shs a peece for wolues killed otherwise, is repealed." (Ibid., vol. 1, pp. 318, 319.)

A special bounty to Indians for killing wolves was adopted on "The 13th of the 9th Mo, 1644," and here

"It is ordered, yt there shalbe a bushell of Indian corne or three qrts of wine paid to any Indian by ye cunstable of evry towne for evry wolfe killed within ye bounds of ye towne where such cunstable dweleth, upon ye townes account pvided, yt ye Indian bring ye head to ye cunstable, and make good profe where such wolfe was killed, for ye better satisfaction yt it was killed within ye same towne bounds." (Ibid., vol. 2, pp. 81, 84.)

A reenactment of a general bounty law was again resorted to "At a Cort of Election, at Boston, the 14th of the Month, 1645," stipulating that

"Whereas great losse and damage doth befall ye comon wealth by reason of wolues, lock do destroy so great numbers of or cattle, & (notwithstanding pvision hath formly bene made by ye Cort for supprsing of ym, we find little hath bene done yt way) for ye bettr incuraging of any to set about a work of so great concernmt,—

"It is therefore ordered yt any pson, either English or Indian, that shall kill any wolfe or wolues within ten miles of any plantation in ys iurisdiction, shall have for every wolfe by him or ym so killed 10 shs, to be paid out of ye treasury of ye country; pvided, d(ue) profe be made thereof unto ye plantation next adioyning, where such wolfe or wolves were killed, & also yt they bring a certificate undr some matrats hand, or ye cunstable of ye place, unto ye Tresurer; pvided also yt ye ordr doth onely intend such plantations as do contribute to publike charge, & for such plantations upon ye river of Pascataq, yt do not ioyne wth us to carry on publike charge, they are to make payment upon their owne charge." (Ibid., pp. 96, 103.)

However, repeal of the 1644 bounty to Indians also was effected. "The ordr for alowing 3 qrts of wine, or a bushell of Indian corne, to any Indian for killing of a wolfe, is hereby repealed." (Ibid.)

The next Massachusetts wolf bounty of interest was that which gave Englishmen larger payments than those granted to Indians, "At a Session of the Genrall Courte, at Boston, 18th of the 8th Mo, 1648,"

"It is ordered, & by the authority of this Courte enacted, that every inhabitant, English or Indian, within this jurisdiction, that shall kill any wolfe or wolues, making good prufe to the cunstables of the towne where such wolfe is killed bringing of their heads, wch the cunstable is to bury, if any English shall kill any, he shall be alowed thirty shillings at the least by the cunstable of such townes for the time being, ten shillings whereof the Treasurer in the next levy that issues out of that towne to the country, he shall alow to the cunstable; & for every Indian that shall kill any wolfe shall be alowed twenty shillings, ten shillings whereof shalbe alowed by the Treasurer, as before, back againe to the cunstable, as aforesaid.

"This law to be of force for foure years." (Ibid., pp. 249, 252.)

Ample evidence of wolf depredations in the early days of the Massachusetts Bay Colony is afforded by the variety of legislative enactments tried out in the first eighteen years of the existence of the General Court.

The General Court was the governing body of the colony. It attended to all of the usual governmental functions—administrative, legislative, and judicial. Originally it consisted of the governor, the deputy governor, eighteen assistants, and all "freemen." At first, the only "freemen" were the stockholders of the corporation that owned the charter of the colony, perhaps not more than a dozen. However, upon strong representations from the populace, the number of "freemen" was gradually increased, although strict requirements as to church membership and property ownership were enforced.

Twelve separate pieces of legislation relative to bounty payments were adopted during this period (1630-1648). Among the various schemes was the ingenious attempt to assess a bounty tax according to the number of domestic animals on a "plantacon" at the rate of one penny for each "beast and horse" and one halfpenny for each "weaned swyne and goate."

In 1640 the Puritans gave special recognition to hunting dogs, since the Court in June of that year ordered payment of 40 shillings for each wolf taken with hounds while only 10 shillings each was allowed for those taken by other means. Also, any keeper of suitable hunting dogs was exempt from taxation for bounty payments. This regulation must have created some dissatisfaction as it remained in operation only eight months.

Again, a special inducement was offered to Indian wolf hunters in the form of a bounty of one bushel of corn or three quarters of wine for each wolf killed, payable by the town constable, provided the Indian could convince him that the wolf was taken within the town limits. This regulation was in force only three months.

Nevertheless parallel legislation was enacted May 22, 1661, as follows:

"Besides all other considerations and provitions for the destruction of woolves, it is ordered by this Court and the authoritje thereof, that every such Indian or Indians as shall any way destroy any woolfe or woolves, and deliver the heads of such woolves unto the selectmen of any touneship in this jurisdiction, shall receive of such selectmen either two pound of pouder and eight pound of shott, or one pounds of pouder and four pounds of shott and five shillings in corne or other pay, or else they shall receive of the county Tresurer tenn shillings a head, and no pouder and shott, wch such Indian will choose; . . . ." (Massachusetts, 1853-54, vol. 4 (pt. 2), p. 2).

In the bounty law of 1648, distinction was made between English and Indian claimants. The amount allowed the white man per wolf was 30 shillings; the Indian, 20 shillings. The Court seems to have planned at that time for a definite policy in the matter of wolf extermination, for a clause was added stating that this law was "to be of force for foure years."

These awards were renewed in 1653. Nine years later the amount was increased to 40 shillings, 20 shillings payable by the "country," 10 by the county and 10 by the town.

Various schemes were tried in sharing payment between the towns and the colony or "country." In some cases, the treasurer of the colonial government paid the whole amount; in others the town was responsible for full payment; and under another plan the responsibility was divided, one-third of the bounty to be paid by the "country" and two-thirds by the town.

It should be remembered in interpreting the foregoing that the word *town* in New England during colonial days referred not to a village but to a geographical area that might contain several villages and many farms. It was more like a western township, except that it had natural boundaries instead of surveyed boundaries 6 miles apart.

Bounty laws on wolves remained in effect almost continuously for more than two centuries after 1661. In general, Massachusetts did not adopt the practice of enacting special laws for individual counties as did New York and Virginia.

The reward for each grown wolf had risen to 4£ by 1718 and amounted to $15 for most of the 60-year period from 1780 to 1840. Payment was made to claimants by the towns, which were reimbursed by the treasurer of the province. Under the law of 1817, the State bounty could be supplemented by additions from the treasury of any town through action of the voters at regular town meetings.

The General Court set the bounty at 20 shillings in 1693, but restored the former 40 shilling payments within the next quarter century. The regulations of 1695 and thereafter specified that the rewards were payable for any wolf "other than such as shall be taken out of the belly of any bitch wolf."

By 1742 the 4£ award had been reduced to 30 shillings. The law adopted in this year is the only one that offered a larger amount for any animal other than the wolf, namely the catamount (puma), 40 shillings. From this date on the Court gave little or no attention to bounty legislation for 40 years.

Head prices set in 1782 were as follows: wolf, $15; wolf's whelp, $5; bear, $5; wildcat, $5; and fox, $.50. These awards still prevailed in 1836. But in 1838 the State bounty was withdrawn, and the towns were authorized by law to raise whatever amounts of money they chose to encourage the destruction of these animals.

The Massachusetts code of 1860 (Chapter 18) provided that towns might vote such sums as "they judge necessary . . . . for encouraging the destruction of 'noxious animals.' " This permissive regulation is included also in the code of 1882, after which date the nuisance of "noxious animals," including wolves, seems to have declined to the point where legislation was no longer necessary.

In Rhode Island on the basis of fewer records, the first intimation we have of a wolf bounty was the payment for killing an exceptionally destructive individual. Rider quotes a record of 1636 or earlier that "For one 'great gray wolf,' a terrible scourge, the settlers offered five pounds, and John Sweete killed him" (Rider, S. S., 1904: 179).

In 1647 "Newport had passed an order that no deer should be killed for two months, which Portsmouth concurred in, assigning as the reason that in that way the wolves would more readily come to bate and so be caught. At the same time, it was ordered that of the five pounds bounty, on each wolf, which had been established some years before, Newport should pay four and Portsmouth one" (Arnold, S. G., 1859; vol. 1, p. 161).

During the spring of 1688, when the "term of the Common Pleas was held at Kingston, or Rochester as it was then called. . . . a tax of over fifty-three pounds was laid upon the whole Province, or County to pay for the killing of wolves therein. These animals were still very numerous and troublesome" (Ibid., p. 508).

During the years 1654-55, each Indian resident in Rhode Island was obliged to pay an annual tribute of two wolf skins, which if regarded as in lieu of taxes may be considered as a form of bounty. This custom may be traced to tribute taking like that recorded for the English kings. For instance Edgar, 965, in effecting a treaty of peace with the King of North Wales, levied a tribute of three hundred wolves yearly. This tribute, so history tells, was paid for two years; and the year following, the wolf apparently becoming extremely rare in Wales, its King was exempted from the wolf tribute. Also, King Edgar attempted to further wolf control in England "by remitting the punishment of certain crimes on producing a number of Wolves' tongues" (Bewick, T., 1804: 314).

By 1703 we find that in Rhode Island "Wolves had not yet been exterminated. The assembly at an adjourned session offered a premium of twenty shillings a head for every wolf that should be killed" (Arnold, S. G., 1859, vol. 2, p. 55).

Only two years elapsed after the adoption of a wolf bounty by Massachusetts when the Royal Crown Colony of Virginia took similar action. As in Massachusetts, a chronological account shows that the Virginia lawmakers repeatedly changed the bounty act apparently in response to increase in numbers of livestock. Of all the States (and the statement applies also to all of the Canadian provinces), Virginia has had provision for wolf bounties upon its statute books for the longest time—a period of 308 years.

As the first two wolf bounty laws for the Virginia colony are unique, they are quoted verbatim. With respect to the first we find the Grand Assembly "Holden at James Citty the 4th Day of September, 1632," provided in Act XLIX:

"Noe man shall kill any wild swyne out of the forrest or woods, except in his .... or devident [sic], without leave or lycense from the Governor. But it is thought convenient that any man be permitted to kill deare or other wild beasts or fowle in the common woods, forrests, or rivers in regard that thereby the inhabitants may be trained in the use of theire armes, the Indians kept from our plantations, and the wolves and other vermin destroyed. And for encouragement to destroy the wolves, it is thought that whosoever shall kill a wolfe, and bringe in his head to the commander, it shall be lawfull for such person or persons for every wolfe soe kild, to kill also one wild hogg and take the same for his owne use" (Hening, W. W., 1810-23, vol. 1, p. 178).

At this time most of the livestock ran wild, receiving no special care. Under certain conditions a colonist was permitted to kill for his own use an animal so maintained. The areas where wild livestock maintained itself were considered a kind of community area—or commons from which the livestock could be taken when necessary. Hence, the right to kill one wild hog was real compensation and must be considered a bounty as much as it would a cash payment.

Under Act V of 1646 it was ordered that:

"Whereas many losses are lately received by the inhabitants by reason of wolves which do haunt and frequent their plantations; for the better prevention and for the destroying of them, It is inacted that what person soever shall after publication hereof kill a wolfe and bring in the head to any commissioner upon certificate of the said commissioner to the county court he or they shall receive one hundred pounds of tob'o. for soe doeing to bee raysed out of the county where the wolfe is killed" (Ibid., p. 328).

Act IX of 1668 is of interest, for here we find a unique scheme in the requirement it made that Indian tribes should kill wolves for bounty in proportion to their number of hunters. Seventeen groups of Indians estimated to have 725 hunters were involved. The act stated:

". . . . It is enacted that the Indian tributaries be enjoyned and assessed to bring in a certaine number annually, that is to say:

	Bowmen or hunters	Wolves heads
Into Nanzemond county, the Nanzemonds being about	45	9
Surrey		
Powchay-icks	30	6
Weyenoakes	15	3
Charles City County		
Nottoways, 2 townes	90	18
Appamatux	50	10
Henrico County		
Manachees	30	6
Powhites	10	2
New Kent		
Pamunckies	50	10
Chickahomonies	60	12
Mattapanics	20	4
Rapahanocks	30	6
Totas Chees	40	8
Gloster		
Chiskoyackes	15	3
Rapahanock		
Portobaccoes	60	12
Nanzeattio ⎱ Mattehatique ⎰	50	10
Northumberland		
Wickacomico	70	14
Westmoreland		
Appomatux	10	2
	725	145

And for "the putting this act into effectuall execution," the law provided that if some of the Indians were deficient in their wolf quotas the court should issue a summons, and in case of continued neglect the commissioners should "transmitt the contempt to the next assembly." One hundred pounds of tobacco was the Indian's reward for each wolf's head (Ibid., vol. 2, p. 274). This was repealed the following year, 1669, as it had "not produced such effects as was hoped and desired."

From that day to the present (1939), wolf bounty laws of some kind have been in force in the Old Dominion almost continuously.

Act V of the Assembly of 1646 provided for payment of 100 pounds of tobacco for each wolf killed. For a century and a half after this act most of the awards authorized were payable in tobacco, by far the most widely used currency in Virginia. Not until 1744 was a cash payment offered. At that time the authorities in Frederick County were directed to pay 6 shillings for an old wolf and 2 shillings 6 pence for a young wolf. The tax to meet these awards could be collected in money or in grain. A bounty payable in dollars does not appear until 1798. In that year seven counties were permitted to offer $4 for old wolves and $2 for young ones, and the amounts in eight other counties were set at $10 and $5. The colonial legislature, however, for wolf bounty-tax purposes, had standardized the price of tobacco at 12 shillings 6 pence per hundredweight in 1764. As in the case of bounty legislation in other places, the Virginians experienced trouble at times with fraudulent claims.

The law of 1732 stated that "Divers persons have been induced to spare the breading wolves, for the advantage of taking their increase." Hence, there was a reduction in that year of fifty percent in the prevailing two hundred pound tobacco reward. At the same time the law provided that the bounty claimant should take an oath stating, among other things, that he had not knowingly preserved the life of a bitch wolf. If a person submitted a false claim or swore to a false oath, he was to be penalized by forfeiting 1,000 pounds of tobacco, "one moiety [half] to our sovereign lord the king . . . . for the better support of this government, and one moiety to the informer who should disclose the fraud." (Ibid., vol. 1, p. 199.)

Another interesting legal device with regard to the tax for bounties (1662) was the provision that "it be layd only on horses two yeares old belonging to any person in this country not excepting the governour and councell proportioned in every county to the wolves heads there killed, ..." This was repealed in 1665 because of "too greate a burthen on the ffrontier counties which have the most wolves killed, and fewest horses to meet the charge."

The law first mentions pits and traps in the same year that the horse tax was started. Three decades later a distinction was made in the amount of the reward thus: for a wolf taken in pit or trap, 300 pounds of tobacco; for one shot with a gun, 200 pounds of tobacco.

On more than sixty different occasions over a period of three centuries Virginia legislators passed laws looking to the extermination of wolves. As pointed out above, the first known law for this purpose was adopted in 1632; the most recent was in 1930. Twenty-six of these were enacted during the colonial era and the others after statehood was attained following the Declaration of Independence in 1776. In numerous instances the regulations were set up for particular counties or groups of counties. During the last hundred years, as one would suppose, the bounties applied chiefly to the western parts of the State in the Blue Ridge and Alleghany regions, including some counties that later came to be included in West Virginia.

In most cases the Virginia local legislation was permissive, providing for bounty payments, within limited amounts, if the county magistrates considered them necessary and expedient. But the justices of the peace in Frederick County were given a compulsory order by the Assembly in 1745 to pay the legitimately established wolf bounty claims, authorized the year before, or be subject to a fine of 5 pounds (money, not tobacco) for each case of neglect. A hundred years later (1843) Kanawha County was "authorized and *required*" to allow not less than $5 or more than $10 for an old wolf and not less than $4 or more than $8 for a young wolf.

Though special regulations for different counties were common, by 1810 the legislature decided that it should "be lawful for *every* county to allow such reward as the necessity of the case may require." Thus, permissive bounties became state-wide in that year, although the practice of enacting specific rules for individual counties was soon resumed and was continued for 30 years more.

Except for one 7-year period, the expense of bounty payments was borne by the county where the wolf was taken. The law of

1799 stated that such rewards, $2 and $1, should "be paid by the county and repaid by the public"—probably from State funds. This clause was repealed in January 1806.

The amounts of the first money payments (1744) were 6 shillings for an old wolf, and 2 shillings 6 pence for a young wolf. The figures ranged upwards until a maximum of $25 and $12 was reached in 1848 for the counties of Bedford, Franklin, Hardy, Campbell, Roanoke, and Pittsylvania.

General codes of the Virginia statutes were adopted in 1819, 1849, 1874, 1888, 1918, 1924, and 1930 and provision for wolf bounties was included in each. The Code of 1849, Chapter CII, subject "Noxious Animals," provided that any county court could fix or alter, allow or discontinue, rewards for wolves, foxes, wild cats, crows, or blackbirds; any order set forth to remain operative one year. Three years afterwards the legislature passed an act for the control of noxious animals that set the wolf bounty at $10, which price has remained in effect through various minor changes in the law until the present day (1939). The regulations concerning payment of bounties on noxious animals were altered slightly at least eight times from 1888 to 1930; but the price on a wolf's scalp still heads the list at $10, more than six times that on its nearest rivals, the wildcat, catamount (puma), and red fox, priced at $1.50 each. No change has been made in the bounty law since 1930 (Hening, W. W., *The Statutes at Large*. Collection of Laws of Virginia (1619-1792); Shepherd, Samuel, *Statutes at Large of Virginia* (1792-1803), a continuation of Hening; Laws of Virginia, 1804-1938; The Virginia Code, 1849; The Code of Virginia 1888. Section 834. The Virginia Code of 1930. Section 2729).

In New York according to Benjamin F. Thompson's *History of Long Island*, the inhabitants of Jamaica "Agreed, Feb. 6, 1663, that whoever shall kill any wolf, the head being shown to the town or nailed upon a tree, shall have seven bushels of Indian corn." Still earlier the town of Gravesend took similar action, for "on the 8th of August 1650, three guilders were offered for each wolf killed in the town . . . ." (Dutcher, W., 1887: 105).

The town of Hempstead, through its authorized deputies, passed on March 1, 1665, a bounty act which stipulated "The value of an Indian coat [will] be given to anyone who shall bring the head of a wolf to any constable on Long Island, provided it be killed up the island." (Ibid.)

A similar reward was authorized by the town of Flatlands, with the provisos that the head of a wolf should "be nailed over the door of the constable, there to remain; also to cut off both the ears in token that the head is brought in and payed for." (Ibid.)

In 1683 the legislature of the entire New York colony passed a law offering a bounty of 20 shillings for each wolf killed on Long Island. Counties located elsewhere in the colony were permitted to offer bounties at the discretion of the magistrates.

Substantially the same law was reenacted in 1692. Ulster and Westchester Counties were required to pay wolf bounties under the law of 1701, which provided that if any justice should neglect payment of a proper bounty claim he should forfeit "to ye party grieved 5 pounds."

In order that "the breed of Wolves may be whooly rooted out and Extinguished," Suffolk, Queens, and Kings Counties were authorized in 1702 to pay a reward of 3 pounds "currant money of this Colony" for every wolf killed (30 shillings for each whelp).

Additional and similar legislation was passed for Albany, Orange, and Dutchess Counties, naming various amounts of money, in 1715, 1716, and 1719.

The law of 1683, passed on November 1, read as follows:

". . . . That whatsoever Christian shall kill a grown wolf upon Long Island; hee shall bee paid twenty shillings P. head, in the County where itt shall so happen . . . . and for a whelpe about a halfe a Yeare old, he shall bee paid halfe so much.

"That whattsoever Indyans shall in like manner kill any wolfe or wolves, they shall bee paid a Match Coate for each, or the Value which is computed to bee twelve shillings and for a Whelpe halfe so much to be paid as before, of which the Officers for publique affairs in each towne of the Countyes are to take care that the same be duly satisfied.

"And for killing Wolves in other parts of the Government That itt shall be left to the Magistrates to give whatt reward they shall think fitt . . . . Only . . . the same reward . . . for Staten Island as for Long Island" (New York State: 1896, vol. 1, p. 133).

The law of 1726, passed on November 11, an Act for destroying wolves in the counties of Albany, Dutchess, and Orange, read:

"Whereas the Several Inhabitants of the County of Albany Dutchess County and Orange County Suffer great Losses in their Stocks of horses, Neat Cattle and Sheep by the great Number of Wolves in their respective Countys for preventing the like losses for the future and encouraging those who Shall destroy Wolves in the above named Counties. Be It Enacted by his Excellency the Governour Council and General Assembly, and it is hereby enacted by the Authority of the same That every Person and persons whither he be A Christian Indian or a Negroe inhabiting or Sojourning within the respective Countys above mentioned who shall kill any wolf within the above mentioned Countys and Carry the head thereof to any Justice of the peace residing within the County where the said wolf shall be killed Such Justice shall give him or them a Certificate to receive of the Treasurer of the said County the Sum of Six Shillings Currant money of this Colony Allways provided that the said Justice of the peace Shall deem and adjudge the wolf to have been Killed within three days and that the ears of the said Wolf Shall be Cut off in the presence of the said Justice before any such Certificate for such reward shall be given.

"And be it further enacted by the authority aforesaid that for defraying the Charges of destroying Wolves in the aforementioned Countys there shall be raised levyed and Collected and paid by the freeholders Inhabitants Residents and Sojourners of and Inhabiting in the respective Countys afores'd Such sum or sums of money as the Supervisors of the aforementioned Countys or the Major part of them for the time being Shall Seem requisite in Such way and in like manner and under such pains and forfeitures and under Such Regulations and directions as all other publick and Necessary Charges of the respective Countys aforesaid are by Law raised levyed Collected and paid. Any Usage or Custom to the Contrary Notwithstanding.

"And be it further Enacted by the Authority aforesaid that this Act Shall be and Continue in force for two Years from and after the Publication hereof and no Longer" (Ibid., vol. 2, p. 346).

Regulations regarding bounty payments on wolves were adopted by the State Legislature or the Colonial Assembly on approximately 60 different occasions between 1683 and 1898. At least 25 such laws were given a trial in the Colony before 1776. The amount offered for each wolf varied from 6 shillings to 40 dollars.

During the early period a slave occasionally killed a wolf. In that case the master or mistress was entitled to the bounty under the law. Usually the payment was the same in amount to white man and Indian. But the law of 1750 provided that in the County of Albany an Indian should be entitled to one-half the reward due an "Inhabitant" or a "Freeholder."

The wolf appears to have been a hardy creature not easily discouraged by these actions of the colonial legislature. The bounty had risen to 3 pounds by the 1770's, yet bounty laws remained in effect for more than a hundred years to follow. The figure was kept at 3 pounds by the last Assembly of the Colony, in 1775, and was not changed for more than a decade.

First payments in dollars were ordered in 1797. A law of that year empowered county supervisors to set the figure for wolf bounties in their respective counties up to a maximum of $10. In less than 20 years this was doubled to $20 for a grown wolf and $7.50 for a whelp. In 1820 the Legislature gave permission to six counties to pay an additional $10 for each wolf taken, if the supervisors approved.

The highest figure for bounty payment was reached in 1836 when a special act of the Legislature permitted Steuben County to pay $40 for each grown wolf and $20 for each whelp.

A standard state-wide bounty fee, to be paid by the State "to any person who shall kill a wolf within the boundaries of this State" was adopted in 1871. This provision, through reenactments, remained in force until its final repeal in 1898.

Almost all of the changes in the amount to be paid for each wolf were increases, although a few exceptions are to be noted. The $10 payment ordered in 1797 was a decrease from the previous 3 pounds. It is probable, however, that the aggregate outlay under this law was greater, for the $10 rule was to apply throughout the State, and the same amount was to be paid for either grown wolf or whelp. In 1745 the bounty of 20 shillings was found to be too "burdensome and grievous" for the citizens of Orange County and was, therefore, reduced to 12 shillings. It is not stated whether the number of wolves taken was too great or the funds of the county too meager to stand the strain of the larger payment.

Some of the laws passed for wolf control applied only to certain counties or groups of counties when wolf depredations, changed with shifts in the population, menaced different farming centers. One of the special acts for Westchester County (1810) has been lost, only the title appearing among present-day compilations of the laws. Perhaps few of the dwellers of today in famed Westchester, one of the world's most exclusive residential districts, adjacent to our greatest metropolis, would suspect that the ravages of wolves were a serious problem for their predecessors less than a century and a quarter ago.

For the most part, the bounty claims were paid from the treasury of the county in which the wolf was taken. Under the regulations of 1820, the county supervisors could establish a bounty payment of their own choice up to $20 and the State would add an equal amount for each claim paid. But in 1822 a flat price of $10 was prescribed for each wolf, the State to pay half and the county half.

In certain other cases the town, instead of the county, was empowered to set its own bounty prices by popular vote at the town meeting. The towns of Mooers, Dresden, and Fort Ann are examples of places where this plan was in effect during the first third of the nineteenth century.

The provision for a state-wide and state-paid bounty of 1871 was continued for 27 years. Claims were paid by the county treasurer, who was reimbursed from the State treasury upon presentation of proper vouchers.

Under the bounty law in effect in the State of New York in 1871, a total of 98 wolf scalps were submitted between that year and 1897. These bounties averaged $30 per wolf, apparently $10 more than was given for the puma. The wolves turned in came from twelve counties, namely, Broome, Essex, Franklin, Fulton, Hamilton, Herkimer, Lewis, Oneida, Otsego, St. Lawrence, Warren, and Washington. One of these counties (Otsego) paying bounty on a wolf in a fairly recent time is only 150 miles distant in an airline from New York City. The largest number (45) from a single county were from St. Lawrence County bordering on Ontario, Canada.

The wolf was practically exterminated in New York State by the close of the nineteenth century. Under the bounty law of 1871, there were a total of 6 wolves presented in each of the years 1895, 1896, and 1897. Of these 18 individuals, 7 came from St. Lawrence County, 10 from Lewis County, and 1 from Fulton County.

In New York, as elsewhere, opportunity for local use of State money in the early 1800's led to some attempts at fraud. Cooper describes the following interesting instance:

"The principal wild beasts of our forests are the bear, the black and grey wolf and the panther. These are all called noxious animals and so considered by our laws, which give rewards for their destruction, which in these new countries are sometimes as high as from ten to twenty-five dollars, paid on the production of each pair of ears and scalp. . . . The reward is paid by the County Treasurer under a law passed by a majority of the people in open town-meeting. The farmers are always disposed to vote for a high bounty in revenge for the sheep they have lost, and the hunters because they have hope of reward.

"A man by the name of Ellsworth once made a pit-fall with a bait or decoy upon it . . . . on the morning of a town-meeting he found in it a she-wolf with six whelps, supposed to have had their birth after the bitch had fallen in. He left them where he found them and went to the town-meeting, where he made an animated discourse upon the mischievous depredations of these animals; stated in glowing colours the losses and the terrors of the farmers and finished by proposing a bounty such as might encourage some enterprising spirits to devote themselves entirely, and with zeal, to their destruction. His eloquence was popular and successful. The bounty was doubled; next morning he went with a neighbor to examine his pit-fall and taking the seven scalps claimed and received for each, the augmented recompence" (Cooper, W., 1810: 23).

The law of 1822 provided that one of "the assessors, overseers of the poor or commissioners of highways" attend and be "associated with" the justice of the peace, when he considered an application for a bounty payment, and be satisfied that "the application is in all respects regular and fair." It would appear that, now and then, some of the good justices must have indulged in connivance with questionable claimants, probably in the hope of sharing some easy money from Albany.

Further, a special act of the same year limited Franklin County to $500 as the State's share of bounty payments. Court officers were instructed to charge grand juries, particularly in the County of Franklin, to inquire carefully into abuses that had been committed against the provisions for wolf control. Also, the law directed that the governor appoint two "discreet and competent persons . . . for the purpose of examining and determining the legality of certificates and bounties." They were to report to the State treasurer and the county treasurer. In them were placed all powers to conduct a court of inquiry. If the recreant county failed to comply, tax collections could be suspended for all amounts paid out on bounty claims. Franklin County must have grown repentant and properly conformed, as restoration of $1,845 of suspended taxes was made the next year.

Throughout the history of New York bounties, the procedure of making a claim was much the same. The person killing the wolf took the skin before a local officer, as a justice of the peace, who examined the hide and cut off the ears. He then administered an oath to the applicant as to where the wolf was taken, and issued a certificate that the claim was genuine. After the claim was approved by the county board of supervisors it could be paid by the county treasurer.

In preceding paragraphs have been outlined the history in the State of New York of efforts to deal by bounty payments with that notorious despoiler, the wolf, which with amazing persistency stubbornly resisted the advance of civilization and continued to annoy the inhabitants of our most populous State for more than two hundred and seventy-five years after the first appearance of the white settler.

On November 4, 1697 the General Assembly of West Jersey met at Burlington. Both wolf and puma depredations were taken into consideration and the discussions finally led to the adoption of a bounty, "It being seen by daily and detrimental experience that the wolves are very destructive to the cattle and creatures of the inhabitants of this Province . . . . whatsoever Christian shall kill and bring the head of a wolf of prey or panther to any magistrate of any county of this province" (Rhoads, S. N., 1903: 132), a bounty of 20 shillings was to be paid. Here we find a discrimination for the Negro or Indian who might kill a "wolf of prey," only 10 shillings being paid. The bounty for a young wolf or panther was also 10 shillings.

East and West Jersey combined in 1702, and in 1709 a law was passed for the killing of wolves and pumas. By 1730, the bounty on wolves was still stipulated as 20 shillings, but was shortly raised to 60 shillings. (Ibid.)

Pennsylvania, like New York, adopted its first bounty law in 1683. Payment of rewards, varying in amounts, was made in Dutch and English currency. For approximately 40 years, thereafter, the bounty was paid on wolves only, but by 1724, the Pennsylvania authorities of the British Crown began to add other animals deemed nuisances, such as red foxes. By 1740 squirrels were added to the list, then followed the puma and the bobcat. Later, still other mammals and some birds were included in the list of bounties. Thus for more than 250 years the State continued to maintain some form of the bounty that had its beginnings solely for wolves.

We find a statute passed on January 12, 1705, 24 years after Pennsylvania became a colony, reading as follows:
An Act for the Killing of Wolves.

"(Section I) Be it enacted by John Evans, Esquire, by the Queen's royal approbation Lieutenant-Governor under William Penn Esquire, absolute Proprietary and Governor-in-Chief of the Province of Pennsylvania and Territories, by and with the advice and consent of the freeman of the said Province in General Assembly met, and by the authority of the same, That if any person within this province shall kill a dog-wolf, he shall have ten shillings; to be paid out of the county stock; . . . . Indians as well as others, shall be paid for the killing of wolves accordingly" (Pennsylvania, State of, 1896: 238).

Apparently this statute remained in effect in Pennsylvania for 77 years, when in 1782 it was repealed, and a bounty law was adopted setting the wolf bounty at 25 shillings, payable in "good and current money of the 'State of Pennsylvania,' " for every grown wolf; and at 15 shillings for every "Wolf Puppy or Whelp." The bounty was payable by the respective counties (Pennsylvania, Commonwealth of, 1782: 59).

One of the reasons for the change, and for passage of the Act of 1782 was the advent of the Revolutionary War, when the Pennsylvanians did not care to have a statute reading that a wolf bounty must be paid "by the Queen's royal approbation."

We come next to the bounty law of 1819 wherein U. S. currency is first named. This act provided county bounties of $12 each for scalps of full grown wolves or panthers, and of $5 each for "the scalp of a panther or wolf puppy" (Pennsylvania, Commonwealth of, 1819: 114).

Many counties in Pennsylvania had county bounties in effect during the early part of the nineteenth century. Butler County was one of these that not only paid bounties for wolves, but also for pumas, other wildcats, and foxes. The first wolf bounty was paid in 1803; the last, in 1840. In the 38 years that the bounties were paid in Butler County, 240 wolves are recorded as being taken. Apparently the record year was 1809, with a total of 47 bounty payments. Prior to 1825 the bounty was $8 for a grown wolf and $3 for a whelp. After 1825 these amounts were increased to $12.50 for a grown wolf and $5 for a single whelp (Webb, D. K., and Stevens, J. M., 1934: 27 pp.).

During the period from early colonization of New England and the middle Atlantic coast, scarcely more than a decade passed before, as we have noted, the early settlers adopted the bounty system as their main recourse toward the stoppage of wolf depredations. Practically every settlement had some such scheme in effect, but wolf depredations seem to have kept pace with the ever-expanding livestock husbandry. With the closing of the eighteenth century, the wolf bounty plan was in effect in practically all of the colonial settlements. Up to the middle of the nineteenth century Vermont still continued with a State bounty of $20 for the killing of each adult wolf and $10 for each suckling whelp. By this time, according to Thompson, wolves had been so reduced that "the amount paid annually for wolf certificates is usually from one to two hundred dollars" (Thompson, Z., 1853: 34).

In the West, bounties were paid by the States but this form of control was largely developed by associations of stockmen. Enough will be cited of each of these plans to give some idea of their nature and scope.

According to Joseph Neal, of Meeker, Colo.:

"In the early days of the wolf depredations most range states and counties placed a small bounty on the wolf but this was not sufficient to justify a trapper to put in all his time trapping them and mainly resulted in inciting trappers and others to get out and hunt for the pups before they were old enough to leave their dens. This was a primary benefit as these dens would contain from five to as high as eleven pups and their destruction helped to keep down the increase. . . ."[32]

In the 1880's a bounty of $1 apiece was offered by the Territory of Montana; also, nearly every county had a bounty on the animal.

"In 1885 they [wolves] were on the ranges in greater swarms than ever and the damage they did counted heavily against the profits of the year. On the Chestnut range in northeastern Montana the stockmen came to the front with a handsome offer to wolf killers, which will make it a paying business for anybody to engage in that occupation alone" (Carl —————, 1886: 508).

Thus again we note the presence of the "professional wolfer"— that picturesque character who was on the plains in the 1860's and who roamed the western ranges, playing no small part in the total elimination of the "lobo," or "loafer wolf."

The "handsome offer to wolf killers" stipulated that the stockmen's "association will give the wolfer plenty of poison and not less than $5.00 for each skin, after which he is at liberty to sell the hide for what he can get.

"In Yellowstone county the boys have struck quite a bonanza. In addition to the territorial bounty the county offers one dollar on a coyote, and two dollars on a wolf. This just doubles the territorial bounty on each animal killed or brought in.

"A young fellow named Martin with not much on his hands except idle time, practiced a week at the business in Yellowstone county, and the result was nine wolf skins and twenty-six coyote skins. To sum up he got $13 and $26 for coyote ears, and $9 and $18 for those of the wolves; after which he sold the hides for an average of about $1.50 each to a fur dealer in Billings. Total profit, $118.50 and lots of fun; cost about $5.00 for strychnine and time. Bait was had in one dead animal picked up on the range" (Carl —————, 1886: 508).

One of the first meetings of the Oregon pioneers was for the purpose of dealing with the predator problem. "The preliminary meeting of citizens of the Willamette Valley was held at Oregon Institute, February 2nd 1843, and was followed by another at the house of Joseph Gervais, on the first Monday of March of that

[32]Letter of Joe Neal, of Meeker, Colo., sent to Stanley P. Young through Mr. Neal's daughter, Mrs. Blue, and received in Washington, D. C., on February 3, 1939. In files of Fish and Wildlife Service.

year. The latter meeting is generally known in Oregon history as the 'Wolf Meeting,' for a resolution was adopted, to provide for measure of protection against predatory animals; . . . ." (Hastings, L. W., 1932: 12, 13).

"After the proper parliamentary forms, and the choosing of the necessary officers for the Association, the meeting proceeded to fix the rate of bounty for each animal killed by anyone out of the Association, viz: $3.00 for a large wolf; $1.50 for a lynx; $2.00 for a bear; and $5.00 for a panther. The money to pay these bounties was to be raised by subscription, and handed over to the treasurer for disbursement; the currency being drafts on Ft. Vancouver, the Mission, and the Milling Company; besides wheat and other commodities" (Victor, Mrs. F. F., 1870: 318).

Many Iowa counties had adopted the bounty method for combating the wolf menace, and by 1858 there was a state-wide bounty. During 1892 the Iowa State Breeders and Wool Growers Association were instrumental in getting the State to increase the wolf bounty to $5 for every adult, and $2 for each whelp. Typical of the arguments brought to bear were the remarks made by A. J. Blakely, a sheep breeder of Grinnell, who said:

"The wolf, not merely figuratively, is at the door of many an Iowa farmer, but the real wolves, large wolves, prowl over the Iowa farms in increasing numbers, seeking what they may devour. No census like that of their cousins, the dogs, has ever been made. . . . But their name is legion. Much of the best sheep lands of the State, the bluffy, bushy portions along the streams and adjacent to timber belts can not be pastured with sheep. . . . Sheep can't live there now on account of the wolves, and chickens and turkeys must every night roost very high. . . . Really it is a stain, a foul stigma, on the civilization and enterprise of the people of Iowa that these wolves remain and are frequently seen crossing the best cultivated farms, and even near the best towns in our State.

"What is the remedy, do you ask? Wipe out all trifling and unequal bounties and induce the legislature to provide a State bounty of $20 for the scalps of the old wolves and $5.00 for the young ones. The boys will then arm themselves with the best rifles of long range, will watch and hunt for the game, and speedily exterminate the lupine race" (Carman, E. A., and others, 1892: 828).

R. M. Allen, General Manager, Stand Cattle Company, Ames,

Nebr., in a letter of April 3, 1896, said: "In the session of Jan. '93 in Cheyenne (Wyo.) we succeeded in passing a bill for the payment of an $8.00 bounty, to be paid from the general county funds, and at this time I paid at our ranch for the Western Union Company and ours additional bounty, making $13.00 and the hide, or a total of $15.00 to the hunter. Even this did not secure great activity, at least at first, and as counties soon began to issue script instead of paying in cash, the $8.00 bounty was soon reduced to $4.00 in cash. The law was repealed after two years, and in Jan. '95, a bounty paid from the state treasury, of $3.00 a head was passed. Montana also passed a $3.00 bounty law but accompanied by such difficult complications and observations that the law is hampered. In '94 we paid a $5.00 bounty at our ranch on almost exactly 500 wolves."

In North Dakota, Theodore Roosevelt stated: "I never knew the wolves to be so numerous or so daring in their assaults upon stock in the Little Missouri country as in the years 1894 to 1896 inclusive. . . .

". . . . In the early nineties the ravages of the wolves along the Little Missouri became so serious as thoroughly to arouse the stockmen. Not only colts and calves, and young stock, but in mid-winter full grown horses and steers were continually slain. The county authorities put a bounty of three dollars each on wolf scalps to which the ranchmen of the neighborhood added a further bounty of five dollars. This made eight dollars for every wolf, and as the skin was also worth something, the business of killing wolves became profitable" (Roosevelt, T., 1905: 530).

One of the earliest of the local county stock associations formed in the West was the Bent-Prowers County Cattle & Horse Growers Association of southern Colorado. This organization has kept a complete set of the minutes of its annual meetings from the beginning in the early 1870's to the present time. It is typical of many local western stock associations in the causes that led to its formation, namely, what to do about "mavericking" [stealing of unbranded cattle] and wolf depredations.

Among other things, it was decided that all "mavericks" found on the range were to be branded with the association brand and sold, the proceeds to be used to help to defray the expenses of the organization. Among these expenses was that of the wolf bounty, as well as the purchase of poison for use in killing wolves, all of which was for the "protection and advancing the interests of the stock-growers of Bent County." To supplement these funds it was ruled that assessments could be made not to exceed two mills upon each head of stock.

The bounty set on gray wolves was $4.50 a scalp. A further special wolf assessment was added amounting to two cents on each head of stock with 52 stockmen contributing. Individual stockmen within the association owned from 200 to 4,000 head. A perusal of the minutes of the annual meetings that were held shows that the bounty was changed periodically in attempts to obtain more relief from wolf depredations. For instance, on April 7, 1900, 30 years after this organization of cattlemen was formed,

"Motion [was] made and carried that this association shall pay a reward of $5.00 for grown gray wolves, and $2.50 for cub wolves under 3 months old, killed upon the range of any member of this association after this date (Apr. 7, 1900), who is not in arrears of this association for any assessment. This money to be paid by the Treasurer, P. B. Scott. Upon a certificate to him issued by M. H. Murray, certifying that such wolves or cubs have been killed upon the range of some member of this association in good standing. And the fact of such killing of wolves or cubs shall be certified to Mr. M. H. Murray, by the owner of said range upon which the animals were killed."

Skullduggery sometimes took place to obtain the $5 wolf bounty, for we read, "On motion O. G. Strain was allowed $2.50 for one wolf scalp which was caught as pup, but was not killed until grown." In other words, by letting it mature to adult stage in captivity, it was hoped that an extra $2.50 could be collected.

In the hope of interesting neighboring stockmen in joining the association, it was resolved "that any stockowner presenting scalps for bounty, killed on his own range shall be required to join this association or bounty will not be paid him."

Ready cash in the hands of many of these pioneer stockmen was often a minus quantity, so to enable those hard-pressed for cash who might desire to join the association, it was so ordered in the case of one Bill Jess Tanner, that "for one gray wolf scalp $5.00 would be allowed, this $5.00 also paying his admission fee to the stock association" (Bent-Prowers County Cattle and Horse Growers Association, 1870-1938: 3-5, 118, 163, 231, 238).

These early association meetings throughout the West were similar to the so-called "Wolf Meetings" of the early pioneers of Oregon some 30 years before. Means of control for the wolf were discussed, such as bounties and the use of poisons. These early bounty discussions led to the levy plan among local groups of stock interests whereby each producer paid in a certain assessment as his share toward a bounty fund. This plan was the final outgrowth of bounty payments by the several counties and, in addition, oftentimes finally by the State.

Again referring to the Bent-Prowers Cattle and Horse Growers Association as typical in moves taken to obtain county bounty aid, a committee of these stockmen waited "upon the Board of County Commissions of Prowers County to try to get them to assist us in paying wolf bounty. . . . they finally agreed to pay $5.00 per head bounty on 50 wolves and further said when that number had been paid they would consider the matter again and might continue to pay the bounty. All scalps were to be presented to your sec. who had to vouch it to the board who would then draw warrant for same and destroy the scalp" (Ibid., p. 249).

The stock interests of the Western States and Territories took the leading part in fostering county and State bounty legislation, for they felt that, as taxpayers, they were footing a large part of the taxes collected, and bounties were a means of some direct and beneficial aid to them in perpetuating the industry which, in turn, made assessments of taxes a surety, for they held that each head of livestock killed by wolves reduced the number that could be taxed.

In Rio Blanco County, Colo., the stockmen formed what was known as the Piceance Creek Stock Growers Association. Its main objective was cooperative action looking towards the curbing of extensive wolf losses. Money for the payment of bounty—stipulated as $25 for each wolf scalp obtained, later raised to $50, then to $100, and finally to $150 for each wolf killed—was raised voluntarily. This was carried on for nearly eight years, between 1904 and 1912. However, not all of the stock interests paid their just proportion of the fund. To bring this about, another association was finally formed, in which a set of by-laws was adopted for the betterment of the situation, so that all interests shared alike financially. These by-laws stipulated that a cattleman must pay his legitimate assessments for wolf bounty, or he could not join the association, be permitted to join in the cooperative spring and fall cattle round-ups, or join any cooperative ride for the seasonal rounding up of cattle. Members of this association refused to aid those cattlemen in arrears with wolf assessments in any cooperative help with their round-ups, whereby aid from the whole cattlemen's group was of great import in such stock gathering. This meant, therefore, that whosoever reneged on the payment of his wolf bounty fee must singly round up his own cattle, do his own branding, and run his own chuck wagon—work of no small magnitude for a single individual where many square miles of cattle range riding was involved. Thus he received no benefit whatsoever from the community round-up involving several dozen cowhands.

These by-laws brought in the assessments of all those cattle interests who had previously sponged on their neighbors, so that eventually all of the stock interests in this section shared equitably in the collective fight on the wolf. This made for fairness in the pro-rata wolf assessments that were established from time to time as the bounty payments per wolf were increased.

Some of the bounty trappers made good money. To one noted trapper, who during 1912-13 brought in 140 wolves, the association paid $7,000, at the rate of $50 for each wolf. With this money the trapper was able to start a small ranch of his own and equip it with horses, harness, wagon, farm implements, and seed.

In North Park, Colo., in the early 1900's, the stockmen paid a bounty of $35 for each adult gray wolf, and $10 for each whelp. It was reported that at these prices a hunter could easily earn $100 a week because the wolves were so numerous. Particularly good wolf trappers in this section were paid as much as $200 per month plus board, besides a bounty of $50 per head for adult wolves and $20 per head for each whelp by individual stockmen in addition to the State, county, or stock association bounty then offered.

In Canada, also, the bounty system was tried. One of the early schemes involved payment in something more attractive than money to many men, namely, liquor.

At some of its early trading posts the Hudson's Bay Company bred horses for cross-country pack purposes, and cattle for meat and dairy products. Wolves and coyotes were a constant nuisance to the livestock, and some means were generally taken to curb the depredations. This was occasionally done by the employment of hunters to kill off these predators near the posts, who were rewarded in most instances with rum as a bounty payment for their services.

Most of the Canadian provinces have at one time or another had in effect bounty systems for wolf control. In 1927 the Dominion Department of the Interior announced the employment of a system of wolf control as follows:

"Wolf-killing campaigns are as old as organized society but the Department of the Interior has introduced a new element into them by endeavoring to make this ravenous beast pay for his own destruction. If wolves were easy to trap there would never be a wolf menace—the trappers would attend to that. But wolves are notoriously the most difficult of all animals to kill or capture and for this reason the trapper naturally gives his attention to fur-bearers more easily taken.

"Canada's northern country is steadily being opened up. Possibilities in hunting, ranching, mining, and other lines are coming into sight but it is a truism that these can only be developed with the aid of the native population of Indians and Eskimos. For generations the natives have depended for a great part of their food and clothing upon the caribou. The wolf preys on this animal and does further damage by destroying the furbearers caught in the traps of the hunters. To check these losses and to protect the subsistence of the Indians and Eskimos the Dominion Government in 1915 offered a bounty of $20 per head for each wolf killed in the Northwest Territories, the hunter being allowed after receiving the bounty to sell the pelt for what it would fetch. This brought about little, if any, increase in the number of wolves destroyed, and to get the situation into hand the North West Territories and Yukon Branch in the winter of 1922-23, and again in 1923-24, sent a wolf-hunting party into the caribou country east of Great Slave lake which resulted in the destruction in the two years of 320 wolves. The pelts thus obtained were sold at auction and the proceeds materially assisted in paying the cost of these expeditions.

"In 1924, following up the success thus attained, the bounty was increased from $20 to $30 per wolf, upon condition that the pelt be surrendered to the Department. The pelts are received from the hunters at the various Royal Canadian Mounted Police posts, and shipped direct to the fur auctions in Eastern Canada to be disposed of at the various sales. This has given a great impetus to the wolf-extermination campaign and at the same time has lessened the cost per wolf to the Department; for while some of the pelts taken under the bounty scheme are only of average value the majority are prime skins of the huge timber wolf of the north, skins which are sought by dealers from all over the world. At the sales held in 1926 and the one in January, 1927, pelts to the number of 964 were disposed of for $13,861. Thus, although the hunter was encouraged, by the increased bounty of $30, to get more wolves, the Government effected a considerable saving as compared with the former bounty of $20, and the expansion of the market caused by the knowledge that such pelts can be secured in quantity will tend to further reduce the cost of combating the wolf menace" (Anonymous, 1927: 3).

Throughout the three centuries that wolf bounties have been paid in North America, millions of dollars have been expended for the extirpation of this animal. The plan has been attended, however, with much fraud.

A review of the bounty laws in force on July 1, 1907, revealed that of the 40 states and territories listed, 39 had bounties in effect on wolves and/or other animals.

Few states now include the wolf in their present bounty legislation, because the animal has disappeared from such a great proportion of its original habitat. Alaska and 29 of the 48 states were authorized to pay bounties on certain animals and birds during 1937. Of these, 12 states and the Territory definitely mention the wolf in their respective bounty acts. The largest payment authorized for a single wolf scalp was $50 in certain counties of Texas.

The wolf bounty for the Northwest Territories of Canada was repealed on February 29, 1940. Most of the Canadian provinces, however, still pay a bounty upon wolves, as do several of the Mexican states. Alaska places the same reward on the wolf as on the coyote, namely, $20 per animal. Between April 1, 1937 and May 31, 1939, bounty was paid by that territory on 8,250 wolves and coyotes. From April 1 to September 12, 1939 bounty was paid on 1,893 wolves and coyotes. About twice as many coyotes as wolves were presented for payment.

Pursuant to a recent action [1941] of its Territorial legislature, Alaska reduced the bounty on coyotes to $17.50 per animal, but did not change the prevailing bounty of $20 per wolf.

It will be well to mention at this point that it was the bounty system that brought the Biological Survey in contact with the Nation-wide attempts that were being made to eradicate mammal pests. A critical review of the scheme showed that throughout its use in America it was an "every colony, state, territory, or county for itself matter." No uniformity of method in applying the plan was or is apparent in its operations, for the rewards offered varied so much for each obnoxious species. Further, the system might be strongly entrenched in one commonwealth, and weakly supported in another, or lacking altogether in a bordering state or states. Generally speaking, wherever the bounty system was favored its loose administration was notorious.

As previously mentioned the bounty system as a predator control measure became honeycombed with fraud. A study of the plan throughout its centuries of use brings to light endless examples of this. A common practice of substituting scalps from domestic animals, such as dogs, for those of wolves, was much in vogue in the West. Substituting coyote ears and scalps for those of wolves was another practice, and often succeeded in duping county or State officials, because of their inability to distinguish between the two animals at the time they would be presented for bounty payments. In operations the bounty system tends to perpetuate itself, since often the most objectionable individual predators and their offspring are left at large, and only the most easily obtained being destroyed by bounty hunters. Instances have been discovered where female wolves were deliberately turned loose after capture in traps, so that the species would be perpetuated, and hence afford continued revenue from the production of whelps to be taken from the den, at $25 or more per whelp. This scheme became commonplace, and was in operation in early Colonial America. For instance, as previously noted the Bounty Act of 1732 in Virginia mentions this fraud. More than two centuries ago a Virginian bounty claimant had to give an oath that: "he had not knowingly preserved the life of a bitch wolf." For one giving a false oath he, if convicted, had to forfeit 1,000 pounds of tobacco (Hening, W. W., 1810-23, vol. 1, p. 199). And as an inducement to make this law truly effective, the informer on the guilty party received one-half of the fine or 500 pounds of tobacco; the other half going to the support of the colony.

Shipment of skins or scalps across State and international boundaries to be presented for bounty in a State or county other than the one in which they were taken was another common practice; so was the presentation of scalps and skins through the front door of the offices of officials dispursing bounty money, only to have the same skins and scalps taken out the back door of the same offices, and later brought around to the front door for another bounty collection, and so on ad infinitum. Furthermore as a control measure, the bounty act is most expensive—even when honest attempts are made to carry out its provisions without fraud. Human nature being what it is as soon as any objective is made a source of income the prevailing idea becomes one of not eradicating but propagating. Thus it has been with bounties on predators, such as wolves, throughout the entire history of the bounty law.

Finally, it cannot be depended upon to bring about the measure of predator control necessary in practical wildlife management. The system, as pointed out, involves so much fraud and has so many undesirable features that it should never be substituted for the more orderly and scientific control that can be applied through the employ ment of trained hunters and trappers whenever wild life conditions warrant.

VII

BRIEF HISTORY OF WOLF DEPREDATIONS AND COOPERATIVE FEDERAL WOLF CONTROL

EARLY American history is replete with the evidence that wolves exacted a costly toll of all farm animals following their introduction from the mother countries of the early colonists. Beasts of prey were attracted to clearings made at the time of early settlements, which were at first confined to the Atlantic seaboard, and gradually spread westward. Stock raising has always been incompatible with great numbers of wolves.

The wolf bounty laws of Massachusetts, Virginia, New York and Pennsylvania as we have noted, were among the earliest attempts to bring relief from wolves for pioneer American husbandry.

Typical of other actions of particular historic interest taken to curb wolf depredations by many early colonial settlements which in many instances preceded the colonial bounty acts is that pertaining to those years after the settlement in 1640 of Woburn, east Middlesex County, Mass. Sewall records that all around the new settlers of Woburn was to be found "a dense forest, or a dreary waste, infested with wolves. . . ." It is indicated that they were very destructive. Bounty was paid accordingly at a price of ten shillings per wolf. Herein we find also a unique order on the part of the town authorities of Woburn:—a wolf trapping area was set aside exclusively for the use of one Izack Brooks, who was engaged to "set traps from time to time in a spring between Woodhill and Maple Meadow." Further, that "all other persons are prohibited to set any traps at the same place, so long as Izack Brooks liveth." (Sewall, S., 1868: 57.) The exclusive right to a trapping area given to Izack Brooks by these early colonial fathers three centuries past is somewhat comparable to a similar plan legalized and enforced by several of our commonwealths at the present time with regard to fur trapping. (Hall, E. R., 1942: 475.)

J. A. Allen, writing mainly of the wolf in the extreme northeastern United States, records: "Most of the carnivorous species existed in such numbers at the time of the first settlement of the country by Europeans that their presence was a great check upon the raising of stock, and even a source of danger to human life. Hence, naturally, an exterminating warfare was speedily begun upon them, which was stimulated by the offer of rewards by the local authorities for their destruction" (Allen, J. A., 1876b: 708).

With regard to wolf depredations farther southward in early Rhode Island, Rider comments: "Wolves were terribly destructive to young cattle, goats, and swine" (Rider, S. S., 1904: 179). It is apparent that this condition led Roger Williams to place hogs on some of the islands that were free from wolves such as Prudence, in Narragansett Bay. In such places the swine, although free-ranging, escaped wolf depredations.

To the westward in Pennsylvania along the Delaware, Davis recorded that the wolves "became so troublesome before 1680, that the Upland Court authorized forty guilders [a guilder was a Dutch coin containing a little less than 55 grains of gold] to be paid for each scalp, but becoming worse the court ordered the setting of fifty-two 'wolf pitts or trap houses'" (Davis, W. W. H., 1876: 32). It is not clear from this record whether the "Upland Court" paid a salary to the persons building the "wolf pitts or trap houses"; whether certain persons had exclusive right to the use of them as in the case of Izack Brooks of Woburn, Mass.; or whether a bounty was the compensation for constructing this large number of pits.

One of the most interesting of the colonial accounts of wolf damage and of defense against it is that relating to General Israel Putnam of Revolutionary War fame. While operating a farm in Pomfret, Conn., which was located about 35 miles northeast of

Hartford, Putnam experienced depredations from wolves, and at some personal risk killed one of the earliest outstanding renegade wolves on record in early Colonial America. By Humphrey we are told that:

"In the year 1739 (Putnam) removed from Salem to Pomfret, an inland fertile town in Connecticut, forty miles east of Hartford: having here purchased a considerable tract of land he applied himself successfully to agriculture. . . . In one night he had seventy-five sheep and goats killed, besides many lambs and kids wounded. This havoc was committed by a she wolf, which, with her annual whelps, had for several years infested the vicinity. The young were commonly destroyed by the vigilance of the hunters, but the old one was too sagacious to come within reach of gunshot; upon being closely pursued she would generally fly to the western woods, and return the next winter with another litter of whelps.

"This wolf at length became such an intolerable nuisance, that Mr. Putnam entered into a combination with five of his neighbours to hunt alternately until they could destroy her. Two by rotation, were to be constantly in pursuit. It was known, that, having lost the toes from one foot, by a steel trap, she made one track shorter than the other. By this vestige, the pursuers recognized, in a light snow, the route of this pernicious animal. Having followed her to Connecticutt river and found she had turned back in a direct course towards Pomfret, they immediately returned, and by ten o'clock the next morning the blood-hounds had driven her into a den, about three miles distant from the house of Mr. Putnam: The people soon collected with dogs, guns, straw, fire and sulphur to attack the common enemy. With this apparatus several unsuccessful efforts were made to force her from the den. The hounds came back badly wounded and refused to return. The smoke of blazing straw had no effect. Nor did the fumes of burnt brimstone, with which the cavern was filled, compel her to quit the retirement. Wearied with such fruitless attempts (which had brought the time to ten o'clock at night) Mr. Putnam tried once more to make his dog enter, but in vain; he proposed to his negro man to go down into the cavern and shoot the wolf; the negro declined the hazardous service. Then it was that the master, angry at the disappointment, and declaring that he was ashamed to have a coward in his family, resolved himself to destroy the ferocious beast, lest she should escape through some unknown fissure of the rock. His neighbours strongly remonstrated against the perilous enterprise; but he, knowing that wild animals were intimidated by fire, and having provided several strips of birch-bark, the only combustible material which he could obtain, that would afford light in this deep and darksome cave, prepared for his descent. Having, accordingly, divested himself of his coat and waistcoat, and having a long rope fastened around his legs by which he might be pulled back, at a concerted signal, he entered head fore-most, with the blazing torch in his hand.

"The aperture of the den, on the east side of a very high ledge of rocks is about two feet square; from thence it descends obliquely fifteen feet, then running horizontally about ten more, it ascends gradually sixteen feet towards its termination. The sides of this sub-terraneous cavity are composed of smooth and solid rocks, which seem to have been divided from each other by some former earth-quake. The top and bottom are also of stone, and the entrance in winter being covered with ice, is exceedingly slippery. It is in no place high enough for a man to raise himself upright, nor in any part more than three feet in width.

"Having groped his passage to the horizontal part of the den, the most terrifying darkness appeared in front of the dim circle of light afforded by his torch. It was silent as the house of death. None but monsters of the desert had ever explored this solitary mansion of horror. He, cautiously proceeding onward, came to the ascent, which he slowly mounted on his hands and knees until he discovered the glaring eye-balls of the wolf, who was sitting at the extremity of the cavern. Started at the sight of fire, she gnashed her teeth, and gave a sullen growl. As soon as he had made the necessary dis-covery, he kicked the rope as a signal for pulling him out. The people, at the mouth of the den, who had listened with painful anxiety, hearing the growling of the wolf, supposing their friend to be in the most imminent danger, drew him forth with such celerity that his shirt was stripped over his head and his skin severely lacerated. After he had adjusted his clothes, and loaded his gun with nine buck-shot, holding the torch in one hand and the musket in the other, he descended the second time. When he drew nearer than before, the wolf assuming a still more fierce and terrible appear-ance, howling, rolling her eyes, snapping her teeth, and dropping her head between her legs, was evidently in the attitude, and on the point of springing at him. At the critical instant he lavelled and fired at her head: Stunned with the shock, and suffocated with the smoke, he immediately found himself drawn out of the cave. But having refreshed himself, and permitted the smoke to dissipate, he went down the third time. Once more he came within sight of the wolf, who appearing very passive, he applied the torch to her nose, and perceiving her dead, he took hold of her ears, and then kicking the rope (still tied around his legs) the people above with no small exultation dragged them both out together" (Humphreys, D., 1818: 19).

Zadock Thompson, the Vermont historian, relates on the wolf problem of that State that: "For some years after the settlement . . . wolves were so numerous . . . that the keeping of sheep was a very precarious business" and that wolves "have always been so great an annoyance that much pains have been taken for their extermination" (Thompson, Z., 1853: 34).

Two renowned Americans, George Washington and Thomas Jefferson, whose worldly fame includes expertness as tillers of the soil, together with other agriculturists and livestock breeders of early Virginia, have left records with respect to the wolf problem at the time Virginia was a colonial possession, and the following period after it came into the Union. Near the close of the eighteenth century, Washington owned approximately 800 head of sheep that were kept on his Mount Vernon estate, which was probably at that time one of the largest herds in the infant United States. Always keen for the improvements of his herd as well as the pastures for them, Washington was induced from time to time to correspond with various authorities, foremost amongst whom was Arthur Young in London. He was a zealous contributor to agricultural progress, being president of the Agricultural Society of Great Britain, and considered at the time one of the world's leading agriculturists. In a letter to Young transmitted from Mount Vernon in early December of 1788, Washington wrote: ". . . . I cannot help thinking that increasing and improving our herd of sheep would be one of the most profitable speculations we could undertake; especially in this part of the Continent, where we have so little winter, ... and where we are sufficiently distant from the frontiers not to be troubled with wolves or other wild vermin, which prevents the inhabitants there from keeping flocks" (Washington, G., 1801: 41).

To this Young replied from London: "Wolves are named as a motive for not raising sheep: surely they cannot be serious, who urge it. They abound all over Europe; in France and Spain, among the greatest flocks in the world, and no wolf could get into my sheep houses, or at least, I may say, nothing is so easy as to keep him out. . . . By night, if secure from wolves, they are secure from dogs; and by day sheperds may have loaded fire arms to kill all that approach." (Ibid.)

At this time public lands in colonial America could not be inclosed by fencing, and unless the small domestic flocks of sheep were closely attended, oftentime the resultant wolf depredations were so severe as to cause complete loss.

Washington apparently felt that Young had no conception of the wildness of the American frontier, and that he did not realize the impossibility of handling sheep there by the same methods as then in use in the Old World.

Washington at times discussed the wolf problem with his friend, Richard Peters, a very prosperous and practical Pennsylvania farmer, and one time President of the Philadelphia Agriculture Society, sending Peters' comments on to Young at London. Washington enclosed in a letter to Young in September 1792 a letter received in the middle of June 1792 from Peters, who was then at Belmont, 6 miles from Philadelphia. This letter read in part: ". . . For some time hence this will not be a great sheep country; we keep too many dogs, who destroy them and our country is much intersected with mountains, inhabited by wolves, which cannot be extirpated" (Washington, G., 1801: 41).

In June of that year, however, Washington had stated in a letter to Young: "Sheep thrive very well in the middle states, though they are not exempt from diseases, and are often injured by dogs; and more so as you approach the mountains, by wolves. (Ibid.) With this letter Washington enclosed a letter from Thomas Jefferson, with whom he also had discussed the wolf problem, Jefferson remarking that "Sheep are subject to many diseases which carry them off in great numbers. In the Middle and Upper parts of Virginia, they are subject to the wolf, and in all of it to dogs; these are great obstacles to their multiplication." (Ibid.)

The wolf problem in the eastern portion of the infant United States was thus a matter of importance as indicated by the writings quoted. A letter from Young to Washington with reference to the wolves on the Pennsylvania lands was commented upon by Richard Peters, as follows: "Wolves are a serious enemy to the sheep plan [that is, running sheep as Young had suggested in reply to Washington's letter of December 1788] in places where there are the largest ranges. Time may, perhaps, subdue them. But we have paid, for forty or fifty years past, out of county rates, 20s for each wolf's head: and though they are chiefly banished from our plains and older settlements, yet on our mountains they are plenty. Where a large ridge runs through a country, in other parts ever so well peopled, they find retreats and breed prodigiously. . . . I know not a speedy remedy. I lay not long ago at the foot of the South Mountain in York County, in this State in a country very thickly settled, at the house of a Justice of the Peace. Through the night I was kept awake by what I conceived to be a jubilee of dogs, assembled to bay the moon. But I was told in the morning that what disturbed me was only the howling of wolves which nobody there regarded. When I entered the *Hall of Justice*, I found the 'Squire' giving judgment for the reward of two wolf whelps a country man had taken from the bitch. The judgment seat was shaken with intelligence that the she wolf was coming—not to give bail . . . . but to devote herself, or rescue her offspring. The animal was punished for this daring contempt, committed in the face of the court, and was shot within an hundred yards of the tribunal." (Ibid.)

These comments of Peters were sent by Washington to Young in a letter dated September 1, 1793, during Washington's first term in the Presidency. Up to this time, some scheme of bounty against wolves had been in effect in Pennsylvania for more than a hundred years.

The remarks of Richard Peters lead to the conclusion that in spite of the Pennsylvania bounty, the wolf apparently was holding its own. Early historical records of practically all the new settlements, and during the time following the formation of the counties in Pennsylvania, seldom fail to include elucidating accounts of wolf depredations. Typical of such pertains to Tioga County located in the northern part of the State. Here the historian states: "The wolves particularly were a source of constant trouble to the farmers on account of killing their sheep if they were not securely housed at night. Frequently, whole flocks were decimated in a night by these rapacious and prowling pests of the wilderness settlements" (Anonymous, 1897: 44).

Abundant evidence, therefore, shows that wolves were a menace to all kinds of farm stock in the earliest colonies, and after statehood, continued well into the nineteenth century. As agriculture progressed beyond the Alleghenies, the settlers experienced an equal, if not a greater, hazard from wolves that continued westward across the country. A few of the voluminous accounts bearing on the early times of the pioneer explorers, ranch and stockmen, are here quoted.

In his journal of a voyage up the Missouri River in 1843, Audubon noted with respect to wolves that: "These animals are extremely abundant on the Missouri River, and in the adjacent country. On our way up that extraordinary stream we first heard of wolves being troublesome to the farmers who own sheep, calves, young colts, or any other stock on which these ravenous beasts feed, at Jefferson City, the seat of government of the State of Missouri" (Audubon, J. J., and Bachman, J., 1851-54, vol. 2, p. 159).

Writing about the emigrant trails of the Far West, on the Sweetwater River, Wyo., in 1846, Bryant stated: "We have passed today some eight or ten dead oxen which belonged to emigrant companies in advance of us. Oxen, when foot-sore or exhausted by fatigue, are left by the emigrants, and immediately become the victims of wolves, who give them no rest until they fall. I have sometimes traced an ox pursued by wolves along the trail for ten or twenty miles, and noticed places where he would turn and give battle to his remorseless pursuers. The result in every instance was that I found the dead carcass or skeleton of the ox, upon which the wolves and ravens had been feasting. Domesticated animals, unprotected, cannot resist the persevering attacks of wolves, urged on as they are by their appetites, and conducting their warfare with all the skill of instinct, sharpened often by famine." (Bryant, E., 1885: 132.)

Peter Corney, who was on the Columbia River, in Oregon, at intervals between 1813 and 1818, mentions the wolf as an economic factor even at old Fort George, at the mouth of the Columbia River, but a short distance from where Lewis and Clark built their most westerly fort. Describing Fort George in October 1817, he says: "At this settlement they have cleared about 200 acres of ground, and planted about 20 acres with potatoes for the use of the gentlemen, their object being to collect furs, and not to cultivate or improve the land. They have about twelve head of cattle with some pigs and goats imported here from California; their stock does not increase, for want of proper care, the wolves often carrying off goats and pigs" (Corney, P., 1896: 81).

The historian Bancroft recorded that: The early Oregon settlers, and especially those emigrants of the trek of 1843, suffered losses "of stock of every kind by panthers, wolves, and cougars" (Bancroft, H. H., 1882-90, vol. 29, p. 300).

Hastings, in commenting upon the wolf problem in the Far West in 1843, wrote: "All the different kinds of wolves are very troublesome in all the various settlements into which they make frequent inroads, not only destroying the hogs and sheep, but also frequently attacking and destroying the grown cattle. The cause of there being such an abundance of all the different kinds of wolves is, perhaps, that they are never killed, either by Mexicans or foreigners. They do not kill them because they are entirely worthless [meaning worthless as to skin value], and because the people in that country have not a superabundance of ammunition" (Hastings, L. W., 1932: 98).

As a problem to our military establishments in the pioneer West Marcy records that: "The wolves were formerly so numerous around some of our frontier military posts that it was difficult to keep sheep or poultry in the vicinity, and their depredations were perpetrated with such fearlessness that they did not hesitate to enter into the inclosures and out-buildings of the garrisons to secure their prey" (Marcy, R. B., 1888: 297).

What eventually intensified the wolf problem in the West, however, and more than any other factor, was the building up of a cattle industry following discovery by the westward emigrants that the matured short grasses of the Great Plains were so nutritious that livestock pastured thereon often fattened as well as stall-fed animals. Once that was realized and the buffaloes done away with, the cattle industry grew with surprising rapidity, high-grade stock was introduced, and wolf damage became of greater importance than ever before. Many believed that with the passing of the buffaloes, the wolf would do likewise, but such opinions were destined to change.

However, increase in the number of wolves reported by cattle interests of the period probably was not as great as supposed. What happened was that depredations by these animals, formerly largely satisfied by attacks upon buffaloes and other big game, were being more and more directed toward livestock as a substitute prey.

The wolf was thus brought into direct competition with the livestock producer, and provoked continued warfare. Every known means such as guards, guns, traps, poisons, bounties, wolf-proof enclosures, were sooner or later employed to obtain relief from wolf depredations. Some of the details of these preventive measures have been discussed in the preceding chapter. Although disease might decimate his flocks and herds, or drought or severe winters might result in starvation or extreme cold losses, none of these factors seemed to arouse such outstanding resentment and determination of the stockman-farmer to adopt every means of elimination, as when the wolves killed on the open prairie or mountain range, or maimed and mutilated his range cattle and entered corrals to prey upon domestic stock. The cowman of the Old West wrought special vengeance on the wolf.

Combating the wolf was not, however, a matter of mere revenge. Losses caused by this animal were often the chief factor in determining whether a season's range operations were to produce a profit, or the reverse, to the individual stockman, particularly the small producer.

Under date of April 3, 1896, R. M. Allen, then General Manager of the Standard Cattle Company, of Ames, Nebr., wrote the Biological Survey, now a part of the Fish and Wildlife Service, as follows: ". . . . I went to Wyoming in '79, and in the next few years I never saw any grey wolves. From the fall of '81 I was not on the range in Wyoming for a good many years, but I do not think that any grey wolves appeared until after the winter of '86-'87. About this time Nebraska became more completely settled to its western limits, and it is believed by some people that this drove wolves from Western Nebraska into Wyoming. Whatever the origin of the wolves may be, they began to appear after the winter of '86-'87 and have continued to increase in most of the district east of the mountains ever since. The matter was neglected for a great many years, and finally the number of wolves has become so considerable that all means of extermination used for the last five years have only succeeded in keeping them at about a standstill.

". . . I consider that the extent of the loss to the community is much greater than is commonly supposed, and that it is greater than that from cattle thieves, which I estimated to be very heavy indeed. There is absolutely no way of estimating the extent of the loss to a state like Wyoming, but I should judge it to be not far from a million dollars a year, four times the entire revenue needed to run the state government."

Arthur J. Tisdall, of Bell Ranch, located in San Miguel County, N. Mex., informed the Biological Survey on December 26, 1897, of the "excessive damage by wolves all over the western states and territories, especially where cattle and horses run loose on the range." Mr. Tisdall believed "that they destroyed not less than 500,000 animals annually, principally calves and yearling cattle." To effect relief he recommended "a United States law making wolf scalps legal tender for payment of taxes, at say $10.00 per head." He also suggested a plan whereby "the Government issue to responsible men in every county, poison free of charge, to be by him distributed to the owners of stock, on application." Here we have one of the first suggestions for federal aid in combating wolves which, however, was not to become an actuality until 1915.

Though the sheep industry of the West was much slower in its development than the cattle industry, nevertheless when it did get under way, the losses occasioned by wolves soon became just as severe as those occurring in the cattle industry. In the former, however, coyotes augmented the depredations by wolves. A resume of the picture near the close of the nineteenth century by Palmer states: "It was estimated in 1892 that in New Mexico, where the sheep were valued at $4,556,000, such losses varied from 3 to 7 percent; in Nebraska the value of sheep was about $2,000,000, while the losses amounted to 5 percent, or $100,000; and sheep owners in central Texas suffered losses on account of wild animals to the extent of 10 to 25 percent" (Palmer, T. S., 1896: 55).

The late Senator Thomas B. Kendrick, of Wyoming, one of the foremost and honored citizens of that State, besides being one of the pioneer stock producers of the Rocky Mountain area, says of the wolf problem: "The gray wolf appeared in largest numbers on the northwestern ranges about 1893. It was demonstrated there that between the time of the branding season of one year and the spring roundups of the next season, even after a mild winter, where there were infinitesimal losses from other sources, the gray wolf destroyed sometimes as high as 50 percent of the calf crop within those few months" (U. S. Senate, 1930: 6).

Senator Kendrick further stated: "The gray wolves were more destructive on the smaller and younger cattle, because they were easier prey, but they were none the less viciously destructive of grown cattle.

"Our fight on the ranges over which I had supervision and management at the time began in the fall of 1893. The campaign was conducted through the work of two men on horseback with guns, poison, and traps, and within the short period of two or three months they had a record of 150 gray wolves that they had destroyed.

". . . . all told on this one cattle ranch, covering territory of probably 30 or 35 miles square, we had a record when I left the ranch, and lost track of it, of about 500 gray wolves that we had killed. And the coyotes we threw in for good measure; they numbered hundreds, but we had no disposition to either count them or keep track of them." (Ibid.)

Thus the enmity of the western livestock interests toward the wolf continued to increase. Consequently by the turn of the century many insistent requests were received by the Department of Agriculture for a study of the economics of this problem looking toward more efficient wolf control.

Most of the range states, in addition to the counties, had sanctioned various bounty acts for many years, nearly all of which were attended by disastrous financial results, and had brought but little relief. It was believed by many authorities during this period that the bounty plan was plain legalized fraud. As a result of patchwork defense of the western bounty system some consideration was given for a unified bounty, the so-called "west-wide" plan. This scheme formed one of the main topics at the annual convention of the American National Livestock Association held in Denver, Colo., during January 1899. It favored not only uniformity for all western and territorial bounty laws, but a reward "sufficiently large to be effective" (Palmer, T. S., 1899: 65). Accordingly, Colorado, Minnesota, Montana, and Wyoming attempted to enact new "wolf bounty laws, or amend old laws; and in Utah to substitute a State bounty for existing county bounties." (Ibid.) Apparently, all of this came to naught during the next five years. The "west-wide" bounty plan though first conceived more than forty years ago, and has in that interval died "several natural deaths" for want of unified action, nevertheless, it still at times forms a topic among stockmen during annual meetings as a control measure for such of the predators as the coyote. The range States, however, have never been able to agree unanimously on the plan; some have always been diametrically opposed to it in favor of the paid hunter system.

Early in the present century, in response to the requests received, field naturalists of the Biological Survey were chosen to conduct a series of range studies of wolf damage in the West. These studies eventually led to the publication of four reports by the Department of Agriculture, between 1907 and 1909, on the predator-big game-livestock relationship within and outside the boundaries of the existing national forests. Foremost among these publications was that entitled "Key to Animals on Which Wolf and Coyote Bounties Are Often Paid" (Bailey, V., 1909). This document was issued as an aid to the States and counties in an attempt to reduce some of the fraud that had become apparent in the widely used bounty system, through which monies were being paid upon various animals other than the predators to be eliminated. As previously mentioned, thousands of dog, fox, and stretched rabbit ears and scalps had flooded the various State and county treasuries, being substituted as bounty evidence on which to collect compensation for wolves and coyotes. Statistics show that by 1914 more than $1,000,000 annually were being paid out in bounties. This sum does not include the local bounties paid by various livestock associations—itself a tidy sum.

During the year 1907 the Biological Survey, based on careful analysis of field studies, came to the conclusion that losses from wolves and other predators could be prevented only by carefully planned and concerted action throughout the wolf-infested country. This Bureau at the same time volunteered to furnish any information in its possession that would aid in obtaining the best results through cooperative undertakings to reduce the losses. It further reported that: "In the western part of the United States wolves and coyotes levy a heavy tax on stock, especially colts, calves, and sheep —a loss aggregating several millions of dollars annually." Further, "At the request of the Forest Service [this Bureau] undertook a special investigation of the wolf problem. It was found that in early spring the breeding dens of wolves may be located and the young destroyed at small expense. The application of this discovery, in connection with experiments with [traps and] scent baits for adult wolves, and certain other information obtained in previous field work, has already resulted in a saving of stock worth upward of a million dollars." (U. S. Senate Doc. 132, 1907: 14.)

The Secretary of Agriculture, in his annual report for 1907 (p. 98) to the President, said in part with respect to the Departmental wolf publications of that year: "The adoption by stockmen of the methods recommended—especially killing the young in the breeding dens—has already resulted in a material reduction in the number of wolves and a corresponding saving of stock and game."

More effective means of wolf control continued to be stressed, because of the mounting volume of complaints regarding wolf infestations on many of the newly established western national forests. The stock interests felt, and forcefully expressed, that it was unfair to collect a grazing fee for the use of forage on a forest area heavily infested with wolves and other predators, unless some degree of protection from predation was simultaneously afforded.

The Department of Agriculture, through the Forest Service, soon recognized this general situation. To effect some means of relief, therefore, its field officers, and in particular the forest rangers, were supplied with wolf traps purchased with federal funds allotted to that Service for use in trapping operations against the wolf.

The wolf trap that was used most commonly by the forest rangers was the double-spring No. 4½, which had been developed in the 1890's. It was manufactured by the Newhouse Trap Company as a result of the wolf menace in Texas, and it soon found a ready sale throughout the western livestock country. Containing a double steel spring, it weighed 5¼ pounds, and, in its main component parts, was an enlargement of the former No. 4 beaver trap. Wide use of this trap afforded some relief, but there still remained large areas of public and private domain outside the boundaries of the national forests upon which no organized wolf control was in force. Consequently the wolf control work that was done by the forest rangers and their cooperators afforded only temporary relief, because of re-infestation by wolves from the surrounding lands. Then too wolf control was but one of the forest ranger's many official tasks, and he could not give the problem his undivided attention. Nevertheless, a great deal of good was being accomplished, for as Cameron states:

"As a result of the efforts of the stockmen and of the rangers and special hunters on the forest reserves along the lines recommended in these [wolf] publications, a record kill of predatory animals was made in 1907. Over one thousand eight hundred wolves and twenty-three thousand coyotes were accounted for. The estimated resulting savings in stock was $2,000,000" (Cameron, J., 1929: 46). This kill included wolves from 39 western national forests, comprising an area of 72,760 square miles, in addition to the acreage from outside areas that brought the total to 145,520 square miles, which was about one-tenth of the total range then inhabited by these animals in the United States.

Strong sentiment continued to develop to the effect that the National Government should take more of an active part in wolf control because of the vast acreages of wolf-infested national forests and the federal public domian. Finally, the Congress responded to the persistent pleadings of the western stock interests, which were joined in their requests for relief by sportsmen's groups, and others. Momentum that had been gradually gathering for many years thus resulted in an appropriation of federal funds as a partial aid in bringing relief from wolves.

Of all the agencies then comprising the federal organization, the Biological Survey by this time had become the recognized national agency charged with all matters relating to wild life in its relation to agriculture, forestry, and stock-raising. By some it had been thought of as the natural history agency of the Federal Government, because of its far-flung activities that dealt with life histories, the habits, the habitats, the ranges and the distribution, the economic, and esthetic values of America's fauna. Consequently, it became the agency chosen to assume the most difficult task of wolf control. The Bureau accordingly was authorized under the Act of Congress of June 30, 1914 (38 Stat. L., 415)—An Act, Making appropriations for the Department of Agriculture for the fiscal year ending June thirtieth, nineteen hundred and fifteen—to expend money for "experiments and demonstrations in destroying *wolves*, prairie dogs, and other animals injurious to agriculture and animal husbandry."

In rounding out the historical record dealing with wildlife in relation to economic interests, it may be well at this time to point out again that as shown by the language used in the foregoing authorization it was primarily wolf depredations that led to the initiation of cooperative injurious animal control by the Federal Government.

Thus with the beginning of the fiscal year, July 1, 1915, the first appropriation, of $125,000, specifically providing federal funds to assist in organizing predator control on national forests and other public lands, became effective. In addition, this action also presented an opportunity to correlate the activities of all those agencies at work on the problem at that time along the most effective and economical lines, reducing thereby much of the existing chaos in wolf control work, some of which was found to be detrimental to many beneficial forms of wildlife. Wherever field studies indicated the need of wolf control, operations were begun. Hence by the close of the fiscal year 1916 a large portion of the western livestock ranges was organized into control districts under competent supervisors, together with field control personnel.

Approximately three decades have passed since the Fish and Wildlife Service has been engaged in predatory animal control work. During this time many of the States and counties have repealed their bounty laws, and in lieu thereof have legislated modest appropriations for cooperation with the Federal Government. These monies have been further supplemented by funds raised cooperatively through direct assessments on livestock, in addition to contributions at times from private stockmen and farmers, either in cash, labor, or materials.

Owing to the investigative and educational work of the Service as to the hazards involved to many forms of wildlife that should always be maintained because of its value to mankind, the once wide use of poison by the stock interests in predator control has practically ceased. Field experiments constantly devoted toward the improvement of predator control technique has to date resulted in more selectivity whenever the elimination of locally injurious animals becomes necessary. Furthermore, these experiments are also resulting in making possible more and more humane control practices than were possible in the earlier years. To these ends the Service has worked continually ever since the first year it was called upon to assume the leadership in this necessary but most difficult project often unjustly criticized by certain nature lovers, with a highly theoretical concept of a biological balance. These are individuals apparently unmindful of all the accumulated knowledge of the food habits of wolves and other large predators and the hard practical bearing of these animals on human welfare through the centuries.

Today, the wolf has been definitely brought under control and presents a very minor problem except in limited areas in the United States, in connection with man's interests. It still remains, however, practically uncontrolled throughout most of its vast range in Alaska, northern and western Canada, and in Mexico. Except in local areas where wolves have continued to present a pressing economic problem the Fish and Wildlife Service has felt that little wolf control work is now justified. There still remain, even in the United States, some areas of considerable size in which we feel that both the red and gray species, in their respective habitats, may be allowed to continue their existence with little molestation.

Thus the story of the wolves has been one of continual conflict throughout the centuries—a story with more intimate bearing on human welfare than that of any other carnivore.